Women and Minorities in Science and Engineering

National Science Foundation
January 1988

NSF 88-301

Foreword

Scientists and engineers play a vital role in addressing many critical national issues ranging from strengthening the educational system and increasing our industrial competitiveness to advancing the frontiers of knowledge.

The importance of scientific and engineering activities to the United States makes it essential that the best talent from every available source be attracted to careers in science and engineering. Women and members of minority groups, however, have had historically low rates of participation in science and engineering. These low rates must be cause for concern.

Another concern must be the market conditions encountered by women and minorities who have earned science and engineering degrees. The data suggest less favorable conditions as compared to male and majority scientists and engineers. The reasons for these market experiences may be the result of a number of factors including differences in socioeconomic characteristics, career preference, or a combination of these and other factors; these differences may also reflect inequitable treatment.

A clear factual picture of the current situation and recent trends in participation is an important prerequisite to rational and effective policy formulation. This volume, the fourth biennial report in this series, is designed to meet this need by providing a sound basis for informed discussion and constructive policy and program development.

This report supplies facts and information needed by Congress, the Administration, and others concerned with the overall vitality of U.S. science and engineering and specifically with the furtherance of equal opportunities and equal treatment for women and minorities in science and engineering.

Erich Bloch
Director
National Science Foundation

Acknowledgments

This report was developed within the Division of Science Resources Studies, Surveys and Analysis Section, by Melissa J. Lane, Economist, Scientific and Technical Personnel Characteristics Studies Group (STPCSG), under the direction of Michael F. Crowley, Study Director, STPCSG. John A. Scopino, Senior Science Resources Analyst, STPCSG, contributed to the initial analysis. David Edson of Mathematica Policy Research, Inc., generated the data on the science and engineering population as well as the statistical tables appearing in this report; Nita Congress of Evaluation Technologies Incorporated provided professional editing services; and Patricia D. Hughes of NSF's Printing Services Branch coordinated the production of the document.

The report benefited from comments provided by the National Science Foundation's Committee on Equal Opportunities in Science and Engineering. Guidance and review were provided by Charles H. Dickens, Head, Surveys and Analysis Section; William L. Stewart, Director, Division of Science Resources Studies; and Richard J. Green, Assistant Director of the National Science Foundation for Scientific, Technological, and International Affairs.

Contents

Executive Summary

This report, the fourth in a biennial series mandated by the Science and Technology Equal Opportunities Act (Public Law 96-516) of 1980, presents information on the participation of women, racial/ethnic minorities, and the physically disabled in science and engineering. In keeping with its purpose as an information resource, this report makes no recommendations on programs or policies. The report does present facts and information that may be used to address issues concerned with the full utilization of the Nation's human resources in science and engineering.

Employment of women and minorities in science and engineering (S/E) has increased much more rapidly than that of men and the majority over the 1976-86 period. Nonetheless, women, blacks, and Hispanics remained underrepresented in S/E employment in 1986 based on their representation in the overall U.S. work force. Asians and native Americans, on the other hand, were not underrepresented in S/E fields.

The general underrepresentation of women, blacks, and Hispanics reflects their relatively low participation in precollege science and mathematics courses and in undergraduate and graduate S/E education. However, those women and minorities who do earn degrees in science and engineering and subsequently seek employment in the S/E work force generally encounter less favorable market conditions than men and the majority.

Several major themes emerge from the data and analyses in this report. First, despite a significant increase in their number, women scientists and engineers continue to report higher unemployment rates and lower annual salaries. Second, the fundamental concern for underrepresented minorities continues to be the quality of their precollege experience. Most minorities are less likely than the majority either to be in an academic curriculum or to take advanced mathematics courses in high school. These and other differences are reflected in scores on examinations measuring mathematics and science achievement (e.g., the Scholastic Aptitude Test).

Major findings presented in this report on women, racial minorities, Hispanics, and the physically disabled are summarized below.

WOMEN

Employment

- Employment of women scientists and engineers increased by 250 percent (13 percent per year) over the 1976-86 decade, compared with an employment increase of about 84 percent (6 percent per year) for men. In 1986, women accounted for 15 percent of the S/E work force, up from 9 percent in 1976. Women continue to constitute a smaller ratio of the S/E work force than they do of either total U.S. employment (44 percent) or total employment in professional and related occupations (49 percent).

- Representation of women varies substantially by S/E field. In 1986, more than 1 in 4 scientists was a woman compared to only 1 in 25 engineers. Among science fields, the proportion of women ranged from 12 percent of environmental scientists to 45 percent of psychologists.

- Because of their relatively recent influx into science and engineering fields, women generally are younger and have fewer years of professional experience than men. In 1986, almost three-fifths of the women, but only about one-quarter of the men, had fewer than 10 years of experience.

- Overall, annual salaries for women averaged 75 percent of those for men in 1986 ($29,900 versus $39,800). Salaries for women are lower than for men in essentially all fields of science and engineering and at all levels of professional experience. There were a few exceptions at the entry level, however, where salaries were comparable (e.g., recent bachelor's degree recipients in electrical/electronics engineering).

- About 75 percent of employed women scientists and engineers were working in S/E jobs in 1986; the comparable figure for men was 86 percent. S/E employment rates vary substantially between science and engineering. Among scientists, 72 percent of women and 78 percent of men were in S/E jobs. Among engineers, the rate for women (94 percent) was slightly higher than that for men (92 percent).

- The unemployment rate for women was about double that for men in 1986: 2.7 percent versus 1.3 percent. Unemployment rates for both women and men have declined since 1976 when they were 5.4 percent and 3.2 percent, respectively.

- Available data show greater underemployment of women than of men among scientists and engineers. If those working involuntarily in either part-time or non-S/E jobs are considered as a proportion of total employment, about 6 percent of women compared to 2 percent of men are underemployed.

Education and Training

- About the same proportions of females and males enroll in an academic curriculum in high school. Males, however, are more likely than females to take courses in chemistry, physics, and advanced mathematics (e.g., calculus).

- In 1986, males continued to score somewhat higher than females on the verbal component of the Scholastic Aptitude Test (SAT), and substantially higher on the mathematics portion. Although there have been some fluctuations over the decade, score differences between males and females have increased on the verbal section and remained constant on the mathematics component.

- SAT mathematics scores for college-bound seniors planning to major in science or engineering are generally higher for males than females. Throughout the eighties, however, females intending an undergraduate major in engineering had SAT mathematics scores consistently higher than those for males.

- Score differences between women and men vary among the components of the Graduate Record Examination (GRE). Of women and men with undergraduate majors in S/E fields, women scored slightly higher than men on the verbal component, much lower on the quantitative section, and slightly lower on the analytical portion.

- By the mid-eighties, women accounted for about one-half of both total higher education enrollment and the overall number of degrees awarded. At the baccalaureate level, they accounted for 45 percent of degrees granted in science fields and 15 percent of those in engineering. In 1985, more than two-thirds of women received their degree in either the social sciences, psychology, or the life sciences.

- Between 1975 and 1985, degree production patterns changed markedly. The number of science and engineering baccalaureates earned by women increased by 30 percent compared with a 1-percent decline for men. By field, the most notable gains for women have been in computer science (from almost 1,000 to more than 14,000 10 years later) and in engineering (from 900 to 11,000).

- In 1985, women received 30 percent of all S/E master's degrees, up from 20 percent a decade earlier. Women received 40 percent of science degrees awarded and 11 percent of those granted in engineering. Over the 1975-85 decade, the number of women earning S/E master's degrees rose by 66 percent; the corresponding number of men was virtually unchanged.

- Women accounted for 26 percent of the doctorates granted in science and engineering in 1986, up from 17 percent in 1976. For the 10-year period, the number of S/E doctorates earned by women rose 65 percent to 4,900; the number awarded to men declined by 7 percent to 13,900. Among U.S. citizens only, women represented 31 percent of S/E doctorates awarded in 1986, up from 18 percent a decade earlier.

Minority Women

- Minorities are more highly represented among women than among men. Of the 698,600 employed women scientists and engineers in 1986, roughly 5 percent were black (34,500) and 5 percent were Asian (36,300); less than 1 percent (2,700)

was native American. On the other hand, in 1986, about 2 percent of male scientists and engineers were black, 5 percent were Asian, and less than 1 percent was native American.

- Asian women are more highly represented among scientists and engineers than in the general work force. While they account for about 5 percent of women scientists and engineers, they represent only about 2 percent of all women in the U.S. work force. Black women account for 11 percent of all employed women and 5 percent of women scientists and engineers.

- In 1986, almost 3 percent (19,600) of women scientists and engineers were Hispanic compared with 6 percent of all employed women.

RACIAL MINORITIES

Employment

- In 1986, blacks accounted for 2.5 percent of all employed scientists and engineers. Although this proportion was up from 1.6 percent in 1976, it was still lower than their proportion elsewhere. Blacks accounted for 10 percent of total U.S. employment in 1986 and almost 7 percent of all employed professional and related workers.

- Asians represented about 5 percent of all scientists and engineers in 1986, but only about 2 percent of the overall U.S. labor force.

- The representation of native Americans is about the same among scientists and engineers as in the overall U.S. work force (less than 1 percent). Data on native Americans, however, should be viewed with caution since they are based on an individual's perception of his or her native American heritage; such perceptions may change over time. Additionally, sample sizes for native Americans are small and statistical reliability is thus lower for data on this racial group.

- Racial groups differ with respect to their participation in S/E fields. The proportions of racial minorities who were engineers ranged from about 59 percent of Asians to 36 percent of blacks. Among scientists, blacks were more likely than whites and Asians to be social scientists or psychologists.

- Unemployment among black scientists and engineers averaged 3.8 percent in 1986; among Asians, unemployment averaged 1.8 percent while among native Americans, it was 1.2 percent. In comparison, the rate was 1.5 percent for whites.

- Underemployment (the fraction of total employment representing those involuntarily working in either a part-time or non-S/E job) for scientists and engineers varies by race. Whereas the S/E underemployment rate for blacks was more than 5 percent, the rates for whites, Asians, and native Americans were roughly one-half this rate.

- Blacks and native Americans, on average, have fewer years of professional experience than do white and Asian scientists and engineers. Almost 40 percent of blacks compared to roughly 30 percent of whites and Asians had fewer than 10 years of professional experience in 1986. Among native American scientists and engineers, about 20 percent had fewer than 10 years of experience.

- Black, white, and native American scientists and engineers are all equally as likely to report management or administration as their major work activity. In 1986, roughly 28 to 30 percent of each group were in management. In contrast, about 22 percent of Asians reported this activity as their major work in 1986.

- Black scientists and engineers, on average, earn lower salaries than do whites, Asians, or native Americans. In 1986, the average annual salary reported by blacks was $31,500. Average salaries for other racial groups ranged from about $39,000 for whites and Asians to $41,000 for native Americans.

Education and Training

- Trends in Scholastic Aptitude Test scores have varied greatly over the 1975-85 decade. Scores for blacks have risen substantially on both the verbal and mathematics components while scores for whites and Asians have either remained unchanged or fallen. However, whites continue to score highest on the SAT verbal component; Asians receive the highest score on the mathematics portion. For native Americans, scores have increased on the mathematics section and remained about the same on the verbal section.

- Between 1975 and 1985, scores for blacks on the SAT mathematics component rose 22 points compared to a 3-point decline for whites. In 1985, blacks scored 376 on the mathematics component, 114 points lower than whites (490). In the same year, Asians scored 518 on the mathematics component, 28 points above whites. The mathematics score for native Americans was 428, 62 points lower than that for whites.

- The socioeconomic characteristics of college-bound seniors vary by racial group. Parents of Asians are more likely than other parents to have graduate degrees. Also, college-bound Asian students are more likely to report a high school grade point average above 3.75 (out of a possible 4.00) and to plan for graduate education.

- Blacks and native Americans appear not to have the same access to S/E education as whites and Asians. For example, although blacks and native Americans aspire to higher levels of education than that achieved by their parents, their grade point averages are in the 2.75 range. In addition, the family incomes of black and native American students are lower than those for other students and they are much more likely to state the need for financial aid. Parental income reported by white students was about $35,000 per year, compared to about $17,000 for blacks and $24,700 for native Americans.

- Blacks account for a larger fraction of S/E baccalaureates granted than of the advanced-level S/E degrees conferred. For example, blacks earned 5 percent of the S/E baccalaureates and 2.5 percent of the doctorates. In contrast, Asian representation increased at advanced levels: they earned only 4 percent of the S/E bachelor's degrees but almost 6 percent of the S/E doctorates.

HISPANICS

Employment

- In 1986, Hispanics of all racial groups represented 2 percent of all employed scientists and engineers; this fraction was down from 2.2 percent in 1984. For the same year, roughly 7 percent of all employed persons and more than 3 percent of those in professional and related fields were Hispanic.

- Approximately 30 percent of employed Hispanic scientists and engineers were Mexican American; 15 percent were Puerto Rican. The remaining 55 percent were "other Hispanic" or did not report their specific Hispanic origins.

- About one-half of Hispanics were engineers and the other one-half were scientists; this split was roughly similar to the overall scientist-engineer split. Hispanics in science are somewhat more likely to be social scientists and less likely to be computer specialists.

- Hispanics report significantly fewer years of professional experience than do all scientists and engineers. Almost 44 percent of Hispanics reported fewer than 10 years of experience in 1986; the comparable figure for all scientists and engineers was 31 percent.

- Hispanic scientists and engineers were more likely than non-Hispanics to be unemployed or underemployed.

- Annual salaries for Hispanics averaged $34,600 in 1986; the average for all scientists and engineers was $38,400.

Education and Training

- The proportion of Hispanics in academic programs is smaller than that of all high school seniors; those Hispanics who are in such programs take fewer mathematics and science courses. Hispanic versus non-Hispanic variations in coursetaking is reflected in the respective SAT scores of college-bound seniors. Scores for Hispanics on the mathematics component averaged 426 for Mexican Americans and 405 for Puerto Ricans. Scores for all college-bound seniors averaged 475.

- In 1985, scores for Hispanics were lower than the national average on the SAT verbal component: 382 for Mexican Americans and 373 for Puerto Ricans. These scores were 49 and 58 points, respectively, below the average for all college-bound seniors. A language barrier may be one factor contributing to these lower scores for Hispanics. In 1985, between 7 percent and 9 percent of Hispanic seniors reported that English was not their best language.

- The socioeconomic background of Hispanic college-bound seniors differs from that of non-Hispanics. For example, annual parental income of Mexican Americans was $20,500 compared with $32,200 for all such seniors in 1985.

- Hispanics account for a larger percentage of degrees at the undergraduate than at the graduate level. For example, they earned about 3.1 percent of S/E degrees at the bachelor's level in 1985 (down from 3.2 percent in 1979) and 2.1 percent of the S/E doctorates (up from 1.7 percent in 1979).

PHYSICALLY DISABLED

- In 1986, about 94,000 scientists and engineers (about 2 percent of the total) reported a physical disability. Of these, 22 percent reported an ambulatory condition, 22 percent a visual condition, and 18 percent had an auditory disability. The remainder did not specify the nature of their disability.

- Those reporting a disability are much more likely than all scientists and engineers to be out of the labor force. The 1986 labor force participation rate for disabled scientists and engineers was 76 percent; for all scientists and engineers, the rate was 95 percent.

- The field distribution of employed disabled scientists and engineers differs only slightly from that of all scientists and engineers.

- Both the physically disabled and all scientists and engineers in the labor force reported an unemployment rate of 1.5 percent in 1986. Those with a physical disability, however, were more likely than all scientists and engineers to hold an S/E job: 90 percent versus 83 percent.

Introduction

The Science and Technology Equal Opportunities Act, passed in December 1980, calls for the National Science Foundation (NSF):

... to promote the full use of human resources in science and technology through a comprehensive and continuing program to increase substantially the contribution and advancement of women and minorities in scientific, professional, and technical careers, and for other purposes.[1]

Under this act, NSF is required to report to Congress on the status of women and minorities in science and engineering (S/E) professions on a biennial basis. This report is the fourth in the series and, like its predecessors, it provides a comprehensive overview of the participation of women, minorities (including Hispanics), and the physically disabled in science and engineering employment and training.

The report has been designed as a reference document that allows readers to easily locate information on particular subgroups or on specific aspects of participation or utilization. Readers preferring a more concise overview of the findings are encouraged to read the executive summary.

The body of the report is organized into three chapters. The first two chapters focus on the characteristics of the Nation's S/E population. Specifically, the first chapter examines the representation and utilization of women, including members of racial and ethnic minority groups, in science and engineering. The second chapter presents similar information for five minority groups: blacks, Asians, native Americans, Hispanics, and the physically disabled. The third chapter examines the acquisition of scientific and mathematics skills by both women and minorities

and highlights differences from men and the majority in achievement test performance, academic preparation, and degree production.

The issues addressed in the first two chapters relate to S/E employment. They include:

- The representation of women and minorities in science and engineering employment;

- Differences in employment characteristics between sexes and across minority groups; and

- Measures that indicate underutilization of those with science and engineering skills.

Labor market representation may be assessed by comparing the proportion of employed scientists and engineers who are women and members of minority groups with the proportion of these groups in some relevant population, such as overall U.S. employment or all professional and related workers. Level of representation, however, reveals nothing about the experiences of women and minorities once they are in the labor market. These experiences are instead addressed by differences in employment characteristics.

Employment characteristics are analyzed in terms of field of employment and career patterns. Information on field of employment is valuable for at least two reasons: (1) to indicate whether women and minorities are underrepresented in some fields vis-a-vis men and the majority, and (2) to reveal differences by sex and racial/ethnic group. Employment opportunities vary by field; these differences may be significant in determining such variations in work characteristics as employment in S/E jobs, unemployment, and salaries. Career patterns are important because they may illuminate differences in experi-

ences within fields. These patterns are measured in terms of proportions in management positions; for those employed in academia, tenure status and rank are indicators.

The third issue addressed in chapters 1 and 2 is the utilization of individuals with science and engineering training. Insights in this area may be gleaned from a variety of labor market indicators: labor force participation and unemployment rates are standard indicators. These rates are useful in assessing whether market conditions for women and minority scientists and engineers differ from those encountered by men and the majority and also by women and minorities in the general population.

Labor force participation rates measure the fraction of the S/E population in the labor force, that is, the proportion working or seeking employment. Low rates suggest that a significant fraction of those with S/E training and skills are not using these skills in science and engineering or in any other jobs.

A second indicator of utilization is unemployment. Unemployment rates measure the proportion of those in the labor force who are not employed but who are seeking employment. Higher rates for women and minorities may signify that these groups encounter labor market problems different from those of men and the majority in the S/E work force. Unemployment rates, however, are incomplete market condition indicators for scientists and engineers. These rates do not indicate the degree to which those with the necessary education and training succeed in finding S/E jobs. The National Science Foundation has, therefore, developed three measures unique to scientists and engineers: the S/E employment rate, the S/E underemployment rate, and the S/E underutilization rate:

- The S/E employment rate provides a way to assess the market conditions for scientists and engineers performing S/E work. This rate measures the degree to which employed scientists and engineers report that their jobs are related to S/E work.

- The S/E underemployment rate indicates the extent to which scientists and engineers use their training and skills. For example, when full-time jobs are not available, individuals may accept part-time jobs. Similarly, when jobs in science and engineering are not available, some individuals accept jobs in other areas. Thus, some part-time employment (i.e., seeking full-time jobs) and some non-S/E employment (i.e., belief that S/E jobs are not available) may indicate underemployment. The S/E underemployment rate provides an overall statistical measure of both involuntary part-time and involuntary non-S/E employment.

- The S/E underutilization rate combines numbers of both unemployed and underemployed and presents them as a percent of the labor force. This rate is only a partial measure of potential underutilization, since it does not account for those persons whose S/E skills are greater than their jobs require.

Observed differences in labor market experiences between women and men and between minorities and the majority may highlight potential areas of concern. Although disparities may indicate inequitable treatment, they are not in themselves enough to justify such an inference.

The third chapter of this report focuses on issues related to education and training, specifically the acquisition of those skills requisite to an S/E career. These issues are of increasing importance for several reasons. For example, the population's changing demographic mix results in a rate of influx for minorities at all educational levels that is higher than that for whites. As a group, however, minorities do not participate in science and engineering undergraduate and graduate training to the same extent as does the majority. It is therefore critical to increase minority participation in S/E education, both to ensure that they have the same opportunities in and access to the acquisition of skills in science and mathematics, and to ensure that the demand for S/E personnel may always be met from all available human resource pools.

Chapter 3 explores differences between women and men and between minorities and the majority in five areas of education and training: precollege preparation, undergraduate preparation, science and engineering degree production, graduate education, and postdoctoral experiences. Most of the data presented in this chapter are from sources outside the National Science Foundation and are not always based on regularly recurring surveys. As a result, updates of information presented in previous reports (especially for data on precollege preparation) are not available for inclusion here. Alternate information sources have been substituted where possible; these explore differences in the educational experiences and opportunities for women and minorities compared with men and the majority. Scores on standardized tests measuring mathematics and science achievement are also used as indicators of participation patterns. For example, students who take fewer years of coursework in mathematics generally score lower on exams measuring mathematical knowledge. Scores on these exams reflect a variety of factors including social, demographic, and economic characteristics. For example, there is evidence linking student performance on standardized tests to family income; a disproportionate number of minority families are at lower economic levels.

The final sections of this report contain technical notes (Appendix A) and statistical tables (Appendix B). The technical notes present information on the underlying concepts, data collection techniques, reporting procedures, and statistical reliability of the primary NSF data sources used in this report. These notes also contain several tables of standard errors for the science and engineering personnel estimates. Because of the relatively small number of women and minorities in the sample surveys of scientists and engineers, data for these groups are not as statistically reliable as those for men and whites. However, any comparisons made in this report between women and men and between minorities and the majority are statistically significant at the 0.05 level; that is, the reported difference is due to chance only 5 or fewer times in 100.

To review information on current research on women and minorities in science and engineering, the National Science Foundation sponsored two workshops—one focusing on women and the other on minority groups—in the fall of 1986. These workshops provided a forum for experts to exchange information on both current research findings and newly emerging issues. Information on the reports resulting from these workshops can be obtained from the Division of Science Resources Studies, National Science Foundation.[2]

ENDNOTES

1. "National Science Foundation Authorization and Science and Technology Equal Opportunities Act," Public Law 96-516, 42 USC 1861, December 12, 1980.

2. National Academy of Sciences, Women: Their Underrepresentation and Career Differentials in Science and Engineering, Proceedings of a Workshop and Minorities: Their Underrepresentation and Career Differentials in Science and Engineering, Proceedings of a Workshop, workshops sponsored by the National Science Foundation under Contract No. SRS-8515461 (Washington, DC: National Academy Press, 1987).

CHAPTER 1

Women in Science and Engineering

OVERVIEW

In 1986, 698,600 women scientists and engineers were employed in the United States. This number represents 15 percent of all scientists and engineers and is up from 9 percent in 1976. This proportional change was caused by a 250-percent increase (13 percent annually) in employment of women. For men, the corresponding increase was 84 percent (6 percent per year). Women, however, remain underrepresented in science and engineering (S/E) employment as compared, for example, to the overall U.S. work force where they constituted about 44 percent of all workers.

Women account for a much larger share of employment in science than in engineering. In 1986, while more than 1 in 4 scientists was a woman, only 1 in 25 engineers was female.

Women scientists and engineers are more likely than their male colleagues to be unemployed and underemployed. The unemployment rate for women in 1986 was more than double that for men: 2.7 percent versus 1.3 percent. This gap has declined over the decade. In 1976, the rate for women was 5.4 percent compared to 3.2 percent for men. While the current unemployment rate for women scientists and engineers (2.7 percent) was lower than that for all women in the U.S., it is similar to the rate for all women college graduates (2.4 percent).

Women are three times as likely as men to report they were underemployed (6.3 percent versus 1.9 percent). Women also report lower annual salaries than do men: in 1986, annual salaries for women ($29,900) were about 75 percent of those for men ($39,800). Yearly earnings for women are lower than those for men among all S/E fields and, with few exceptions, at all levels of professional experience. In some fields (e.g., electrical/electronics engineering), however, salaries are comparable at the entry level.

Because of the relatively recent influx of women into science and engineering, they are generally younger and have fewer years of professional experience than do their male colleagues. Almost three-fifths of women, compared to roughly one-quarter of men, reported fewer than 10 years of professional work experience.

Relatively few women scientists and engineers are members of minority groups. In 1986, about 5 percent were black, another 5 percent were Asian, and less than 1 percent was native American. Among men, about 2 percent were black and 5 percent were Asian. Only Asians were more highly represented among women scientists and engineers than in the general work force. Hispanic women also account for only a small fraction (3 percent) of all women scientists and engineers; their representation, however, is higher among men.

EMPLOYMENT LEVELS AND TRENDS

Women continue to constitute a smaller fraction of the science and engineering work force than they do of total U.S. employment or employment in professional and related occupations. In 1986, women represented 44 percent of all employed persons[1] and 49 percent of those in professional and related occupations,[2] but only 15 percent of employed scientists and engineers. Nonetheless, their fraction of the S/E work force has risen dramatically over the last decade; in 1976, they accounted for only 9 percent of this work force.

The increased representation of women in science and engineering underscores their much faster employment growth rate than that for men over the last decade. Between 1976 and 1986, employment of women rose by 250 percent (13 percent per year) compared to an 84-percent increase for men (6 percent per year). More recently (1984-86),

employment of women scientists and engineers accelerated to a rate of almost 17 percent per year; concurrently, employment growth for men scientists and engineers remained at about 6 percent. In terms of absolute growth, the number of women scientists and engineers rose from 199,700 in 1976 to 512,600 in 1984, and to 698,600 in 1986.

Employment of women doctoral scientists and engineers has also shown substantial growth over the decade. Between 1975 and 1985,[3] their employment grew by 165 percent (10 percent per year) compared to 46 percent (4 percent annually) for men. In 1985, there were almost 58,500 women doctoral scientists and engineers. This number represented 15 percent of the total Ph.D. work force and was up from 9 percent (22,100) in 1975.

Among all scientists and engineers, about the same percentage of women and men hold doctorates; however, within each field, the proportion of women is lower. The relatively small difference at the aggregate level reflects the differing field concentrations for women and men. Women, for example, are more highly concentrated in those sciences where a doctorate is frequently required for advancement. Most men, on the other hand, are in engineering fields where a doctorate is not a critical element for career advancement.

In 1986, the doctoral intensity rate[4] was between 8 percent and 9 percent for both women and men (figure 1-1). By field, however, a lower proportion of women than of men hold doctorates. Among science fields, the largest differences occur in physical science and psychology. Regardless of gender, engineers are less apt to hold doctorates than scientists. The doctoral intensity rate in 1986 for engineers was 1.5 percent for women and 2.7 percent for men.

The number of science and engineering degrees awarded to women[5] has increased rapidly over the last decade. Consequently, women account for a

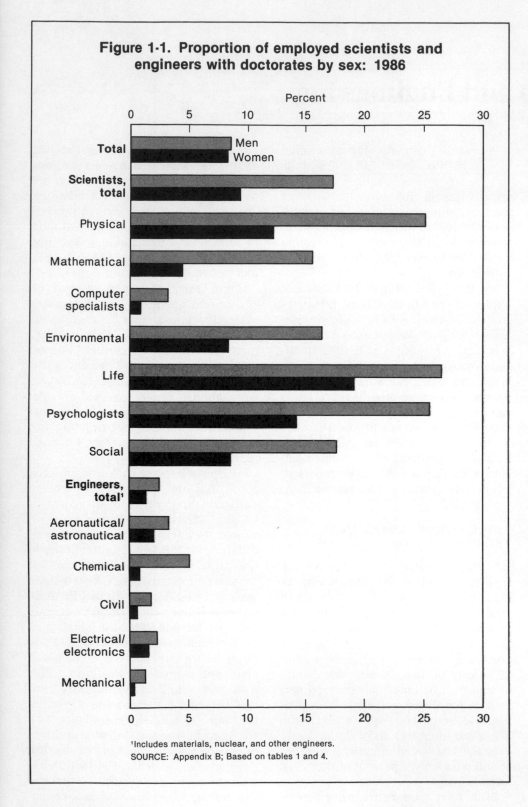

Figure 1-1. Proportion of employed scientists and engineers with doctorates by sex: 1986

Percent

- Total — Men / Women
- Scientists, total
- Physical
- Mathematical
- Computer specialists
- Environmental
- Life
- Psychologists
- Social
- Engineers, total[1]
- Aeronautical/astronautical
- Chemical
- Civil
- Electrical/electronics
- Mechanical

[1]Includes materials, nuclear, and other engineers.
SOURCE: Appendix B; Based on tables 1 and 4.

FIELD

Women represent a much larger proportion of employment in the science work force than in engineering (figure 1-2).[7] In 1986, while more than 1 in 4 scientists was a woman, only 1 in 25 engineers was female. Among science fields, the proportions of women ranged from 12 percent of environmental scientists to 45 percent of psychologists. In engineering, the range was from 3 percent of both mechanical and electrical/electronics engineers to almost 8 percent of chemical engineers.

S/E field distributions differ markedly between women and men (table 1-1). For example, about 86 percent of employed women and 40 percent of men were in a science field in 1986. These distributions have changed somewhat since 1976 as a result of differing growth patterns. In the sciences, employment of women rose 13 percent per year while that of men increased at an annual rate of 7 percent.

The fastest growing field for both women and men was computer specialties, up at annual rates of 23 percent and 15 percent, respectively. In 1986, about one-quarter of women and one-tenth of men were computer specialists; these proportions increased from one-tenth and one-twentieth, respectively, in 1976.

Among women scientists, above-average employment growth rates were also experienced in psychology and the environmental, mathematical, and life sciences (figure 1-3). In contrast, one of the slowest growing fields for women was social science, registering an annual growth rate of about 9 percent over the decade. Because of this growth rate, the fraction of women in social science fell from 28 percent in 1976 to 19 percent in 1986.

About 60 percent of men, compared with 14 percent of women, were engineers in 1986. Employment of women engineers, however, has increased at a much more rapid rate than that of men over the 10-year period: 17 percent and 6 percent per year, respectively. For both women and men, the fastest growing field over the decade was electrical/electronics engineering. Above-average employment increases were also registered for women in aeronautical/astronautical and mechanical engineering.

larger fraction of employment of recent science and engineering graduates than of total S/E employment. In 1986, about 34 percent of employed graduates who were granted science and engineering baccalaureates in 1984 were women.[6] Similarly, at the S/E master's degree level, 27 percent of employed 1984 degree recipients were women. These proportions have increased since the late seventies: in 1980, women represented about 33 percent of employed 1978 S/E baccalaureate recipients and 23 percent of master's degree holders.

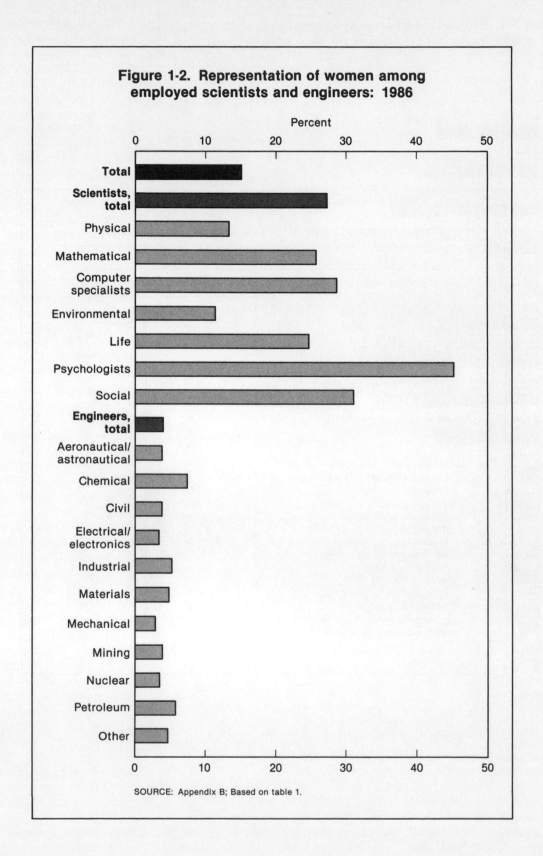

Figure 1-2. Representation of women among employed scientists and engineers: 1986

Percent

SOURCE: Appendix B; Based on table 1.

Table 1-1. Employed scientists and engineers by field and sex: 1986

Field	Men	Women
Scientists and engineers	3,927,800	698,600
	Percent	
TOTAL	100.0	100.0
Scientists, total	40.4	85.8
Physical	6.4	5.5
Mathematical	2.5	4.9
Computer specialists	10.2	23.3
Environmental	2.5	1.8
Life	7.9	14.7
Psychologists	3.5	16.5
Social	7.5	19.2
Engineers, total	59.6	14.2
Aeronautical/astronautical	2.7	0.6
Chemical	3.5	1.6
Civil	8.5	1.8
Electrical/electronics	14.1	2.7
Industrial	3.3	1.0
Materials	1.3	0.4
Mechanical	12.2	2.0
Mining	0.4	0.1
Nuclear	0.6	0.1
Petroleum	0.7	0.3
Other	12.2	3.5

SOURCE: Appendix B; Based on table 1.

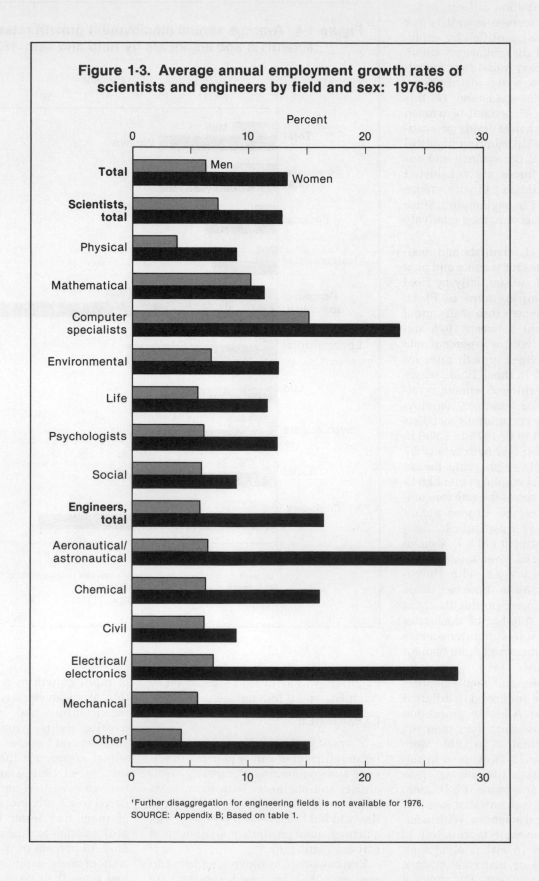

Figure 1-3. Average annual employment growth rates of scientists and engineers by field and sex: 1976-86

Percent

[1] Further disaggregation for engineering fields is not available for 1976.
SOURCE: Appendix B; Based on table 1.

The field distribution differences between men and women scientists and engineers may be quantified by applying the index of dissimilarity,[8] which provides a summary measure of overall differences between two distributions. In 1986, the index measured 47; this ratio means that 47 percent of women would have to change fields or occupations to have a distribution identical to that of men. If the science and engineering work forces are considered separately, the index is 24 in the science work force and 23 in engineering. Since 1976, the index has remained relatively stable.

Among doctoral scientists and engineers, growth rates for women and men have also varied substantially by field (figure 1-4). Employment of Ph.D. women in the sciences rose at an annual rate of 10 percent between 1975 and 1985, compared with a 4-percent rate for men. The highest growth rates for women occurred in those fields where the number of employed women is relatively small. For example, employment of women as computer specialists rose from about 150 in 1975 to 1,600 in 1985, representing a growth rate of 27 percent per year. In engineering, the annual growth rate in employment of Ph.D. women was five times the rate for comparable men over the 10-year period (20 percent versus 4 percent). In absolute terms, the number of Ph.D. women engineers increased from about 230 in 1975 to 1,500 in 1985. The above-average growth rates in these two fields partially reflect degree production: over the decade, the number of doctorates granted to women in computer science and engineering increased more than for all other S/E fields.

Doctoral women and men scientists and engineers are employed in different fields (figure 1-5). A higher proportion of women (98 percent) than men (81 percent) were scientists in 1985. More than four-fifths of Ph.D. women in science were in either life science, psychology, or social science. Ph.D. men, in contrast, were concentrated in either the life or physical sciences. Within engineering, women were more likely to be concentrated in either electrical/electronics (350) or materials science (250) engineering in 1985. The index of dissimilarity for doctoral scientists and

Figure 1-4. Average annual employment growth rates of doctoral scientists and engineers by field and sex: 1975-85

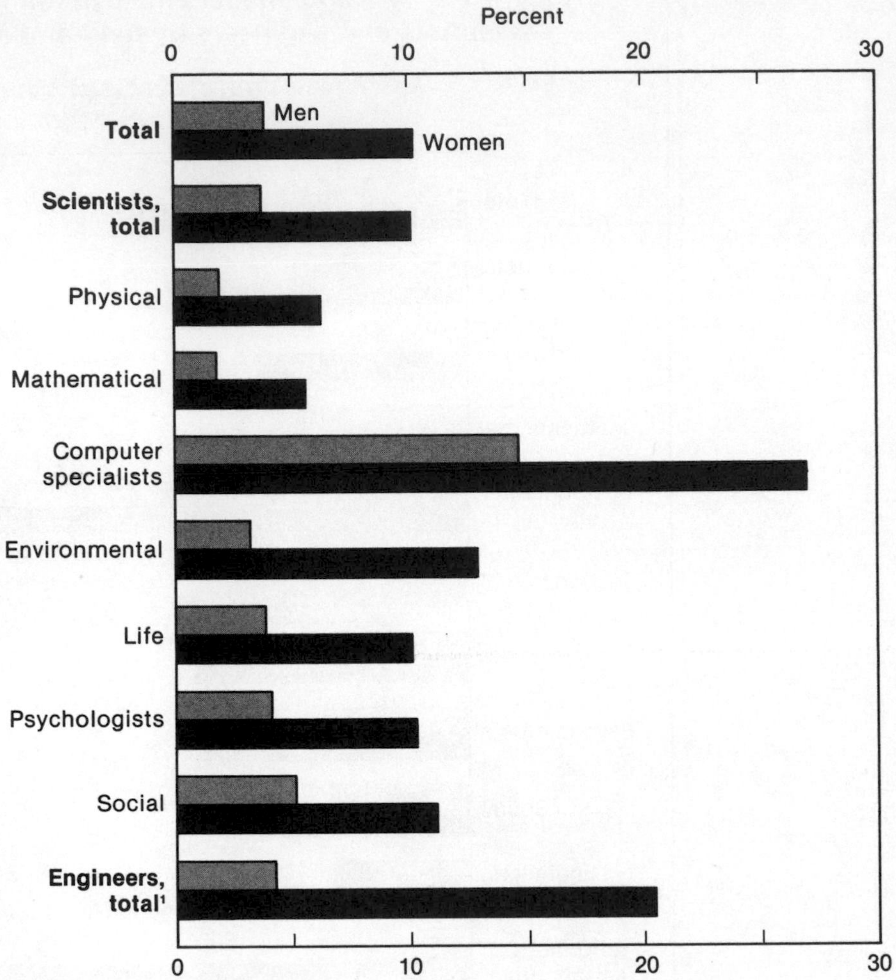

[1]Because the number of Ph.D. women engineers is small (1,500 in 1985), growth rates for engineering subfields are not presented.
SOURCE: Appendix B; Based on table 4.

engineers was 37 in 1985—29 for Ph.D. scientists and 8 for engineers.

EXPERIENCE

Years of professional experience may be an indicator of career patterns in science and engineering. For instance, scientists and engineers with more years of professional experience will be more likely to hold senior-level positions, e.g., a management position or attainment of full academic rank.

Employment of women scientists and engineers has increased substantially over the 1976-86 decade mostly because of rapid growth in S/E degree production at all levels. Given this relatively recent influx into science and engineering fields, women are generally younger and have fewer years of professional experience than their male colleagues. In 1986, almost three-fifths of women scientists and engineers, compared to slightly more than one-quarter of men, had fewer than 10 years of professional experience. Furthermore, only 15 percent of women, but 46 percent of men scientists and engineers, had more than 20 years of work experience.

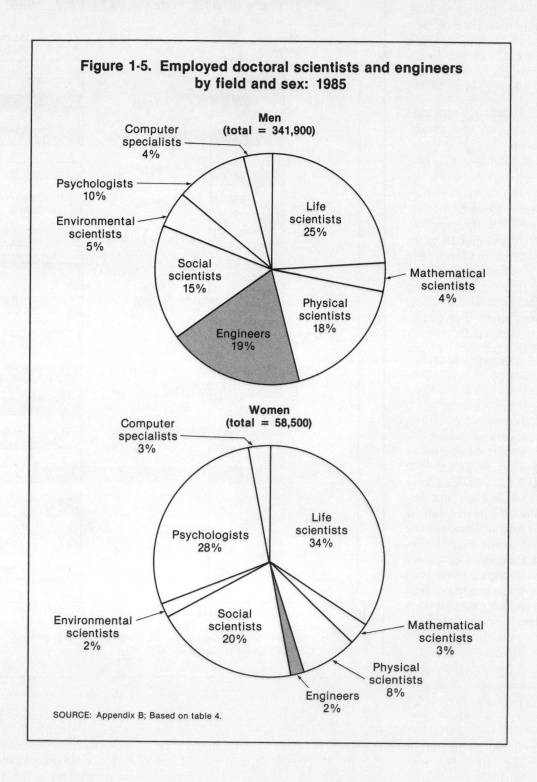

Figure 1-5. Employed doctoral scientists and engineers by field and sex: 1985

Men (total = 341,900)

- Computer specialists 4%
- Psychologists 10%
- Environmental scientists 5%
- Social scientists 15%
- Engineers 19%
- Physical scientists 18%
- Mathematical scientists 4%
- Life scientists 25%

Women (total = 58,500)

- Computer specialists 3%
- Psychologists 28%
- Environmental scientists 2%
- Social scientists 20%
- Engineers 2%
- Physical scientists 8%
- Mathematical scientists 3%
- Life scientists 34%

SOURCE: Appendix B; Based on table 4.

Years of work experience for women vary among S/E fields (figure 1-6). For example, in engineering—a field which has experienced a very large increase in employment of women—almost 68 percent of women have less than 10 years of professional work. In science fields overall, about 56 percent of women reported fewer than 10 years of work experience.

Doctoral women scientists and engineers also have fewer years of work experience than do doctoral men. In 1985, the proportion of women who had less than 10 years of work since receiving their doctorate was almost twice that of men: 54 percent versus 28 percent. Similarly, the fractions of Ph.D. scientists and engineers with more than 20 years of professional experience were 8 percent for women and 22 percent for men. The field variation in these proportions for women was not as great as among all scientists and engineers. For example, about 54 percent of Ph.D. women scientists, but 60 percent of doctoral women engineers, had fewer than 10 years' work experience.

CAREER PATTERNS

Since direct indicators of career development for scientists and engineers are not available, proxy measures that examine career-related activities may be substituted. For all scientists and engineers, the number and proportion in management, especially management of research and development (R&D) activities, are indirect indicators of career opportunities. In academia, tenure status and faculty rank of doctoral scientists and engineers similarly may be used to assess career development patterns.

Management

Women scientists and engineers were less likely than men to report their major work activity as management, either of R&D or other types of activities (e.g., educational programs). In 1986, about 19 percent of women, but 29 percent of men, reported management as their major work. These proportions varied substantially by field. Among engineers, the difference widened to 18 percentage points—13 percent for women versus 31 percent for men. Within engineering fields, the proportions of women pri-

Figure 1-6. Percentage of men and women with fewer than 10 years of work experience by field: 1986

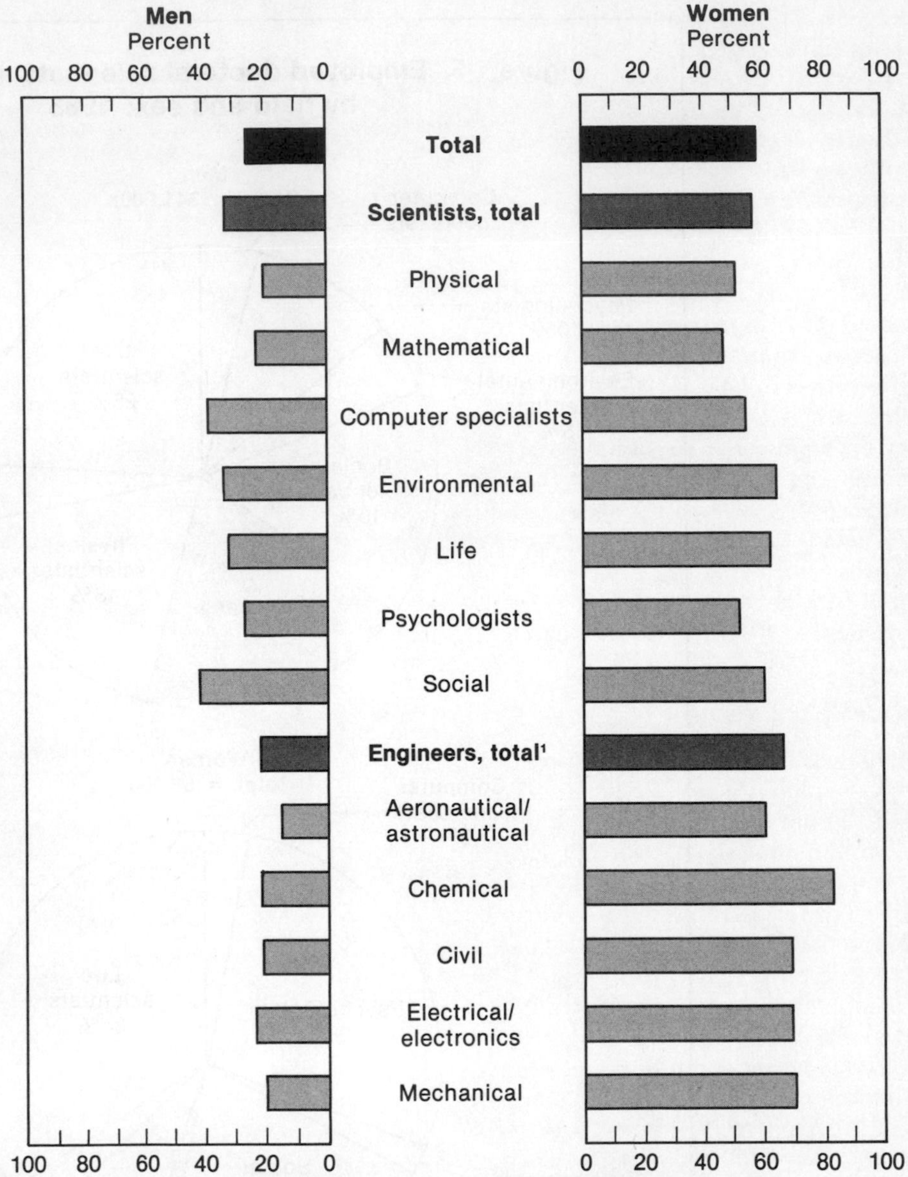

[1]Includes industrial, materials, mining, nuclear, petroleum, and other engineers.
SOURCE: Appendix B; Based on tables 9 and 10.

marily engaged in management activities ranged from 6 percent of petroleum engineers to 17 percent of industrial engineers. The range for men was 21 percent of petroleum engineers to 37 percent of civil engineers. Among scientists, the proportional differences were not as large: 20 percent of women reported management activities versus 27 percent of men. Although a higher fraction of men than women reported management activities among all science fields, this gap narrows considerably in some fields. For example, about 37 percent of men social scientists, compared with 33 percent of women, report management as their major work.

Within management, a larger share of men than women reported their primary work activity as R&D management: 32 percent versus 24 percent in 1986. However, this pattern did not hold across all fields of science and engineering (table 1-2). Among social scientists and psychologists, for example, a larger fraction of women than men in management reported R&D management as their primary work. Among engineers, about one-third of both women and men were primarily engaged in managing R&D activities.

Since 1976, the proportion of men who reported management as their major activity has fallen from 31 percent to 29 percent; concurrently, the proportion of women has increased, rising from 17 percent to 19 percent. This change partially reflects different sectoral growth patterns between men and women. For example, growth in the number of women employed in industry has far outpaced that of men over the decade. This sector has traditionally accounted for most scientists and engineers who report management as their primary work activity (two-thirds in 1986).

Sector of Employment

Between 1976 and 1986, employment of women scientists and engineers grew fastest in the industrial sector, rising at an annual rate of 17 percent (figure 1-7). The proportion of women employed in industry therefore rose from 36 percent to 51 percent. By field, above-average growth rates were experienced in computer specialties, engineering, and psychology. For men, employment in industry grew at about the same annual rate (6 percent) as that of total employment. About two-thirds of men were employed by industry in both 1976 and 1986. By field, there was relatively little difference by gender in the proportions employed in this sector. For example, a majority of female and male physical scientists, computer specialists, and engineers were employed in the industrial sector.

Employment of women in academia, primarily in 4-year colleges and universities, registered a below-average growth rate over the 10-year period (10 percent per year versus 13 percent for total employment of women). As a result, the proportion of women scientists and engineers working in this sector fell from 28 percent in 1976 to 21 percent

in 1986. In contrast, academia was the fastest growing sector of employment for men (8 percent per year). This sector, however, accounted for only 12 percent of employed men in 1986.

Tenure Status and Academic Rank

Among doctoral scientists and engineers employed in 4-year colleges and universities, men are more likely than

Table 1-2. Proportion of men and women in management who are primarily engaged in R&D management by field: 1986

Field	Men	Women
	Percent	
TOTAL	32.0	23.5
Scientists, total	31.9	22.4
Physical	60.0	40.4
Mathematical	43.0	34.7
Computer specialists	38.5	34.6
Environmental	35.2	26.3
Life	28.0	23.7
Psychologists	13.7	15.0
Social	15.9	18.2
Engineers, total	32.0	32.6
Aeronautical/astronautical	67.5	25.0
Chemical	36.6	30.0
Civil	8.6	4.8
Electrical/electronics	47.2	48.0
Mechanical	34.5	37.5
Other	26.0	35.7

SOURCE: Appendix B; Based on tables 18 and 19.

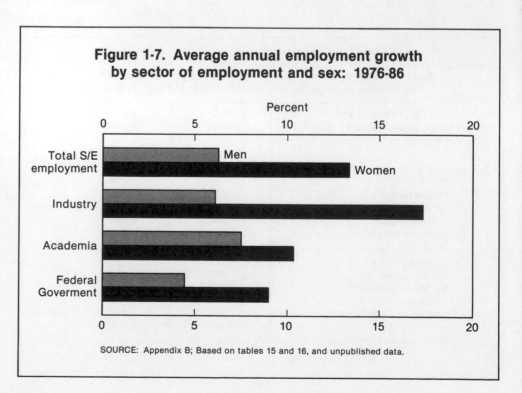

Figure 1-7. Average annual employment growth by sector of employment and sex: 1976-86

SOURCE: Appendix B; Based on tables 15 and 16, and unpublished data.

women to be tenured or hold full professorships (table 1-3). In 1985, almost four-fifths of Ph.D. men were either tenured or in tenure-track positions compared to three-fifths of Ph.D. women. Of those on tenure-track, almost 81 percent of men, compared to 61 percent of women, held tenure. Between 1983 and 1985, however, the number of doctoral women in tenured positions rose 12 percent while the number on tenure-track but not yet tenured rose 32 percent. Comparable growth rates for men were 2 percent and 20 percent.

In 1985, a smaller proportion of doctoral women (71 percent) than men (84 percent) held professorial rank (i.e., full, associate, or assistant professor). Women were much less likely than men to hold full professorships but more likely to hold assistant professorships. Between 1983 and 1985, however, the number of doctoral women holding professorial rank at all levels rose faster than that of men. For example, the number of Ph.D. women scientists and engineers who were full professors rose 13 percent compared to a 2-percent increase for men.

LABOR MARKET INDICATORS

Labor market indicators,[9] such as labor force participation and unemployment rates, are useful in assessing relative market conditions (i.e., employment opportunities relative to available supply) for scientists and engineers. Disparities in market conditions between women and men scientists and engineers may reflect differences in labor market behavior, demographic characteristics, behavior of employers, or a combination of these factors.

Labor Force Participation Rates

The labor force participation rates for both men and women scientists and engineers were about the same (95 percent versus 94 percent) in 1986. These rates are higher than those for the general population or the college-educated population. In 1986, about 55 percent of all women, and 73 percent of college-educated women, were in the labor force; for men, these rates were 76 percent and 88 percent, respectively.[10] Over the decade, participation rates increased for women scientists and engineers, rising from 90 percent in 1976; rates remained stable for men.

Labor force participation rates vary more for women than men among S/E fields (appendix table 26) although the rate for women scientists was the same as that for women engineers: 94 percent. Within science fields, rates ranged from 90 percent of life scientists to 97 percent of computer specialists; in engineering, the range was from 90 percent of chemical or electrical/electronics engineers to 99 percent of aeronautical/astronautical engineers in 1986.

The small fraction of women scientists and engineers who do not participate in the labor force cite different reasons than do men. In 1986, about 34 percent of women, but less than 1 percent of men, reported family responsibilities as their primary reason. In contrast, almost 78 percent of men, compared to 13 percent of women, indicated they were retired by 1986. Women were more than twice as likely as men to report that they were outside the labor force because they were students: 35 percent versus 15 percent. This pattern of responses for women scientists and engineers differed from that for all women outside the labor force. In 1986, about 67 percent of all women cited family responsibilities ("Keeping house"), 14 percent were retired, and 8 percent were students ("Going to school").[11]

Despite a relatively large fraction of women scientists and engineers outside the labor force citing family responsibilities, a number of women with children do actively participate in the S/E labor force. In 1986, this participation rate for women scientists and engineers with children present was 93 percent, about the same as that for all women scientists and engineers. Differences in rates, however, arise with respect to childrens' ages. For example, the labor force participation rate for women with children under the age of 6 was 94 percent; this percentage decreased, however, for those with children between the ages of 6 and 17 (88 percent).

Among doctoral scientists and engineers, women were slightly less likely than men to be employed or seeking employment. In 1985, the labor force participation rate for doctoral women was 93 percent compared with 95 percent for men (appendix table 27). Rates for women scientists were below those for comparable men, although there was variation by field. Among doctoral engineers, rates for women and men were essentially the same.

Among recent S/E graduates, labor force participation rates for women were

Table 1-3. Doctoral scientists and engineers in 4-year colleges and universities by tenure status, academic rank, and sex: 1985

Tenure status and academic rank	Ph.D. men	Ph.D. women
	Percent	
TENURE STATUS............	100.0	100.0
Tenure-track................	78.9	60.9
Tenured	63.1	37.3
Not tenured	15.8	23.6
Non-tenure-track...........	13.8	31.0
Other & no report...........	7.3	8.1
ACADEMIC RANK		
Full professor	43.7	16.4
Associate professor	24.0	24.9
Assistant professor	15.9	30.0
Other & no report...........	16.4	28.7

SOURCE: Appendix B; Based on tables 21, 22, 24, and 25.

also below those for men. In 1986, the rates for individuals who received S/E baccalaureates in either 1984 or 1985 were 99 percent (men) and 97 percent (women). This gap widens at the S/E master's level to 99 percent for men and 95 percent for women.

Unemployment Rates

Although most women and men scientists and engineers participate in the labor force, women report a higher unemployment rate than do men. In 1986, the rate for women was more than twice that for men: 2.7 percent versus 1.3 percent. Unemployment rates, however, have fallen for both women and men over the decade. In 1976, rates were 5.4 percent and 3.2 percent, respectively. The 1986 unemployment rate for women scientists and engineers was substantially lower than that for all women in the United States (7.1 percent)[12] but similar to that for women in professional occupations (2.3 percent)[13] or women college graduates (2.4 percent).[14]

Unemployment rates by gender vary between and within science and engineering fields (figure 1-8). Among all science fields, unemployment rates for women were above those for men. The largest differential was between women and men environmental scientists with 1986 rates of 8.2 percent and 3.9 percent, respectively. In contrast, unemployment rates for women (2.7 percent) and men (2.3 percent) social scientists were roughly similar. The lowest rates for both women and men were reported by computer specialists in 1986: 1.6 percent versus 0.6 percent.

Within engineering fields, rates for women were above those for men with one exception. In 1986, the unemployment rate for women electrical/electronics engineers (1 percent) was about the same as that for men.

The unemployment rates reported by both women and men doctoral scientists and engineers are lower than those of all scientists and engineers. However, rates for doctoral women were above those for doctoral men among all S/E fields. In 1985, the unemployment rate for women (1.8 percent) was more than twice that for men (0.7 percent). Over the 1975-85 decade, the rate for

women has declined from 2.9 percent, but has remained virtually unchanged for men (0.8 percent in 1975). By field, the largest differences by gender occurred for doctoral scientists, especially among social and physical scientists in 1985.

Unemployment rates for men and women who are recent S/E degree recipients are similar at the baccalaureate level; some differences begin to arise, however, at the master's degree level. For those who received their degrees in 1984 or 1985, unemployment rates for

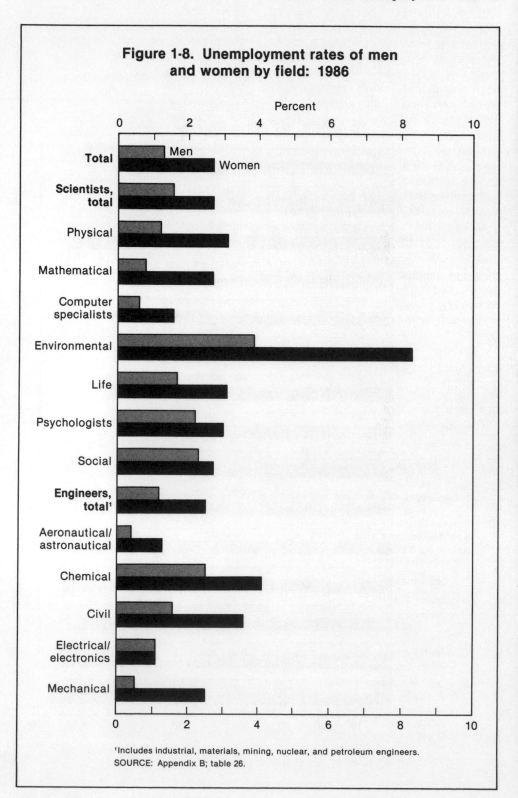

Figure 1-8. Unemployment rates of men and women by field: 1986

[1] Includes industrial, materials, mining, nuclear, and petroleum engineers.
SOURCE: Appendix B; table 26.

recent S/E bachelor's recipients were 3.4 percent (men) and 3.7 percent (women) in 1986. At this level, unemployment rates for women were below those for men in mathematics, environmental science, psychology, and among almost all engineering fields.[15] At the S/E master's degree level, the rate for women (3.2 percent) was almost twice that for men (1.7 percent). With little exception, women's unemployment rates were higher than men's across all fields.

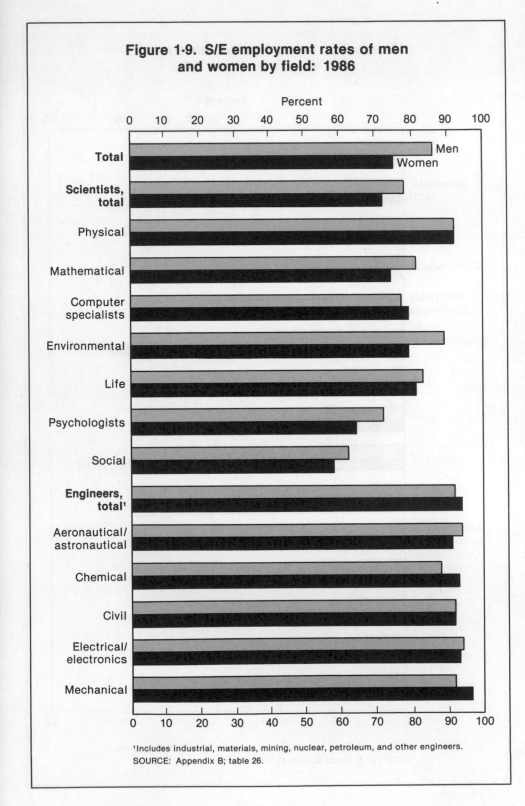

Figure 1-9. S/E employment rates of men and women by field: 1986

Percent

[1]Includes industrial, materials, mining, nuclear, petroleum, and other engineers.
SOURCE: Appendix B; table 26.

S/E Employment Rates

The S/E employment rate measures the extent to which employed scientists and engineers have a job in science or engineering. Women scientists and engineers are less likely than men to work in science- or engineering-related activities. In 1986, the S/E employment rate for women was 75 percent compared to 86 percent for men. These rates have declined steadily for both women and men throughout the eighties: in 1982, the rates were 80 percent (women) and 88 percent (men). The somewhat larger decline for women partially reflects their high concentrations in psychology and social science. The S/E employment rates in these fields have fallen dramatically during the eighties for both women and men. More than one-third of women, compared with about one-tenth of men, were in one of these fields in 1986.

S/E employment rates vary by field; the widest fluctuations occur in the sciences (figure 1-9). In 1986, the S/E employment rate for women scientists was 72 percent compared with 78 percent for men. In engineering, however, the rate for women (94 percent) was above that for men (92 percent).

Among doctoral scientists and engineers in 1985, the S/E employment rate for women (90 percent) was slightly lower than that for men (92 percent), and showed little variation by field (appendix table 27). The S/E employment rate for Ph.D. scientists and engineers has fallen for both women and men from 93 percent and 94 percent, respectively, in 1975.

The largest difference between S/E employment rates of women and men occurred among recent science and engineering graduates. In 1986, the rate for women S/E baccalaureate recipients (1984 or 1985 graduates) was 53 percent. This rate was much lower than the 70-percent rate for men and reflects the high concentration of women in social science and psychology where the overall S/E employment rate is about one-third.

Among science and engineering fields, variation is not as large as it is at the aggregate level. For example, about 90 percent each of women and men computer specialists were employed in S/E jobs, and the rates for electrical/electronics engineering graduates were 90 percent (women) and 92 percent (men). The difference in S/E employment rates narrows somewhat at the S/E master's degree level; in 1986, these rates were 78 percent for women and 87 percent for men.

S/E Underemployment Rates

Low rates of S/E employment could be indicators of underutilization depending on specific reasons for non-S/E employment. In 1986, women employed outside of science and engineering were more likely than men to report either preference, location, better pay, or lack of S/E job opportunities. Men, in contrast, were substantially more likely to report promotional opportunities as their reason for non-S/E employment. One way to measure potential underutilization among employed scientists and engineers is to use the S/E underemployment rate. Underemployment may be quantified and measured for scientists and engineers by calculating the number who are involuntarily working in non-S/E jobs (i.e., those who report a lack of available S/E jobs) and the number involuntarily working part-time (i.e., those actively pursuing full-time job opportunities) as a percent of total employment.

The S/E underemployment rate for women scientists and engineers was three times more than that for men in 1986: 6.3 percent versus 1.9 percent. The rates were higher for women among almost all major fields of science and engineering; the widest variation was exhibited in science fields (figure 1-10). In science, the underemployment rate for women was 7.0 percent compared to 3.3 percent for men. Only among computer specialties did women and men report identical rates—2.5 percent. In engineering, respective rates were 2.3 percent and 1.0 percent.

Among doctoral scientists and engineers, S/E underemployment rates were relatively low (compared to those for all scientists and engineers). The rate for women (3.9 percent), however, was above that for men (1.3 percent) in 1985.

S/E Underutilization Rates

To derive a more comprehensive indicator of potential underutilization, the numbers for those who are unemployed and those who are underemployed may be combined and expressed as a percentage of the labor force. This rate is only a partial measure, however, since it does not take into account the number of scientists and engineers who may have jobs requiring skills below those they actually possess.

The pattern exhibited in underutilization rates by gender mirrors that in underemployment rates. The S/E un-

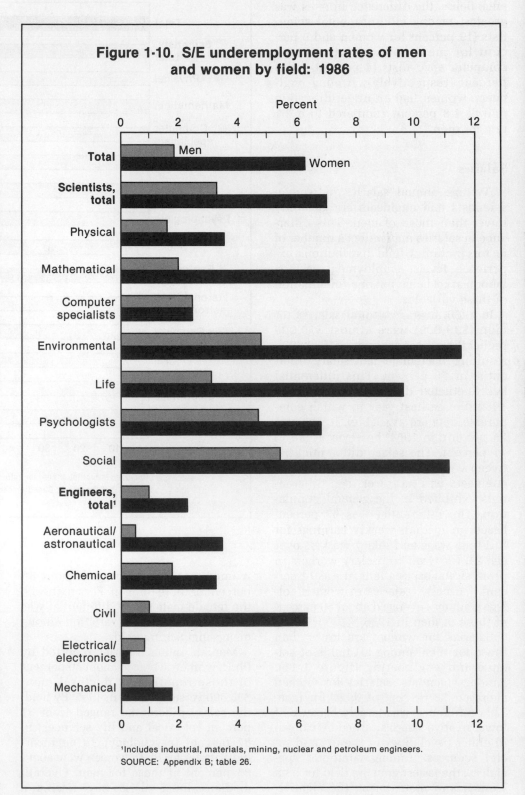

Figure 1-10. S/E underemployment rates of men and women by field: 1986

Percent

Total — Men / Women
Scientists, total
Physical
Mathematical
Computer specialists
Environmental
Life
Psychologists
Social
Engineers, total[1]
Aeronautical/astronautical
Chemical
Civil
Electrical/electronics
Mechanical

[1]Includes industrial, materials, mining, nuclear and petroleum engineers.
SOURCE: Appendix B; table 26.

derutilization rate for women scientists and engineers was substantially higher than the rate for men in 1986: 9 percent versus 3 percent. In addition, the rates for women were above those for men across all fields of science and engineering (appendix table 26). Within science fields, the difference in rates was greatest among environmental scientists (19 percent for women and 9 percent for men) and smallest among computer specialists (4 percent and 3 percent, respectively). Among engineers, women had an underutilization rate of 4.8 percent compared to a 2.1 rate for men.

Salaries

Average annual salaries of women scientists and engineers are generally lower than those of men. This difference in salaries may reflect a number of factors including field distributions, experience levels, employment sectors, labor market behavior, or a combination of these variables.

In 1986, average annual salaries for men ($39,800) were almost $10,000 higher than those for women ($29,900), resulting in a female-male salary differential of 75 percent. This differential has fluctuated during the eighties. In 1982 (the earliest year in which comparable data are available), it was also 75 percent; in 1984, however, it fell to 71 percent. The salary differential between women and men scientists and engineers was narrower than differentials exhibited in the general population. The differential was 67 percent based on median weekly earnings for full-time wage and salary workers over age 24; for wage and salary workers in professional occupations, it was 71 percent.[16] Finally, salaries of women college graduates averaged about 60 percent of those of men in 1986.[17]

Salaries for women are lower than those for men among all fields of science and engineering (figure 1-11). Among scientists, salaries for women averaged 76 percent of those for men. This difference was largely because of lower relative salaries earned by women in either psychology or the life and social sciences. Among computer specialists, the fastest growing field for both women and men during the eighties,

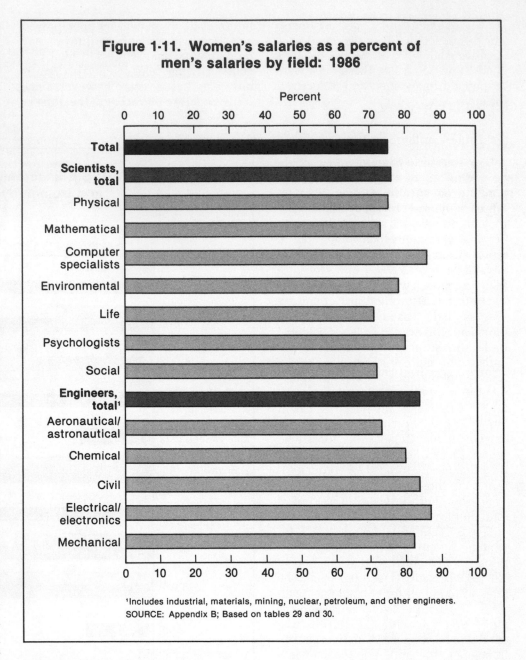

Figure 1-11. Women's salaries as a percent of men's salaries by field: 1986

[1]Includes industrial, materials, mining, nuclear, petroleum, and other engineers.
SOURCE: Appendix B; Based on tables 29 and 30.

women's salaries averaged about 86 percent of those for men. For engineers, the female-male salary differential was 84 percent with some variation among major engineering fields.

Median annual salaries reported by Ph.D. women averaged about 80 percent of those reported by doctoral men: $35,500 versus $44,500 in 1985. By field, the salary differential ranged from 81 percent (physical and life sciences) to 87 percent (psychology). In engineering, salaries for Ph.D. women were about 85 percent of those for men. Overall, median annual salaries have risen at a

slower rate for women than men over the decade; in 1975, the differential was 81 percent.

For recent S/E graduates, median annual salaries reported by women and men show that at the baccalaureate level, the female-male differential is about the same among all scientists and engineers. In 1986, the median annual salary of 1984 and 1985 women S/E graduates averaged about 74 percent of that for men. There is substantial variation by field. For example, recent women and men engineering graduates reported about the same median annual salaries ($30,000-$31,000) in 1986. At the S/E master's degree level, salaries for women averaged about 77 percent of those for men.

MINORITY WOMEN

The following section focuses first on racial minorities (blacks, Asians, and native Americans) and then on Hispanics. Data presented here are necessarily limited given the small sample sizes from which to generate estimates of minority women in science and engineering. Changes in data presented here are statistically significant at the 0.05 level.

Racial Minorities

Employment Levels and Trends

Racial minorities account for a larger share of employed women than of men scientists and engineers. In 1986, about 13 percent (89,700) of women were members of racial minority groups; the comparable fraction for men was 9 percent. During the eighties, this proportion did not change for women but has risen slightly for men from 7 percent in 1982 (the earliest year in which comparable data are available).

The racial background of women in 1986 was 87 percent white, 5 percent (34,500) black, 5 percent Asian (36,300), and less than 1 percent (2,700) native American.[18] The remaining 2 percent were either of mixed racial backgrounds or did not report their race. Among men, about 2 percent were black, 5 percent were Asian, and less than 1 percent was native American. In comparison with total U.S. employment, black women accounted for a higher fraction of all employed women (11 percent)[19] than of women in the S/E work force. Asians, however, were more highly represented among women scientists and engineers (2 percent of women in the U.S. work force were Asian).[20] Finally, about 22 percent of Asian women scientists and engineers were non-U.S. citizens in 1986, much higher than corresponding percentages among white or black women (about 1 percent each).

The representation of racial minorities among women varies substantially by S/E field (table 1-4). For example, in

Table 1-4. Racial minorities as a percent of employed women scientists and engineers by field: 1986

Field	Total	Black	Asian	Native American
Women scientists and engineers	698,600	34,500	36,300	2,700
	Percent			
TOTAL	100.0	4.9	5.2	0.4
Scientists, total	100.0	5.0	4.8	0.4
Physical	100.0	4.4	11.0	(1)
Mathematical	100.0	6.8	2.4	0.3
Computer specialists	100.0	4.4	5.4	0.2
Environmental	100.0	0.8	1.6	0.8
Life	100.0	3.2	5.4	1.0
Psychologists	100.0	5.2	3.8	0.4
Social	100.0	7.0	3.7	0.3
Engineers, total	100.0	4.4	7.4	0.3

(1)Too few cases to estimate.
SOURCE: Appendix B; Based on table 3.

1986, about 4 percent of women physical scientists were black and 11 percent were Asian. Among women environmental scientists, however, the proportions were much smaller: 0.8 percent and 1.6 percent, respectively. In examining representation as the proportion of each racial group accounted for by women, it was found that a higher proportion of black scientists and engineers were women than of other racial groups. In 1986, almost 30 percent of employed blacks were women compared to 15 percent of whites, 16 percent of Asians, and 11 percent of native Americans. Because of the more rapid growth rates for women scientists and engineers than for men, these proportions have increased since 1984.

Between 1984 and 1986, employment of black women scientists and engineers rose faster than that of either whites or Asians. These respective annual rates were 23 percent and 16 percent.

Among doctoral scientists and engineers, about 6,500 women (11 percent of all Ph.D. women) were members of racial minority groups in 1985. Of these, about 3.0 percent (1,700) were black, 7.0 percent (4,100) Asian, and 0.1 percent (less than 100) native American. For men, about 1.0 percent of doctoral sci-

entists and engineers were black, 9.0 percent were Asian, and 0.1 percent were native American.

Field

Table 1-5 illustrates differences in field distributions of women by racial group. The most significant dissimilarity is in the proportions in engineering. In 1986, about 20 percent of Asian women, compared to between 11 percent (native American) and 14 percent (white) of women in other racial groups, were engineers. This distributional difference between Asians and other groups is also evident at the aggregate level. For example, in 1986, about 59 percent of Asians were in engineering compared with 53 percent of whites and 36 percent of blacks.

Experience

Regardless of racial group, larger fractions of women than men scientists and engineers have less than 10 years of work experience. Among women, white and Asian scientists and engineers were more likely than blacks to report fewer than 10 years' professional work: 58 percent each versus 52 percent in 1986.

15

Table 1-5. Field distributions of women by racial group; 1986

(Percent)

Field	Total	White	Black	Asian	Native American
TOTAL...	100.0	100.0	100.0	100.0	100.0
Scientists, total	85.8	86.2	87.2	79.9	88.9
Physical	5.5	5.2	4.9	11.6	(1)
Mathematical	4.9	5.0	6.7	2.2	3.7
Computer specialists	23.3	23.5	20.9	24.2	14.8
Environmental	1.8	2.0	0.3	0.6	3.7
Life	14.7	14.6	9.6	15.4	37.0
Psychologists	16.5	16.8	17.4	12.1	18.5
Social	19.2	19.0	27.2	13.8	14.8
Engineers, total	14.2	13.8	12.8	20.1	11.1

(1)Too few cases to estimate.
SOURCE: Appendix B; Based on table 3.

Career Patterns

The proportion of women scientists and engineers who reported management as their primary work activity varied among racial groups. Black women (24 percent) were most likely to be primarily engaged in management activities, followed by Asian women (22 percent), and white women (19 percent) in 1986. Regardless of racial group, lower proportions of women than men reported their major work as management.

Sectoral distributions vary by racial group. For example, whereas about one-half each of white women and black women worked in industry in 1986, this sector employed almost three-fifths of Asian women. The proportions employed in academia ranged from 17 percent each for blacks and Asians to 22 percent for whites.

Other measures of career patterns among minority women are tenure status and academic rank. In terms of tenure status, Ph.D. black women were more likely to be in tenure-track positions—either tenured or waiting for tenure—than were white and, especially, Asian women. In 1985, these fractions were 72 percent, 61 percent, and 51 percent, respectively. Of those who were in tenure-track positions, however, about the same fraction of black, white, and Asian women (three-fifths) were tenured.

Variations are also evident in terms of the academic rank of doctoral women scientists and engineers by racial group. In 1985, a larger fraction of Asian women (27 percent) than either white (20 percent) or black (18 percent) women held full professorships. Blacks were more highly concentrated (39 percent) at the assistant professor level than were whites (36 percent) or Asians (31 percent).

Labor Market Indicators[21]

The labor force participation rates of women scientists and engineers vary only slightly by racial group. In 1986, the lowest rate was 93 percent for Asian women; the highest, 97 percent, was reported for native American women.

Although variation among racial groups was not large, Asians earned the highest average annual salaries among women scientists and engineers. In 1986, Asian scientists reported salaries of $28,700 compared to $29,400 for whites and $25,400 for blacks. These differences are greater in engineering: Asian women engineers earned an annual salary of $35,000; comparable salaries for white women and black women engineers were $34,300 and $32,900, respectively, in 1986.

Women scientists and engineers of all racial groups reported annual salaries lower than those for men. The differential between Asian women and Asian men was larger than among other racial groups. In 1986, Asian women earned 74 percent of men's salaries while the salary differential for black women and white women was, respectively, 78 percent and 76 percent.

Hispanics

Hispanics are a diverse ethnic group including individuals whose Spanish heritage could be from Central or South America, Asia, or Europe. It would be desirable to differentiate among these groups because they may face differing experiences in the S/E work force; however, because of data limitations, Hispanics will be treated in the aggregate. Among Hispanic women scientists and engineers, about 23 percent (4,600) were Mexican American, an additional 30 percent (5,800) were Puerto Rican, and 45 percent (8,900) were classified as "other Hispanic" in 1986; the remainder (300) did not report their Hispanic origins. Hispanic women were more likely than all women scientists and engineers to be non-U.S. citizens: 7 percent versus 3 percent in 1986.

Employment Levels and Trends

Almost 3 percent (19,600) of women scientists and engineers in 1986 were Hispanic, up from 2 percent (9,500) in 1982 (the earliest year in which comparable data are available). In contrast, about 2 percent of men were Hispanic. Although Hispanics were more highly represented among women than men scientists and engineers, their proportion of all employed women was double that of S/E women; in 1986, Hispanics constituted about 6 percent of all employed women in the United States.[22] Among doctoral women scientists and engineers, Hispanics accounted for 1.6 percent (less than 1,000) in 1985.

Field

Between 1984 and 1986, employment of Hispanic women grew at a slower rate than that of all women scientists and engineers: 29 percent versus 36 percent. In terms of field distributions, both Hispanic and all women were more apt to be scientists than engineers but within the sciences, differences emerged. For example, more than two-thirds of Hispanic women were either psychologists, or life or social scientists in 1986; less than three-fifths of all women were in these fields (figure 1-12).

Experience

Hispanic women scientists and engineers have substantially fewer years of professional work experience than do all women. In 1986, almost three-quarters of Hispanics, compared with less than three-fifths of all women, had less than 10 years' experience. The percentages of those with less than 5 years of experience were 45 percent for Hispanics and 31 percent for all women.

Career Patterns

Both Hispanic and all women scientists and engineers are about as likely to report management as their primary work activity; they also exhibit similar distributions in terms of employment sector. In 1986, less than one-fifth of Hispanic women scientists and engineers reported their major work as management. In that same year, about one-half of Hispanic women were employed in the industrial sector and an additional one-fifth worked in academia.

Among academically employed doctoral scientists and engineers, similar proportions of Hispanic and all women were tenured or in tenure-track positions. Additionally, about the same fractions of both held the rank of full professor. In 1985, about 61 percent of both doctoral Hispanic women and all Ph.D. women were in tenure-track positions; of these, about three of every five were tenured. In terms of academic rank, about one-fifth of both were full professors and another one-third held the associate professorship rank.

Labor Market Indicators

Hispanic women scientists and engineers are slightly less likely than all women to be in the labor force. In 1986,

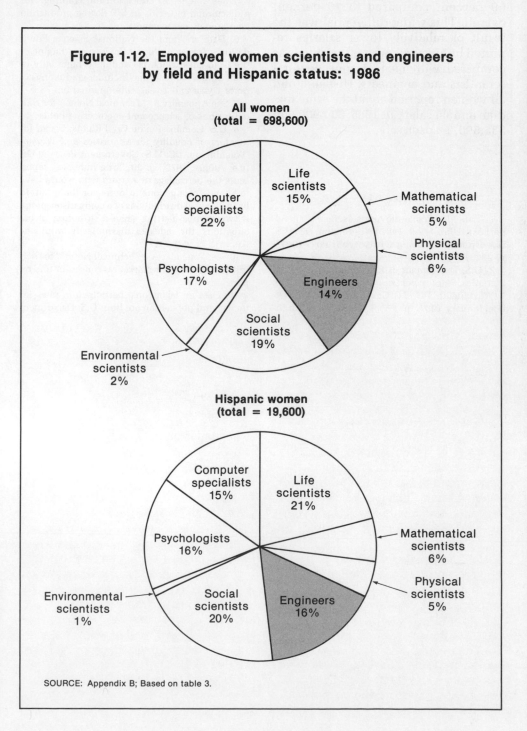

Figure 1-12. Employed women scientists and engineers by field and Hispanic status: 1986

All women (total = 698,600)

- Life scientists 15%
- Mathematical scientists 5%
- Physical scientists 6%
- Engineers 14%
- Social scientists 19%
- Environmental scientists 2%
- Psychologists 17%
- Computer specialists 22%

Hispanic women (total = 19,600)

- Life scientists 21%
- Mathematical scientists 6%
- Physical scientists 5%
- Engineers 16%
- Social scientists 20%
- Environmental scientists 1%
- Psychologists 16%
- Computer specialists 15%

SOURCE: Appendix B; Based on table 3.

respective labor force participation rates for Hispanics and all women scientists and engineers were 92 percent and 94 percent. Hispanic women also reported an average annual salary that was substantially lower than that of all women scientists and engineers: $25,200 versus $29,900. In addition, the salary differential between Hispanic women and Hispanic men was wider than the overall female-male differential. In 1986, the percentage differential for Hispanics was 69 percent compared to 75 percent overall. This wider differential was the result of relatively lower salaries reported by Hispanic women scientists as compared with men. Among doctoral scientists and engineers, Hispanic and all women reported about the same median annual salary in 1985: $34,900 and $35,500, respectively.

ENDNOTES

1. Council of Economic Advisors, *Economic Report of the President, 1987* (Washington, DC: U.S. Government Printing Office, February 1987), p. 282.

2. U.S. Department of Labor, Bureau of Labor Statistics, *Employment and Earnings*, Vol. 34, No. 1 (Washington, DC: U.S. Government Printing Office, January 1987), p. 177. This classification includes nine broad categories of professional occupations: engineering, mathematics and computer science, natural science, health diagnosis, health assessment and treatment, teaching (all educational levels), law, judicial, and other professional specialties.

3. Data on the characteristics of doctoral scientists and engineers in the United States are from the National Science Foundation's Survey of Doctorate Recipients. This survey has been conducted biennially in odd-numbered years since 1973.

4. The doctoral intensity rate is defined as doctoral S/E employment as a percentage of total S/E employment.

5. See Chapter 3, "Education and Training," for a discussion of trends in S/E degree production among men and women.

6. Data are from the National Science Foundation's Survey of Recent Science and Engineering Graduates which is conducted biennially in even-numbered years and includes graduating cohorts 1 year and 2 years after graduation.

7. See Appendix A, "Technical Notes," for NSF definitions of science and engineering fields.

8. U.S. Commission on Civil Rights, *Social Indicators of Equality for Minorities and Women* (Washington, DC: U.S. Government Printing Office, August 1978), p. 39. "The index . . . represents the percentage of a group who would have to change occupations in order for the group to have identical distributions of a comparison group. If two groups had the same distribution of occupations, the index of dissimilarity would be 0.0. . . ." (p. 44).

9. See Appendix A, "Technical Notes," for definitions of the labor market rates used in this report.

10. Data on labor force participation rates for the general population are from U.S. Department of Labor, Bureau of Labor Statistics, *Employment and Earnings*, p. 157. Rates for the college-educated population are from U.S. Department of Labor, Bureau of Labor Statistics, unpublished tabulations.

11. *Employment and Earnings*, p. 197.

12. Ibid., p. 168.

13. Ibid.

14. U.S. Department of Labor, Bureau of Labor Statistics, unpublished tabulations.

15. National Science Foundation, *Characteristics of Recent Science and Engineering Graduates: 1986*, detailed statistical tables (Washington, DC: Division of Science Resources Studies, 1987), in press.

16. *Employment and Earnings*, pp. 214-216.

17. U.S. Department of Labor, Bureau of Labor Statistics, unpublished tabulations.

18. Data for native Americans should be viewed with caution since the estimates are based on an individual's own classification with respect to native American heritage; such perceptions may change over time.

19. *Employment and Earnings*, pp. 158-160.

20. U.S. Department of Commerce, Bureau of the Census, *Detailed Occupation and Years of School Completed by Age for the Civilian Labor Force by Sex, Race, and Spanish Origin: 1980*, Supplementary Report #PC 80-SI-8, 1980 Census of the Population (Washington, DC: U.S. Government Printing Office, 1983), p. 7.

21. An analysis was made of S/E employment, unemployment, underemployment, and underutilization data for women by racial/ethnic group. Although rates varied, the observed differences were not statistically significant (at the 0.05 level) and therefore are not presented.

22. *Employment and Earnings*, p. 205.

CHAPTER 2

Minorities in Science and Engineering

OVERVIEW

Based on their representation in the overall U.S. work force, blacks and Hispanics remain underrepresented in science and engineering (S/E). Asians are not underrepresented, and the representation of native Americans among scientists and engineers is roughly equal to their representation in the total U.S. labor force.

The approximately 115,000 employed black scientists and engineers in 1986 represented 2.5 percent of all scientists and engineers, up from 1.6 percent in 1976 (figure 2-1). Blacks, however, account for 10 percent of total U.S. employment and almost 7 percent of all employed professional and related workers. In 1986, about 2 percent (93,000) of all employed scientists and engineers were Hispanic; the Hispanic shares of all employed persons and those in professional and related occupations were 7 percent and 3 percent, respectively. Asians represented about 5 percent (227,000) of all scientists and engineers, but only about 2 percent of the U.S. labor force. There were about 24,000 native American scientists and engineers in 1986, accounting for less than 1 percent of total S/E employment; this number was roughly similar to their representation in the overall U.S. work force. Less than 2 percent (70,000) of employed scientists and engineers reported a physical disability in 1986.

Over the 1976-86 decade, employment of black scientists and engineers increased more than twice as rapidly as did employment of whites: 200 percent (12 percent per year) versus 96 percent (7 percent per year). Employment of Asians rose by 113 percent (8 percent per year). Between 1984 and 1986, employment of native American scientists and engineers increased at a rate similar to that for whites. Growth in Hispanic employment was about one-half that for all scientists and engineers over the most recent 2-year period.

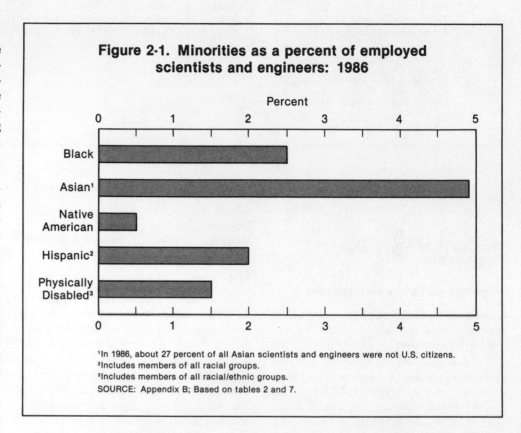

Figure 2-1. Minorities as a percent of employed scientists and engineers: 1986

[1] In 1986, about 27 percent of all Asian scientists and engineers were not U.S. citizens.
[2] Includes members of all racial groups.
[3] Includes members of all racial/ethnic groups.
SOURCE: Appendix B; Based on tables 2 and 7.

Racial/ethnic groups differ with respect to field distributions. The proportions in engineering ranged from about 59 percent of Asians to 36 percent of blacks; about 53 percent of whites were engineers. In the sciences, blacks were more likely than others to be social scientists and psychologists. Asians were least likely to be in these fields.

Asians and, to a lesser extent, Hispanics are less likely than other scientists and engineers to report management or administration as their primary work activity. In 1986, for example, 22 percent of Asians and 26 percent of Hispanics cited management as their major activity. Blacks and native Americans are as likely as whites to hold management positions.

Black and Hispanic scientists and engineers, on average, earn salaries below those earned by either whites or by all scientists and engineers combined. In contrast, Asians and native Americans report salaries equal to or above those for whites. Salaries for blacks averaged 81 percent of those for whites in 1986 (table 2-1). Hispanics earned 90 percent of the salaries paid across all racial/ethnic groups.

On average, minorities are more likely than majority scientists and engineers to be unemployed and underemployed, and are less likely to hold S/E jobs (table 2-1). For example, unemployment among black scientists and engineers in 1986 averaged 3.8 percent; for whites and Asians, the unemployment rates were 1.5 percent and 1.8 percent, respectively. Almost 6 percent of blacks reported that they were underemployed as did 2.5 percent of whites and 2.2 percent of Asians. The proportion of employed scientists and engineers working

Table 2-1. Selected characteristics of scientists and engineers: 1986

Characteristic	White	Black	Asian	Native American	Hispanic(1)	Physically Disabled(2)
Unemployment rate	1.5	3.8	1.8	1.2	2.1	1.5
S/E employment rate	84.9	76.5	87.7	79.3	80.2	90.2
S/E underemployment rate	2.5	5.5	2.2	2.4	4.8	NA
Average annual salary	$38,700	$31,500	$39,100	$41,000	34,600	NA

(1)Includes members of all racial groups.
(2)Includes members of all racial/ethnic groups.
NA: Not available.
SOURCE: Appendix B; Based on tables 7, 26, and 28.

in S/E jobs ranged from 88 percent of Asians to about 77 percent of blacks.

BLACKS IN SCIENCE AND ENGINEERING

Employment Levels and Trends

Despite significant employment gains, blacks remain underrepresented in science and engineering. Over the 1976-86 decade, employment of black scientists and engineers increased more than twice as rapidly as employment of their white counterparts: 200 percent (12 percent per year) versus 96 percent (7 percent per year). More recently, in the 2-year period from 1984 to 1986, S/E employment of blacks rose 27 percent (13 percent annually) compared with 15 percent (7 percent annually) for whites.

In 1986, the approximately 115,000 employed black scientists and engineers made up 2.5 percent of all employed scientists and engineers. While this proportion was up from 1.6 percent in 1976, blacks in 1986 represented 10.0 percent of total U.S. employment and 6.7 percent of those employed in professional and related occupations.[1]

Blacks also remain underrepresented in the doctoral science and engineering work force. Over the 1975-85 decade, employment of black Ph.D.'s increased by 127 percent (9 percent per year), while white employment rose by 53 percent (4 percent per year). In 1985, about 5,700 (1.4 percent) of the doctoral S/E work force was black, up from 2,500 (almost 1.0 percent) in 1975.

Among scientists and engineers at all degree levels in 1986, blacks were about twice as likely as whites to be non-U.S. citizens: 3.0 percent versus 1.5 percent.

Field

By field, the representation of blacks in 1986 ranged from more than 5 percent of mathematical and social scientists to about 1 percent of environmental scientists. Among doctoral scientists and engineers, black representation ranged from 2.7 percent of social scientists to 0.6 percent of both computer specialists and environmental scientists.

Blacks remain more likely than whites to be scientists rather than engineers. In 1986, 64 percent of employed blacks were scientists, compared to 47 percent of whites. Within science fields, blacks were most likely to be social scientists or computer specialists (figure 2-2). Over the 1976-86 period, the most rapid employment gains occurred among black computer specialists (up 28 percent per year) and social scientists (up about 21 percent annually). In comparison, annual employment growth of whites in these fields rose 16 percent and 7 percent, respectively.

An index of dissimilarity[2] can be used to summarize general field differences of various groups. The index between whites and blacks was 20 in 1986; that is, about 20 percent of blacks would have to change fields to have a distribution identical to that of whites.

Among doctoral scientists and engineers, a higher proportion of blacks (91

percent) than whites (85 percent) were scientists rather than engineers. About one-half of all blacks were either social scientists (30 percent) or psychologists (21 percent) in 1985. In contrast, 16 percent of whites were social scientists and 14 percent were psychologists. The index of dissimilarity between black and white doctoral scientists and engineers in 1985 was 24.

Experience

In general, blacks have fewer years' professional experience than do whites. Almost 40 percent of black scientists and engineers in 1986 had fewer than 10 years of work experience, compared with about 29 percent of whites. Black scientists report fewer years of experience than do black engineers: about 42 percent of scientists, but only 30 percent of engineers, reported fewer than 10 years' experience. Among black social scientists, almost 60 percent had fewer than 10 years of experience; more than one-half of these had less than 5 years.

Career Patterns

White scientists and engineers are more likely than blacks to work in industry. In 1986, 62 percent of whites and 52 percent of blacks were working in this sector. Among scientists, 48 percent of whites and 42 percent of blacks were in industry; the comparable figures for engineers were 74 percent and 70 percent, respectively. Black scien-

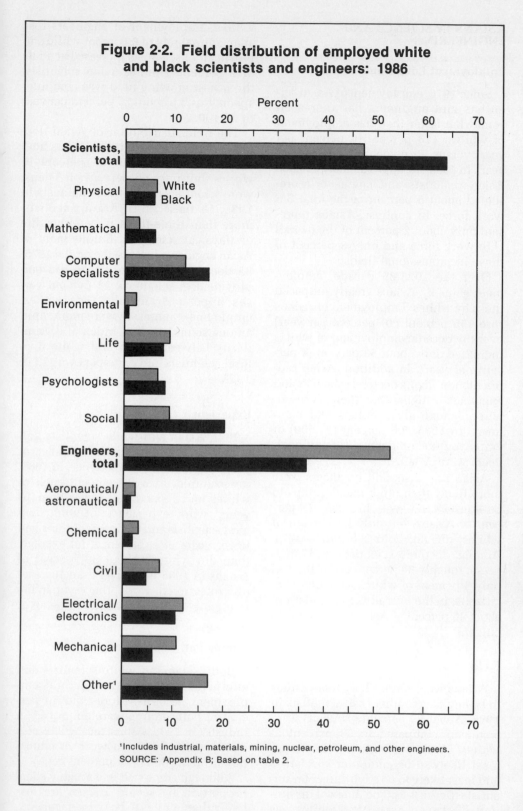

Figure 2-2. Field distribution of employed white and black scientists and engineers: 1986

Percent

- Scientists, total
- Physical — White / Black
- Mathematical
- Computer specialists
- Environmental
- Life
- Psychologists
- Social
- Engineers, total
- Aeronautical/astronautical
- Chemical
- Civil
- Electrical/electronics
- Mechanical
- Other[1]

[1]Includes industrial, materials, mining, nuclear, petroleum, and other engineers.
SOURCE: Appendix B; Based on table 2.

25 percent of whites and 30 percent of blacks were in management; for engineers, the proportions were reversed: 31 percent for whites and 26 percent for blacks.

Black doctoral scientists and engineers employed in 4-year colleges and universities are less likely than their white colleagues to either hold tenure or be full professors. In 1985, 60 percent of whites and 54 percent of blacks held tenure. Roughly equal proportions of whites and blacks (about 17 percent) were in non-tenure track positions. In 1985, 40 percent of whites, but only 29 percent of blacks, were full professors. In contrast, 24 percent of whites and 34 percent of blacks were associate professors.

Labor Market Indicators

Black scientists report different labor market experiences than do whites. While blacks are slightly more likely than whites to be in the labor force, they are also more likely to be unemployed and underemployed and are less likely to be working in S/E jobs.

Blacks in 1986 reported a labor force participation rate of 97 percent; for whites, this rate was 94 percent. The participation rate for blacks was much higher than that for blacks in the overall population (63 percent)[3] or for black college graduates (87 percent).[4] Since 1976, the labor force participation rate for black scientists and engineers has remained relatively stable.

Once in the labor force, blacks are more likely than whites to be unemployed. Unemployment rates for black scientists and engineers averaged 3.8 percent in 1986; this rate was more than twice the 1.5-percent rate for whites. The unemployment rate for black scientists and engineers has, however, declined from 5.9 percent in 1976. The unemployment rate for black doctoral scientists and engineers was 1.2 percent in 1985. In the overall U.S. work force, the unemployment rate for blacks was 14.5 percent,[5] and black college graduates registered a 3.6-percent rate.[6]

By field, unemployment rates for black scientists and engineers range from 6.8 percent among social scientists, to around 1.0 percent for mathematical and environmental scientists. Unemployed

tists and engineers, however, are almost twice as likely as whites to work for the Federal Government: 13 percent versus 8 percent.

Both blacks and whites are about equally as likely to report management or administration as their primary work activity. In 1986, roughly 28 percent of both racial groups were engaged in some aspect of management. However, there were some differences between scientists and engineers. Among scientists, black social scientists accounted for almost two-fifths of the total unemployment among black scientists and engineers (appendix table 26).

In 1976, the S/E employment rates for both blacks and whites were about the same (between 91 percent and 92 percent). Since that time, both rates have declined, largely resulting from above-average growth in fields with relatively low S/E employment rates. Blacks now are employed in non-S/E jobs more often than are whites. In 1986, the S/E employment rate for blacks was 77 percent, compared with 85 percent for whites. The rate is lower for blacks across all major fields of science except mathematical science; here the rate for blacks (90 percent) was above that for whites (79 percent). For engineers, the S/E employment rate was 90 percent for blacks and 92 percent for whites. The S/E employment rate among doctoral scientists and engineers also was lower for blacks than for whites: 86 percent versus 91 percent in 1985.

Black scientists and engineers experience higher rates of underemployment than do whites, 5.5 percent compared to 2.5 percent in 1986. This higher rate primarily results from the underemployment of blacks in science fields (7.5 percent versus 4.2 percent). Across these fields, black social scientists registered the highest rate (13 percent). Underemployment among engineers, on the other hand, averaged only 2 percent for blacks and 1 percent for whites.

Black scientists and engineers earned annual salaries that were, on average, 81 percent ($7,200 less) of those for whites. In 1986, salaries were $31,500 and $38,700, respectively. Annual salaries for blacks were lower than those for whites across all major S/E fields. The greatest differential occurred among social scientists where salaries for blacks ($22,800) were about 71 percent of those for whites. In contrast, salaries for black mathematical scientists averaged 93 percent of those for whites. The overall differential in annual salaries was smaller at the doctoral level. Black doctoral scientists and engineers earned salaries about $40,000 per year in 1985; this average salary was approximately 92 percent (or $3,600 less) of those for white Ph.D. scientists and engineers.

ASIANS IN SCIENCE AND ENGINEERING

Employment Levels and Trends

Since 1976, employment of Asian scientists and engineers has increased somewhat faster than has employment of whites: 113 percent (8 percent per year) versus 96 percent (7 percent per year). In 1986, the approximately 226,800 Asian scientists and engineers represented about 5 percent of the total S/E work force. In contrast, Asians represent only about 2 percent of the overall U.S. work force and only 3 percent of those in professional fields.[7]

Over the 1975-85 decade, employment gains by Asians greatly outpaced those by whites. Employment of Asians rose 155 percent (10 percent per year) over the decade; employment of whites increased only about 53 percent (4 percent per year). In addition, Asian representation among doctoral scientists and engineers is higher than their representation among all scientists and engineers. In 1985, 8.6 percent (34,500) of employed doctoral scientists and engineers were Asian.

Asian scientists and engineers were more likely than other racial groups to be non-U.S. citizens. In 1986, 27 percent of Asians, but only 1.5 percent of whites, did not hold U.S. citizenship. Among doctoral scientists and engineers, roughly 34 percent of Asians and only 3 percent of whites were non-U.S. citizens. In the overall U.S. population, about 40 percent of Asians were not U.S. citizens.

Field

Asians were more likely than whites to be engineers rather than scientists in 1986. About 59 percent of Asians were engineers compared to 53 percent of whites. Among scientists, Asians are most likely to be computer specialists and least likely to be environmental scientists (figure 2-3). The index of dissimilarity between Asians and whites was 15 in 1986; that is, 15 percent of Asians would have to change fields to have a distribution similar to that for whites.

Over the 1976-86 decade, employment of Asian engineers increased more rapidly than did that of Asian scientists: 9 percent versus 7 percent per year. For whites, employment of engineers rose at an annual rate of 6 percent while employment of scientists increased at a rate of 9 percent. Among Asian scientists, the fastest growing field was computer specialties, up about 25 percent per year to 36,100.

The field distribution of Asian doctoral scientists and engineers differs from that of whites. About 85 percent of whites, but only 66 percent of Asians, were scientists rather than engineers in 1985. Of these Ph.D. Asian scientists, more than three-fifths were either life or physical scientists. Employment of Asian engineers increased over the 1975-85 decade more rapidly than did employment of scientists: 11 percent versus 9 percent annually. For whites, employment increases were more rapid among scientists. The index of dissimilarity between Asian and white doctoral scientists and engineers was 23 in 1985.

Experience

Both Asian and white scientists and engineers report a similar number of years of professional experience. In 1986, for example, over 30 percent each of whites and Asians had fewer than 10 years' work experience. Among doctoral scientists and engineers, Asians had fewer years of experience, on average, than did whites. About 39 percent of Asians in 1985 had fewer than 10 years of professional work; the comparable figure for whites was about 31 percent.

Career Patterns

Both Asian and white scientists and engineers show similar sectoral employment patterns. More than 60 percent of both groups were employed in industry in 1986. Asians and whites also were equally likely to work in educational institutions (13 percent each).

Although employed in a roughly equal proportion by sector, Asians are less likely than whites to be in management. In 1986, 28 percent of whites, but only 22 percent of Asians, reported management or administration as their major work activity.

The tenure status and academic rank of Asian scientists and engineers also differ from those of whites. Among doc-

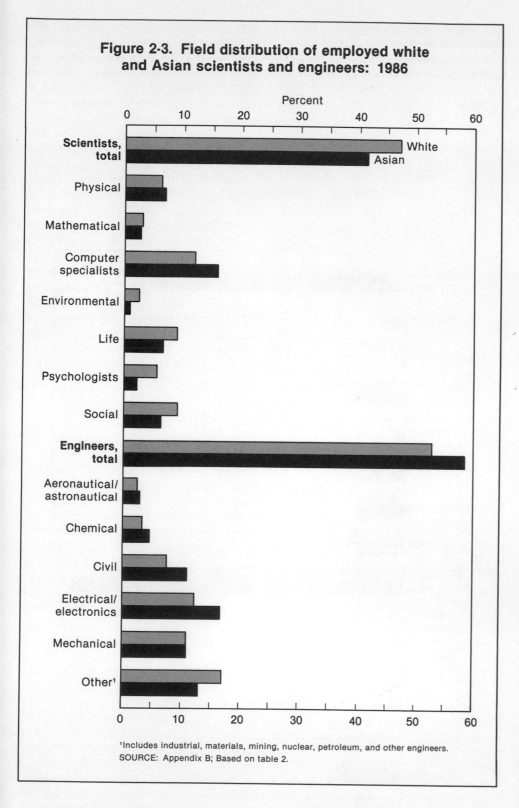

Figure 2-3. Field distribution of employed white and Asian scientists and engineers: 1986

Percent

Scientists, total — White / Asian
Physical
Mathematical
Computer specialists
Environmental
Life
Psychologists
Social
Engineers, total
Aeronautical/astronautical
Chemical
Civil
Electrical/electronics
Mechanical
Other[1]

[1]Includes industrial, materials, mining, nuclear, petroleum, and other engineers.
SOURCE: Appendix B; Based on table 2.

at the associate level, the fraction was about 24 percent for both groups.

Labor Market Indicators

Labor market conditions are about the same for both Asian and white scientists and engineers. Asians are slightly more likely than whites to be in the labor force, have a slightly higher unemployment rate, and are more likely to work in S/E jobs.

The labor force participation rate for Asians in 1986 (96 percent) was slightly above that for whites (94 percent). This rate for Asians, however, has fallen since 1976 when it was 99 percent. In the overall U.S. population, Asians had a labor force participation rate of roughly 70 percent.[8]

Unemployment among Asian scientists and engineers in 1986 was 1.8 percent; for whites, this rate was 1.5 percent. For Asians in the general population, the unemployment rate was about 5 percent.[9] The unemployment rate for Asian scientists and engineers varied over the 1976-86 decade. In 1976, the rate was 1.5 percent; by 1982, this rate had increased to 3.3 percent; and by 1984, it had dropped to 2.4 percent. Among doctoral scientists and engineers, the unemployment rate for Asians was about 1.0 percent in 1985, down from 1.6 percent in 1975.

Asian scientists and engineers are somewhat more likely than whites to work in S/E jobs. In 1986, the S/E employment rate for whites was 85 percent; for Asians, it was 88 percent. This high rate reflects the relatively large proportion of Asians who are engineers rather than scientists. The S/E employment rate for Asian engineers was 95 percent in 1986; for whites, it was 92 percent. Among scientists, both Asians and whites reported similar S/E employment rates of 77 percent. Over the 1976-86 period, the S/E employment rate for Asians remained essentially unchanged. Among doctoral scientists and engineers in 1985, the S/E employment rate for Asians was 95 percent compared with 91 percent for whites.

Only 2.2 percent of Asian scientists and engineers were underemployed in 1986. The corresponding rate for whites was 2.5 percent. Asians' S/E underemployment rate varied by field. For ex-

toral scientists and engineers in 4-year colleges and universities, Asians are less likely than whites to hold tenure: in 1985, roughly one-half of Asians, compared with three-fifths of whites, held tenure. A higher proportion of Asians (22 percent) than whites (17 percent) were in non-tenure track positions. Further, Asians and whites show some differences in measures of academic rank. In 1985, 36 percent of Asians and 40 percent of whites were full professors;

ample, Asian scientists exhibited a rate of 3.5 percent; for engineers, the rate was 1.2 percent.

Asian and white scientists and engineers earned roughly similar salaries in 1986 ($39,100 and $38,700, respectively). While both Asian and white engineers earned approximately similar salaries, among scientists, Asians' salaries averaged 103 percent of those for whites. Within the sciences, salary differences varied substantially by field. For example, Asian psychologists earned salaries averaging about 66 percent of those for whites, while salaries of Asian social scientists were 120 percent of those for whites. At the Ph.D. level, salaries for Asians and whites were roughly similar in 1985: $44,000 and $43,200, respectively.

NATIVE AMERICANS IN SCIENCE AND ENGINEERING

Employment Levels and Trends

Data for native Americans should be viewed with some caution for several reasons. First, estimates for both scientists and engineers, and for the overall U.S. labor force, are based on self-reported data. Second, sample sizes for native Americans are very small; statistical reliability is thus lower for data on native Americans than for other groups.[10]

In 1986, the 23,600 employed native American scientists and engineers represented about 0.5 percent of the science and engineering work force; this proportion was similar to their representation both in professional and related fields and in the overall U.S. work force.[11] Between 1982 (the earliest year in which data are available) and 1986, employment of native American scientists and engineers rose more rapidly than did employment of whites: 51 percent (11 percent per year) versus 40 percent (9 percent per year).

There are relatively few native Americans in the doctoral science and engineering work force. In 1985, about 500 (0.1 percent) were native American, up from about 200 (0.1 percent) in 1975.

Field

Native Americans are about as likely as whites to be engineers rather than

scientists. In 1986, 56 percent of native Americans and 53 percent of whites were engineers. Within science and engineering, however, some differences in field distributions do arise (figure 2-4).

Native American doctoral scientists and engineers were more highly concentrated in the sciences than engineering in 1985: 83 percent versus 17 percent. Within the sciences, almost 3 of every 5 were either life or social scientists. This field distribution has

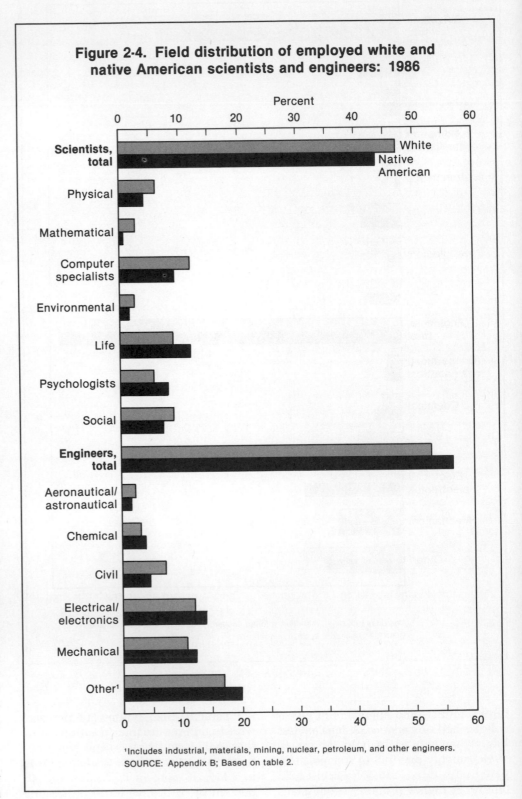

Figure 2-4. Field distribution of employed white and native American scientists and engineers: 1986

¹Includes industrial, materials, mining, nuclear, petroleum, and other engineers.
SOURCE: Appendix B; Based on table 2.

changed somewhat since 1975 when almost all Ph.D. native Americans were scientists.

Experience

Native Americans, on average, report more years of professional experience than do whites. In 1986, about 20 percent of native Americans, compared with 30 percent of whites, reported less than 10 years' work experience.

Career Patterns

The industrial sector employs roughly similar shares of both native American and white scientists and engineers. In 1986, this sector employed slightly more than 60 percent of both native Americans and whites. However, native Americans were less likely than whites to be academically employed: 8 percent and 14 percent, respectively. Native Americans are about as likely as whites to report management or administration as their primary work activity (30 percent and 28 percent, respectively, in 1986).

Among doctoral scientists and engineers employed in 4-year colleges and universities, native Americans were more likely than whites to hold tenure: 67 percent and 60 percent, respectively. Native Americans are more likely then whites to be associate rather than full professors; in 1985, 33 percent of native Americans and 40 percent of whites were full professors. About 67 percent of native Americans, but only 24 percent of whites, were at the associate professor level.

Labor Market Indicators

Native American scientists and engineers generally experience favorable labor market conditions. In 1986, they were more likely than whites to be in the labor force, less likely to be unemployed or underemployed, but also less likely to work in S/E jobs.

In 1986, native American scientists and engineers reported a labor force participation rate of 96 percent; for whites, the rate was 94 percent. Among those in the labor force, 1.2 percent of native Americans and 1.5 percent of whites were unemployed.

The S/E employment rate for native Americans (79 percent) was somewhat below that for whites (85 percent). The relatively lower rate for native Americans largely reflected differences among scientists. In 1986, the rate for native American scientists was 68 percent, well below the 77-percent rate for whites. Among scientists, relatively low rates for native Americans were recorded for life scientists (63 percent versus 83 percent for whites). At about 2.5 percent each, native Americans and whites had similar underemployment rates. Data on annual salaries reflect generally favorable labor market conditions for native Americans. In 1986, native American scientists and engineers had annual salaries of $41,000 compared to $38,700 for whites.

HISPANICS IN SCIENCE AND ENGINEERING

Differentiating among Mexican Americans, Puerto Ricans, and other Hispanics is desirable since socioeconomic backgrounds and reasons for underrepresentation may vary among these groups. Because of data limitations, however, most of this discussion treats Hispanics in the aggregate.

About 30 percent of the employed Hispanic scientists and engineers were Mexican American and 15 percent were Puerto Rican. The remaining 55 percent were either "other Hispanic" or did not report their specific Hispanic origins.[12] In the total U.S. work force, about 61 percent of Hispanics were Mexican Americans and 10 percent were Puerto Ricans.[13]

Employment Levels and Trends

Hispanics remain underrepresented in science and engineering. The approximately 93,400 employed Hispanic scientists and engineers in 1986 represented 2 percent of all scientists and engineers. This proportion was down from 2.2 percent in both 1982 and 1984. Between 1982 (the earliest year in which data are available) and 1984, employment of Hispanic and of all scientists and engineers increased at about the same annual rate (11 percent). Between 1984 and 1986, however, the annual rate of growth for Hispanics averaged only

about one-half that for all scientists and engineers: 4 percent versus 8 percent. Roughly 6.6 percent of all employed persons in the United States were Hispanic in 1986 as were 3.3 percent of those in professional and related occupations.[14]

In 1986, about 11 percent of Hispanic scientists and engineers were non-U.S. citizens; the comparable figure for all scientists and engineers was about 3 percent. Among all Hispanics in the United States, about 20 percent were not U.S. citizens.

Hispanics are also underrepresented among doctoral scientists and engineers. In 1985, the 5,900 Hispanic Ph.D. scientists and engineers represented 1.5 percent of all doctoral scientists and engineers; their employment was up from 2,000 (0.8 percent) in 1975. Among Hispanic doctoral scientists and engineers, about 15 percent were not U.S. citizens in 1985; an additional 25 percent were foreign-born but held U.S. citizenship.

Field

There are relatively small differences between the field distributions of Hispanic and all scientists and engineers; the index of dissimilarity was only 8 in 1986. About 51 percent of Hispanics and 53 percent of the total were engineers in 1986. Among scientists, Hispanics are somewhat more likely to be social scientists and less likely to be computer specialists (figure 2-5). Among doctorates, Hispanics were slightly more likely than all Ph.D.'s to be scientists rather than engineers.

Experience

Hispanics report significantly fewer years of professional experience than do all scientists and engineers. In 1986, about 44 percent of Hispanics reported fewer than 10 years' experience; the comparable figure for all scientists and engineers was 31 percent. Among Ph.D. scientists and engineers, a higher proportion of Hispanics than of all doctoral scientists and engineers had fewer than 10 years of work experience: 46 percent versus 32 percent in 1985.

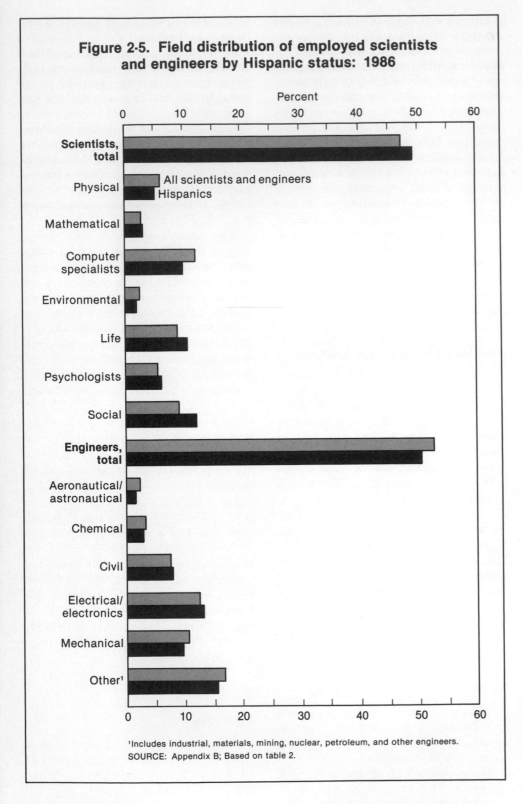

Figure 2-5. Field distribution of employed scientists and engineers by Hispanic status: 1986

Percent

Scientists, total
Physical
Mathematical
Computer specialists
Environmental
Life
Psychologists
Social
Engineers, total
Aeronautical/astronautical
Chemical
Civil
Electrical/electronics
Mechanical
Other[1]

All scientists and engineers
Hispanics

[1]Includes industrial, materials, mining, nuclear, petroleum, and other engineers.
SOURCE: Appendix B; Based on table 2.

There are some differences within educational institutions between Hispanic and non-Hispanic doctoral scientists and engineers regarding tenure status and professional rank. In 1985, 45 percent of Hispanics and 59 percent of all scientists and engineers held tenure. Among Hispanics, about 24 percent were full professors; the comparable figure for all doctoral scientists and engineers was 39 percent.

Labor Market Indicators

Hispanic scientists and engineers face labor market conditions that differ somewhat from those for all scientists and engineers. While Hispanics are as likely as all scientists and engineers to be in the labor force, more are likely to be unemployed and underemployed, and less are likely to hold S/E jobs.

The labor force participation rate for both Hispanic and all scientists and engineers was 95 percent in 1986. The participation of Hispanic scientists and engineers in the labor force is well above the 65-percent rate for the overall Hispanic population,[15] as well as the 84-percent rate for Hispanic college graduates.[16]

The unemployment rate for Hispanic scientists and engineers (2.1 percent) in 1986 was above that for all scientists and engineers (1.5 percent). At the doctoral level, the unemployment rate for Hispanics also was above that for all Ph.D. scientists and engineers: 1.6 percent versus 0.8 percent.

In 1986, about 80 percent of employed Hispanic scientists and engineers held jobs in science and engineering; the comparable rate for all scientists and engineers was 85 percent. S/E employment rates for Hispanics varied between science and engineering and across science fields. The rate for Hispanic scientists (68 percent) was well below that for all scientists (77 percent). The lower rate for Hispanics primarily reflects the large number of Hispanic psychologists, social scientists, and computer specialists working in non-S/E jobs. At the doctoral level, Hispanics reported the same S/E employment rate (91 percent) as did all Ph.D. scientists and engineers.

Hispanic scientists and engineers, on average, experience a higher degree of

Career Patterns

Relatively small differences existed in the sectoral distributions of Hispanics and all scientists and engineers. In 1986, 58 percent of Hispanics and 62 percent of all scientists and engineers were in industry (appendix table 14). Hispanic scientists and engineers are almost as likely as all scientists and engineers to report management or administration as their major activity: 26 percent versus 28 percent.

26

underemployment than do all scientists and engineers. The underemployment rate for Hispanics in 1986 was 4.8 percent, compared with 2.6 percent for all scientists and engineers. Further, Hispanic scientists are much more likely to be underemployed than are Hispanic engineers: 8.2 percent versus 1.4 percent. Among scientists, relatively large numbers of life scientists, social scientists, and psychologists were underemployed.

Salaries for Hispanic scientists and engineers averaged 90 percent of those earned by all scientists and engineers ($34,600 versus $38,400). Hispanic engineers earned 93 percent of the salaries for all engineers; the salary differential was 86 percent for scientists. By science field, the differences ranged from 76 percent for psychologists to above parity for physical and environmental scientists. Hispanic doctoral scientists and engineers earned approximately 96 percent of the salaries for all Ph.D. scientists and engineers ($41,300 versus $43,200) in 1985.

PHYSICALLY DISABLED IN SCIENCE AND ENGINEERING

Definition

As part of the National Science Foundation surveys underlying the employment and related data for scientists and engineers, respondents were asked if they had a physical handicap and, if so, to specify the nature of that handicap (visual, auditory, ambulatory, or other). The data for the physically disabled therefore reflect respondent self-perceptions. Terminology makes it very difficult to precisely measure the number of scientists and engineers who may have a physical disability. Frequently the terms "disability," "impairment," and "handicap" are used synonymously, but their meanings can have important differences. According to the World Health Organization, impairment is a "psychological, anatomical, mental loss, or some other abnormality."[17] Disability is any restriction on or lack of (resulting from impairment) ability to pursue an activity, such as work, in the manner or within the range considered normal. Handicap is a disadvantage resulting from an impairment or disability. Thus, an impairment subject to a prejudice is a handicap, whether or not it is a disability.

NSF's intent in collecting data on the physically disabled is to estimate the number who have a condition that may in some way limit their physical activity. Although the data collection instruments used by NSF refer to a "physical handicap," the term "disabled" will be used since it has emerged as the preferred term in the United States.

Employment Characteristics

In 1986, about 94,200 scientists and engineers, or 2 percent of the total, reported a physical disability. Of those, about 22 percent reported an ambulatory condition, 22 percent cited a visual condition, and almost 18 percent reported an auditory disability. The remainder did not specify the nature of their disability.

Of those citing a physical disability in 1986, about 70,300 were employed. In 1984, about 91,600 reported a physical disability and of those, about 74,800 were employed. The labor force participation rate for the physically disabled thus declined from 83 percent in 1984 to 76 percent in 1986. The corresponding rate for all scientists and engineers in 1986 was 95 percent.

Those reporting a disability are much more likely than all scientists and engineers to be outside the labor force. About 23 percent of the physically disabled cited illness as the reason for not being in the labor force. Among all scientists and engineers, only about 2.6 percent cited illness as their major reason for not working or seeking work.

Both the physically disabled and all scientists and engineers reported an unemployment rate of 1.5 percent in 1986. Those with a physical disability are more likely than all scientists and engineers to hold jobs in science and engineering. In 1986, the S/E employment rate for the physically disabled was 90 percent; for all scientists and engineers, it was 83 percent.

The field distribution of those reporting a physical disability differs only slightly from that for all scientists and engineers (figure 2-6). Those with a disability are about as likely to be scientists and engineers. Among science fields, those with a physical disability are somewhat more likely to be psychologists and are less likely to be mathematical or environmental scientists.

Figure 2-6. Field distribution of employed scientists and engineers and those with physical disabilities: 1986

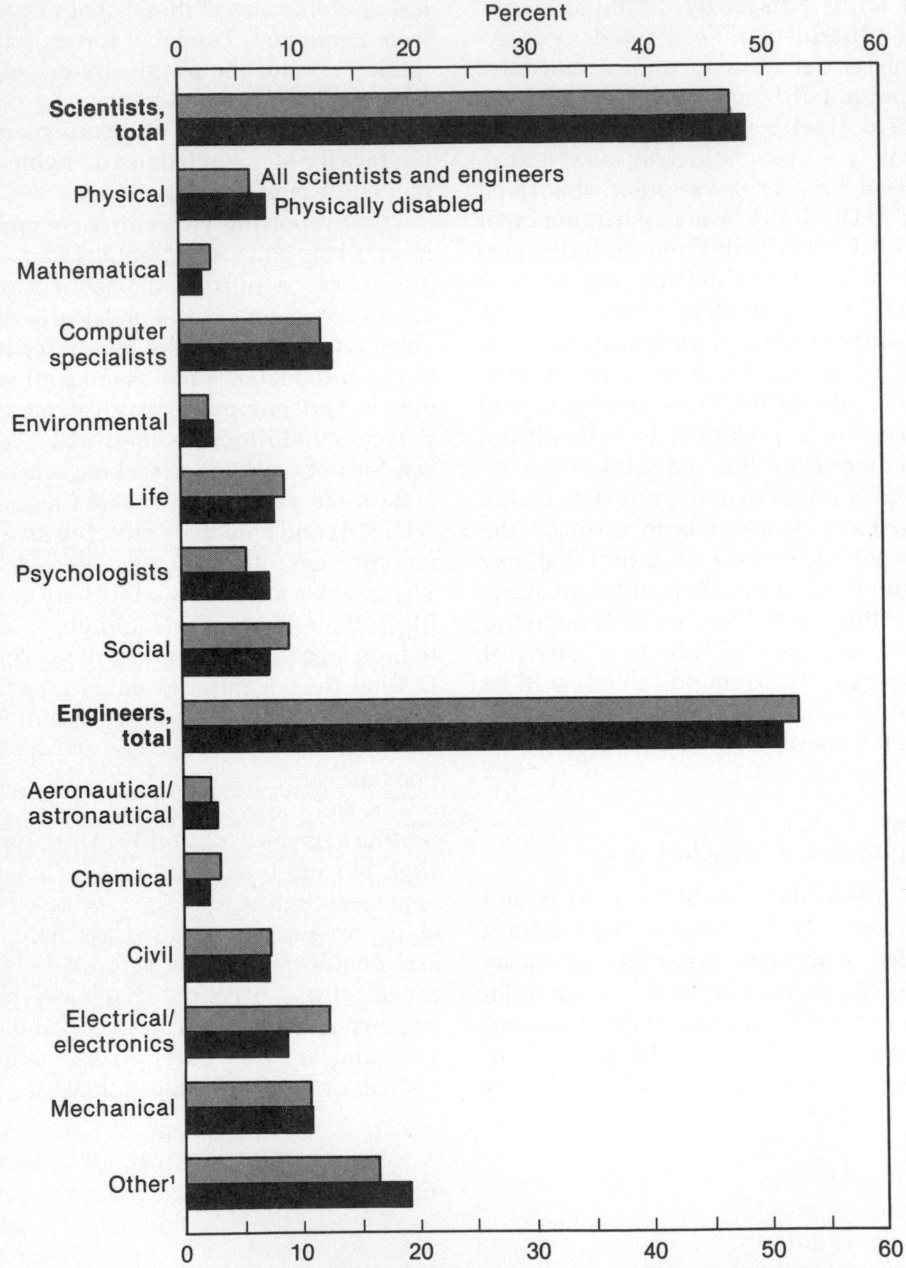
Percent
0
10
20
30
40
50
60
Scientists, total
Physical
All scientists and engineers
Physically disabled
Mathematical
Computer specialists
Environmental
Life
Psychologists
Social
Engineers, total
Aeronautical/ astronautical
Chemical
Civil
Electrical/ electronics
Mechanical
Other[1]

[1]Includes industrial, materials, mining, nuclear, petroleum, and other engineers.
SOURCE: Appendix B; Based on tables 1 and 7.

ENDNOTES

1. U.S. Department of Labor, Bureau of Labor Statistics, *Employment and Earnings*, Vol. 34, No. 1 (Washington, DC: U.S. Government Printing Office, January 1987), p. 179.
2. U.S. Commission on Civil Rights, *Social Indicators of Equality for Minorities and Women* (Washington, DC: U.S. Government Printing Office, August 1978), p. 39. "The index . . . represents the percentage of a group who would have to change occupations in order for the group to have identical distributions of a comparison group. If two groups had the same distribution of occupations, the index of dissimilarily would be 0.0. . . ." (p. 44).
3. *Employment and Earnings*, p. 160.
4. U.S. Department of Labor, Bureau of Labor Statistics, unpublished tabulations.
5. *Employment and Earnings*, p. 160.
6. U.S. Department of Labor, Bureau of Labor Statistics, unpublished tabulations.
7. U.S. Department of Commerce, Bureau of the Census, *General Social and Economic Characteristics, United States Summary*, 1980 Census of Population (Washington, DC: U.S. Government Printing Office, December 1983).
8. Ibid.
9. Ibid.
10. See Appendix A, "Technical Notes," for a discussion of the statistical reliability of the estimates of scientists and engineers.
11. U.S. Department of Commerce, Bureau of the Census, *General Social and Economic Characteristics, United States Summary*.
12. The "other Hispanic" category includes individuals whose origins are in Spain or the Spanish-speaking countries of Central or South America. Also included in this category are those who identified themselves as Spanish, Spanish American, Hispano, Latino, etc.
13. *Employment and Earnings*, p. 202.
14. Ibid., p. 179.
15. Ibid., p. 201.
16. U.S. Department of Labor, Bureau of Labor Statistics, unpublished tabulations.
17. See Johnson and Lambrinos, "Wage Discrimination Against Handicapped Men and Women," *Journal of Human Resources*, Vol. xx, No. 2, Spring 1985, pp. 264-277.

CHAPTER 3

Education and Training

OVERVIEW

One major factor in the underrepresentation of women and minorities in the science and engineering (S/E) work force is their different patterns of participation in science and mathematics at all educational levels. This chapter examines five components of the science and engineering education pipeline: precollege preparation, undergraduate preparation, science and engineering degree production, graduate education, and postdoctoral appointments.

At the precollege level, females and some minority groups take fewer years of mathematics and science coursework and are also less inclined to take advanced coursework in these subjects than are males and whites. Only Asians participate in mathematics and science training to a greater extent than the majority group.

These lower participation rates in precollege education are partially reflected in the lower scores of females and minorities on examinations measuring mathematics and science achievement. For example, in 1985, scores for females were 50 points lower than those for males on the mathematics component of the Scholastic Aptitude Test (SAT). Among minorities, scores for blacks, native Americans, and Hispanics ranged between 100 and 50 points lower than the national average on this portion of the exam. Asians, in contrast, scored more than 40 points higher than the average on the mathematics section. The SAT is often considered to be a critical element in determining college admissions decisions.

In addition to indicating participation in precollege science and mathematics, scores on achievement tests such as the SAT may also reflect a number of social, demographic, and economic factors, especially among minorities.

Information on the characteristics of students who take the SAT reveals many differences in the socioeconomic backgrounds of blacks, native Americans, and Hispanics as compared to the majority and Asians. For example, the family incomes reported by blacks, native Americans, and Hispanics are much lower than the overall average. Furthermore, the parents of these students have much lower levels of educational attainment than the average for all parents, e.g., they were much less likely to hold an undergraduate degree. Finally, the high school grade point averages reported by blacks, native Americans, and Hispanics are also below average. On a more positive note, however, these students plan to complete their education at a much higher level than did their parents. Almost one-third of these students reported that their educational goal was to complete a bachelor's degree; an additional two-fifths reported their degree aspirations to be graduate education.

Precollege mathematics and science experiences help determine participation in science and engineering education at the undergraduate and graduate levels. Women and minorities traditionally have not participated at these levels to the same extent as have men and the majority. For women, however, some progress has been made. The number of S/E bachelor's degrees awarded to women has increased markedly, up 30 percent between 1975 and 1985 compared with a 1-percent increase for men. The largest percentage increases for women, in terms of undergraduate and graduate degrees and graduate enrollments, have occurred in two fields: computer science and engineering.

S/E degrees awarded to minority groups have not shown the same pattern as that for women. For instance, between 1979 and 1985, the increase in the number of S/E bachelor's degrees awarded to blacks, native Americans, and Hispanics was below average. In 1985, these groups accounted for, respectively, 5 percent, less than 1 percent, and 3 percent of the S/E bachelor's degrees granted. Enrollment of minorities in graduate programs increased at above-average rates during the early eighties, but has shown a significant slowdown between 1984 and 1985.

WOMEN

Precollege Preparation

Curriculum and Coursework

Curriculum. Recent data on curriculum and coursework patterns of males and females are not available for the total population of secondary school students. Historical data have shown, however, that about the same proportions of males and females enroll in an academic curriculum in high school. In 1980 (the latest year for which data are available), about two in five high school seniors were in academic programs regardless of sex.[1] The decision to enroll in these programs is critical for students who intend to pursue S/E careers. Enrollment in such programs ensures more exposure to both basic and advanced mathematics and science coursework. Program participants generally score higher than do other students on college entrance exams such as the Scholastic Aptitude Test.

More current and historical data are available on curriculum and coursework for the population of college-bound seniors (i.e., those students who take the SAT and complete the Student Descriptive Questionnaire).[2] These data show that college-bound males and females are more highly concentrated than are all high school students in academic programs. There is, however, little difference in enrollment by gender: in 1985, about 79 percent of males and 78 percent of females were enrolled in academic programs. Since 1981, this fraction has slowly but steadily increased for both males and females, rising from 78 percent and 75 percent, respectively.

Coursework. Historically, the same proportions of males and females take such introductory mathematics courses as algebra I or geometry in high school. Males were, however, more likely to take advanced courses such as trigonometry or calculus. In 1982, for instance, about 54 percent of both male and female high school seniors had completed a geometry course, but 26 percent of males compared to 20 percent of females had enrolled in a trigonometry course.[3]

This pattern is further evidenced by the average number of years of mathematics coursework taken by male and female college-bound seniors. In 1985, males reported completing an average of 3.80 years of mathematics coursework; the average for females was 3.58 years. Although these averages have risen for both males and females over a 4-year period, the differential in courses taken has narrowed only slightly; in 1981, the averages were 3.68 (males) and 3.38 (females).

Data on science courses taken show a more mixed pattern for males and females. Male high school seniors had more often enrolled in physical science (e.g., earth sciences, chemistry, and physics) courses at both basic and advanced levels; females, however, were more likely to have taken either biology or advanced biology. The average number of years of science coursework reported by male and female college-bound seniors reinforces this pattern. In 1985, the average number of years of physical science (including earth science, chemistry, and physics) courses completed by males was 2.08 compared to 1.74 by females. In the biological sciences, the average for females was higher than that for males: 1.44 years versus 1.40 years. Over the 4-year period 1981-85, the pattern remained the same but the differential in average years of coursework narrowed in the physical sciences and increased slightly in the biological sciences (appendix table 36).

Mathematics and Science Achievement

The secondary school experiences of males and females discussed above show differences in behavior that may impede females during undergraduate and graduate S/E study. This section examines the cognitive differences in mathematics and science achievement exhibited by males and females at three precollege levels: elementary, middle, and secondary.

The National Assessment of Educational Progress (NAEP) is designed to assess the achievement levels of precollege students in various areas, including mathematics and science. The objective is to determine how specific groups of U.S. students respond to exercises in different academic areas rather than to measure the performance of individual students. The assessments are administered periodically to 9-, 13-, and 17-year-olds.

Mathematics.[4] Overall results of the most recent NAEP mathematics assessment are mixed.[5] At the 9-year-old level, females outperformed males by about 1 percentage point with the largest differential occurring on the knowledge component. At age 13, males scored higher on the applications component and females outperformed males on the skills portion. Among 17-year-olds, overall scores showed a more than 2-point advantage for males. Since 1978, scores have risen significantly[6] for females at ages 9 and 13 and for males at age 13 (appendix table 37).

Science.[7] Results of the most recent science assessment show that for 9-year-olds, scores for males are slightly higher than those for females regardless of component.[8] This differential tends to widen at the 13- and 17-year-old levels. For example, at age 9, the largest score difference was 2.6 points on the attitude component. Additionally, at age 13, the greatest differential, 5.2 points, occurred on the attitude portion. By age 17, a difference of 5.8 points was recorded on the content component. Scores have fluctuated at all age levels since 1977 (appendix table 38). Noteworthy changes include statistically significant declines among 17-year-old males on the inquiry and content components, a significant score decrease among 17-year-

old females on the inquiry component, and a significant increase on the attitude portion for 17-year-old females.

In summary, the results of the mathematics assessment indicate differences between males and females begin to arise at the 13-year-old level (middle school); the results of the science assessment show males scoring higher than females as early as age 9 (elementary school). These data, in conjunction with information on coursetaking, indicate that not only are potential leakages in the S/E education pipeline greater for females than for males, but also that the leakages for females are occurring at younger ages than for males.

Characteristics of College-Bound Seniors

College-bound seniors represent the largest potential pool of future scientists and engineers. Scores that these seniors achieve on the Scholastic Aptitude Test not only have critical significance in terms of college admissions decisions, but also allow further insight into the precollege experiences of women and minorities compared to men and the majority.

Data collected on college-bound seniors by the Admissions Testing Program of the College Board provide a comprehensive and robust source of material on this population. This section examines several aspects of these data: (1) scores on the Scholastic Aptitude Test, (2) scores on the SAT Achievement Test Series, (3) scores on Advanced Placement (AP) examinations, (4) the undergraduate plans of college-bound seniors, and (5) aspects of the socioeconomic backgrounds of SAT test-takers including parents' education, high school grade point average, and highest degree goals.

Scholastic Aptitude Test.[9] In 1986, males continued to score somewhat higher than females on the verbal component and substantially higher on the mathematics portion of the Scholastic Aptitude Test (figure 3-1). Although there has been some fluctuation over the decade, score differences between males and females have increased on the verbal section and remained constant for mathematics since 1976.

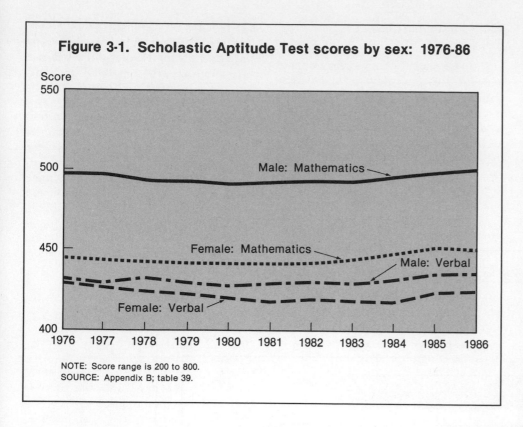

Figure 3-1. Scholastic Aptitude Test scores by sex: 1976-86

Score

- Male: Mathematics
- Female: Mathematics
- Male: Verbal
- Female: Verbal

NOTE: Score range is 200 to 800.
SOURCE: Appendix B; table 39.

Between 1976 and 1986, verbal scores for females fell from 430 to 426 while for males, there was an increase from 433 to 437. However, the overall trend for both females and males has been similar: scores declined until the early eighties and then rose sharply until the mid-eighties. Over the last 2-year period, scores have remained relatively unchanged.

The percentile ranking on the verbal component varies little for males and females. In 1985 (the latest year in which comparable data are available),[10] about 4 percent of males, compared to 3 percent of females, scored more than 650. Rankings were also similar at lower score ranges. The fractions who scored between 400 and 499 were 33 percent (males) and 34 percent (females).

On the mathematics component, scores over the 10-year period rose from 446 to 451 for females and from 497 to 501 for males. The trend in SAT math scores differs from that in verbal scores. Whereas the math score decline for both males and females leveled off in 1980, female math scores did not begin to increase until 1983; math scores for males, however, began to climb in 1981.

Males are much more likely than females to score in the 650 to 800 range on the mathematics component. In 1985, about 12 percent of males, but only 4 percent of females, scored in this range. This difference has increased: in 1981, these fractions were 10 percent for males and 4 percent for females. Furthermore, females were more likely than males to score in the 400 to 499 range in 1985 (30 percent versus 26 percent).

Achievement Test Scores.[11] College-bound senior females are less likely to take achievement tests in science and mathematics[12] than are all college-bound seniors. In 1985 (the latest year in which data are available), females accounted for 46 percent of test-takers who took one or more achievement exams in a science or mathematics field; they also comprised 52 percent of college-bound seniors who took the SAT and 53 percent of seniors who took one or more achievement exams in a non- science or -mathematics field. Females range from one-fifth of test-takers in physics to more than one-half of those in either mathematics level I or biology.

Scores on science and mathematics achievement tests have been consistently higher for males than for females throughout the eighties. In 1985, males scored between 34 and 38 points higher than females on the mathematics levels I and II, chemistry, and biology tests and 56 points higher on the physics exam (figure 3-2). These point differences, however, have narrowed somewhat (2 to 4 points) since 1981.

The SAT mathematics scores for males who took one or more science or mathematics achievement tests are also higher than the scores for comparable females. In 1985, the range in SAT mathematics scores for male college-bound seniors was 587 (mathematics level I) to 664 (mathematics level II). The comparable range for females was 540 to 624, respectively.

Advanced Placement Examinations.[13] Females continue to account for a smaller fraction than the all-field average of those who take AP tests in science and mathematics fields. Their proportion, however, has increased rapidly over the decade. By 1986, females represented about 36 percent of science and mathematics test-takers, up from 25 percent in 1976.[14] Additionally, the proportion of all AP test-takers accounted for by females rose from 42 percent in 1976 to 48 percent a decade later. Representation of females varies significantly across fields of science and mathematics. In 1986, females accounted for 50 percent of the AP test-takers in biology but only 14 percent of those who took the physics C - electricity/magnetism[15] exam (figure 3-3).

The mean grade for males was higher than that for females on each of the science and mathematics AP exams in 1986; the range has narrowed, however, since 1984. In 1986, the largest differences occurred on the computer science exam (0.47 points) while the smallest was on the mathematics/calculus BC[16] test (0.22 points). In 1984, the differences ranged from 0.76 (computer science) to 0.21 (mathematics/calculus AB). For both years, however, score patterns were similar for males and females. For example, in 1986, both scored highest on the mathematics/calculus BC exam (3.57 and 3.35, respectively) and lowest on the physics B test (2.91 versus 2.46) (table 3-1).

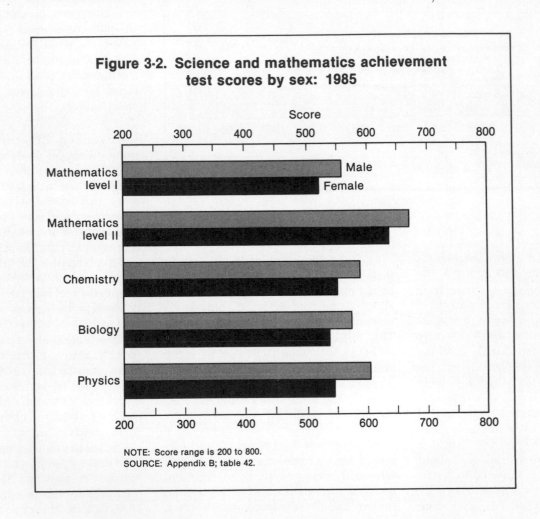

Figure 3-2. Science and mathematics achievement test scores by sex: 1985

NOTE: Score range is 200 to 800.
SOURCE: Appendix B; table 42.

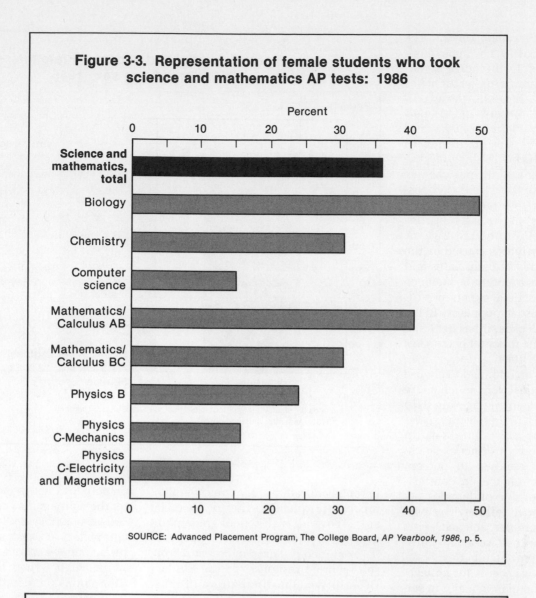

Figure 3-3. Representation of female students who took science and mathematics AP tests: 1986

Percent

SOURCE: Advanced Placement Program, The College Board, *AP Yearbook, 1986*, p. 5.

Table 3-1. Science and mathematics advanced placement examination scores by sex: 1986

Field	Male	Female	Point difference (M-F)
Biology	3.29	3.01	0.28
Chemistry	2.93	2.49	0.44
Computer science	3.05	2.58	0.47
Mathematics/Calculus AB	3.18	2.95	0.23
Mathematics/Calculus BC	3.57	3.35	0.22
Physics B	2.91	2.46	0.45
Physics C - Mechanics	3.54	3.09	0.45
Physics C - Electricity & Magnetism	3.39	3.00	0.39

NOTE: Score range is from 1 to 5: 1 = no recommendation for credit; 2 = possibly qualified; 3 = qualified; 4 = well qualified; 5 = extremely well qualified.
SOURCE: Appendix B; table 43.

Intended Undergraduate Major.[17] The probability of choosing a science or engineering field as an intended undergraduate major is much higher for males than for females. In 1985, these proportions were 48 percent and 28 percent, respectively. Because males and females exhibited similar trends in choice of major during the eighties, the differential by gender did not change. For both sexes, the likelihood of choosing an S/E major rose slightly (1 to 2 percentage points) in the early eighties but tapered off within the last 2 years. This trend primarily was caused by the shifting proportions of both males and females choosing a computer science major. While this field experienced a tremendous increase in popularity in the early part of the decade, it has declined as an undergraduate major for both males and females since 1984.

Among those who intended to choose an S/E major, males were much more inclined to choose an engineering field while females most often selected social science or psychology (figure 3-4). In 1985, about 44 percent of males specified engineering; another 20 percent choose computer science. In contrast, the largest proportion of females selected social science followed by psychology and computer science. This pattern has remained relatively unchanged throughout the eighties.

SAT mathematics scores for college-bound seniors who plan to major in science and engineering are generally higher for males than females. There are, however, exceptions to this pattern. For example, females whose probable undergraduate major was engineering had SAT mathematics scores consistently higher than males throughout the eighties: in 1985, these scores were 561 and 555, respectively. In comparison to all college-bound seniors, both males and females who planned to major in either physical, mathematical, and biological science or an engineering field scored above average on the math component of the aptitude test.

Selected Socioeconomic Characteristics of College-Bound Seniors. This section compares several aspects of the socioeconomic backgrounds of male and female college-bound seniors. Specifically, differences in terms of (1) level of

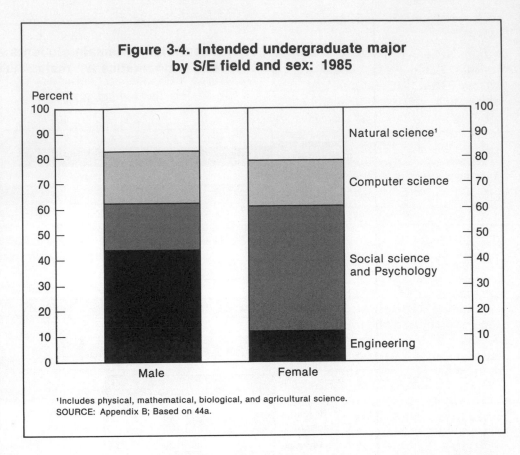

Figure 3-4. Intended undergraduate major by S/E field and sex: 1985

Percent

Natural science[1]
Computer science
Social science and Psychology
Engineering

Male   Female

[1]Includes physical, mathematical, biological, and agricultural science.
SOURCE: Appendix B; Based on 44a.

parents' education, (2) annual parental income, (3) plans to file for financial aid, (4) overall high school grade point average, and (5) degree-level goals will be examined.[18] These data result from self-reported responses to the Student Descriptive Questionnaire and must therefore be treated on their relative, rather than absolute, merits.

Parents' Education. In 1985, the median numbers of years of education completed by fathers and mothers of college-bound seniors were about 14.0 years and 13.5 years, respectively, for both males and females. Examining these levels more closely, a larger proportion of their fathers than mothers completed a bachelor's degree (roughly 18 percent versus about 14 percent) or attended graduate or professional school (approximately 26 percent versus 16 percent); among mothers, the largest proportion (about one-third) had received a high school diploma.

The level of education completed by each parent did not explain differences between male and female test scores. Regardless of level of parental education, males scored higher than females

on both SAT components. For example, on the mathematics component, among college-bound seniors whose parents had completed at least a high school diploma, males scored approximately 50 points higher than females; the score differential increased to 60 points for those whose parents completed less than a high school diploma.

Annual Parental Income. While the distributions of annual parental income for males and females are similar, males score higher on both components of the SAT with the largest differential occurring on the mathematics section. In 1985, males were more likely than females to report their parents' annual salary to be more than $30,000 (57 percent versus 53 percent), but throughout the income range, males outperformed females on the SAT. This differential narrowed, however, as reported annual salary increased (appendix table 45).

Financial Aid Plans. In 1985, most college-bound seniors reported that they would seek financial aid; females were slightly more likely than males to seek such assistance (79 percent versus 76 percent).

High School Grade Point Average. Females reported a higher grade point average (GPA) than males in 1985: 3.07 compared to 2.98 (on a 4.00-point scale). Nonetheless, their SAT scores were lower especially on the mathematics component. This differential widens as GPA increases: for instance, for college-bound seniors whose GPA was between 3.50 and 3.74, math scores for males were 70 points higher; in the 2.50 to 2.74 GPA range, the difference narrowed to 60 points.

Degree-Level Goals. In 1985, about one-third each of male and female college-bound seniors sought a baccalaureate as their highest degree. Males were slightly more likely than females, however, to plan a more advanced degree. For instance, 47 percent of males planned to seek graduate education compared with 44 percent of females.

The trend in SAT scores by degree-level goals is comparable to that of other socioeconomic variables: males consistently score higher on both SAT components with the largest gap occurring on the mathematics portion. The gap in SAT mathematics scores, however, widens appreciably at advanced degree levels. In 1985, scores for males who indicated that the baccalaureate would be their terminal degree were 38 points higher than comparable females; for those who reported a doctorate or professional degree, this difference rose to 69 points.

Undergraduate Preparation

The Educational Testing Service offers a series of exams to potential graduate students. The Graduate Record Examination (GRE)[19] is taken by students who plan further study in the arts and sciences. Primarily used by graduate and professional schools to supplement undergraduate records, it may also be used to examine the undergraduate preparation of women and minorities compared to that of men and the majority.

Although more women (102,700) than men (89,600) took the Graduate Record Examination in 1985,[20] women test-takers were much less likely than men

to have majored in a science or engineering field at the undergraduate level (46 percent versus 70 percent).[21] Those test-takers who majored in S/E fields outscored all test-takers, regardless of sex, on every component of the exam (figure 3-5).

In 1985, among those who majored in S/E fields, women generally scored slightly higher than did men on the ver-

bal component, much lower on the quantitative section, and slightly lower on the analytical portion. These differences generally persisted across fields, although wide variation occurred (table 3-2). For example, men who majored in engineering scored lower than women on both the verbal and analytical sections by 40 points and 50 points, respectively, but scored slightly higher (8

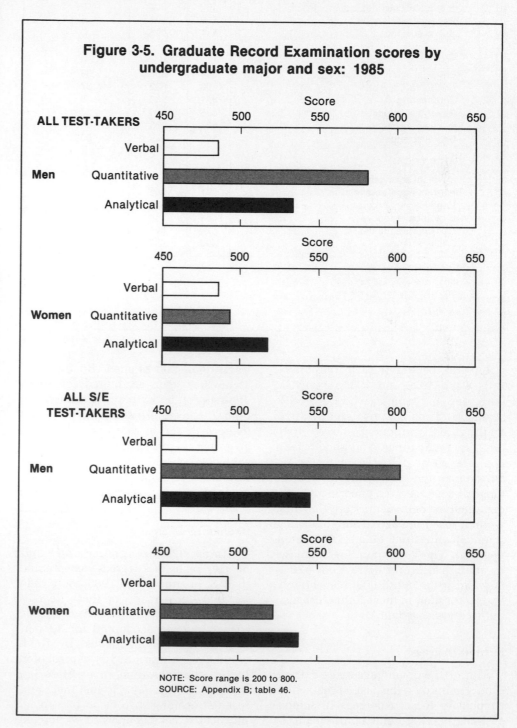

Figure 3-5. Graduate Record Examination scores by undergraduate major and sex: 1985

NOTE: Score range is 200 to 800.
SOURCE: Appendix B; table 46.

Table 3-2. Graduate Record Examination scores by undergraduate major and sex: 1985

Component and undergraduate major	Men	Women	Point difference (M-W)
VERBAL			
Physical sciences	501	509	−8
Mathematical sciences	489	478	11
Engineering	458	499	−41
Biological sciences	502	511	−9
Behavioral sciences	506	501	5
Social sciences	454	451	3
QUANTITATIVE			
Physical sciences	642	606	36
Mathematical sciences	669	632	37
Engineering	671	663	8
Biological sciences	585	558	27
Behavioral sciences	535	488	47
Social sciences	509	449	60
ANALYTICAL			
Physical sciences	568	577	−9
Mathematical sciences	591	586	5
Engineering	553	603	−50
Biological sciences	551	564	−13
Behavioral sciences	524	524	0
Social sciences	490	485	5

NOTE: Score range is 200 to 800.
SOURCE: Appendix B; table 46.

points) on the quantitative component.

Between 1979 and 1985, scores for both men and women who majored in science and engineering fields declined on the verbal component but rose on the other two components (appendix table 46). The most dramatic increases occurred for women majoring in either biological science or engineering. On the quantitative component, scores for these women rose from 528 to 558 (biological science) and from 603 to 663 (engineering). The corresponding increases in analytical scores were from 526 to 564 and from 534 to 603, respectively. Scores for men in these fields rose also, but to a lesser extent.

Earned Degrees

Although women have made extraordinary gains over the past 10 years, their propensity to earn degrees in science and engineering fields continues to be lower than that of men. By the mid-eighties, women accounted for about one-half of both total enrollment in higher education institutions[22] and all degrees (baccalaureate and advanced) awarded. In comparison, they represented 44 percent of all degrees granted in science fields and 14 percent of those conferred in engineering fields in 1985.

Bachelor's Degrees[23]

Almost 322,000 science and engineering bachelor's degrees were granted by U.S. institutions in 1985; more than 121,000 (38 percent) of these degrees were earned by women. One decade earlier, women accounted for 32 percent of S/E baccalaureates. By field, women were more highly represented in the sciences than in engineering (table 3-3). In science fields, their representation ranged from 28 percent of physical science degrees to 68 percent of the degrees granted in psychology. In contrast, representation of women in engineering was between 8 percent (aeronautical) and 29 percent (industrial).

Consistent with their pattern of representation in S/E employment, women are more apt than men to earn degrees in life and social sciences and psychology; men are more heavily concentrated in engineering fields. In 1985, more than two-thirds of women earned degrees in either social science, psychology, or life science. In contrast, only 9 percent of women received degrees in engineering; they were concentrated mostly in the electrical, chemical, and mechanical fields. For men, one-third earned degrees in engineering, with the largest shares in electrical, mechanical, and civil specialties. In science, more than one-half of men earned degrees in either social or life science.

Between 1975 and 1985, these patterns of S/E degree production changed markedly. Overall, the number of science and engineering baccalaureates earned by women has increased by 30 percent compared to a 1-percent decline for men. By field, the most notable gains for women have been in computer science, up fourteenfold from 956 to 14,431, and in engineering fields, up twelvefold from 860 to 11,316. Other fields showing relatively large increases were physical science (up 75 percent) and life science (up 21 percent). The number of degrees granted to women in the mathematical and social sciences declined over the 10-year period. Men, on the other hand, experienced absolute declines or no growth in the number of degrees granted in all fields except computer science (up 505 percent) and engineering (70 percent).

Master's Degrees[24]

In 1985, women represented 30 percent (18,300) of the master's degrees conferred in science and engineering, up from 20 percent (11,000) a decade earlier (table 3-3). By field, women accounted for 40 percent of science degrees and 11 percent of those granted in engineering.

The field distribution of women who earn master's degrees parallels that exhibited at the bachelor's degree level.

Table 3-3. Science and engineering degrees granted to women by degree level

Science and engineering field	S/E baccalaureates[1]		S/E master's degrees[1]		S/E doctorates[2]	
	Number of women	Percent of total	Number of women	Percent of total	Number of women	Percent of total
Total	121,439	37.7	18,298	29.9	4,906	26.1
Sciences, total	110,123	45.2	15,970	39.9	4,681	30.4
Physical[3]	6,698	28.1	1,352	23.3	605	16.4
Mathematical	7,036	46.1	1,011	35.0	121	16.6
Computer	14,431	36.9	2,037	28.7	49	12.3
Life..........................	25,149	43.5	3,491	39.9	1,448	30.2
Psychology	27,422	68.2	5,417	63.9	1,564	50.9
Social	29,387	43.5	2,662	37.8	894	32.5
Engineering, total	11,316	14.5	2,328	11.0	225	6.7
Aeronautical/astronautical	241	8.4	31	5.1	1	0.8
Chemical.....................	1,875	26.0	268	17.3	53	11.1
Civil	1,233	13.4	337	10.6	19	4.9
Electrical	2,422	11.1	434	8.4	33	4.7
Industrial....................	1,167	29.1	227	15.5	14	13.9
Mechanical	1,754	10.4	205	6.7	14	3.2
Other	2,553	16.4	741	12.5	91	7.9

[1]1985
[2]1986
[3]Includes environmental sciences.
SOURCE: Appendix B; Based on tables 47, 48, and 49.

Women were most likely to earn their degrees in psychology (30 percent), life science (19 percent), or social science (15 percent). About 13 percent of women were granted engineering degrees; these were concentrated in the electrical, civil, and chemical fields. In contrast, almost 44 percent of men earned engineering degrees; another 24 percent each were granted degrees in either life or computer science.

The growth rate for women earning S/E master's degrees far exceeded that for men over the decade: 66.0 percent versus 0.3 percent. The fastest growing fields for women were computer science and engineering. The number of men earning degrees in these two fields was also substantial but was masked by large declines in degree production among the remaining science fields.

Doctorates[25]

Trends in degree production at this level do not differ substantially from those at either the bachelor's or master's degree levels. The representation of women earning doctorates in science and engineering fields has increased dramatically over the decade, rising from 17 percent (3,000) in 1976 to 26 percent (4,900) in 1986. In addition, women accounted for a larger proportion of the Ph.D.'s in science fields (30 percent) than of engineering doctorates (7 percent) in 1986 (table 3-3). Among S/E doctorate recipients who were U.S. citizens, the proportion granted to women was 31 percent in 1986, up from 18 percent 10 years earlier.

About 61 percent of women earned their doctorates in either psychology or life science in 1986. Only 5 percent had earned engineering doctorates, most often in chemical and electrical specialties. The field distribution of men earning doctorates differs from this pattern: almost 70 percent had earned doctorates in either life science, physical science, or engineering.

While the number of S/E doctorates granted to women has increased 65 percent between 1976 and 1986, the number awarded to men has fallen by 7 percent. For women, above-average growth rates were experienced in engineering (up 317 percent to 225 degrees) and computer science (up 206 percent to 49 degrees). For men, only computer science (165 percent) showed any significant growth over the decade.

Graduate Education

The juncture between undergraduate and graduate education represents another critical interval in the science and engineering pipeline. In many fields of science and engineering, an advanced degree is considered an entry-level requirement. In examining this crucial stage, the following section concentrates on several aspects of graduate education including (1) graduate enrollment in science and engineering programs, (2) graduate degree attainment rates in science and engineering fields, (3) sources of graduate support for those pursuing S/E doctorates, and (4) characteristics of NSF fellowship recipients.

Graduate Enrollment[26]

In 1986, women represented 33 percent of graduate enrollment in science and engineering programs; this fraction, in 1977, was 26 percent. Representation of women varies considerably by field (figure 3-6). For example, within science fields, women accounted for more than three-fifths of enrollment in psychology programs whereas within engineering, the largest fraction (one-fifth) of women was in industrial engineering.

Most women who were enrolled in graduate programs were in one of three fields in 1986: social science, psychology, or life science. Only about 10 percent were enrolled in engineering fields, most often civil, electrical, and industrial engineering. Men, in contrast, were most highly concentrated (one-third) in engineering fields, primarily in electrical, civil, and mechanical graduate programs. Among other fields, about 18 percent of men were enrolled in social science programs; another 13 percent pursued graduate education in life science.

Since 1977 (the earliest year in which comparable data are available), there have been substantial changes in these distributions, resulting from very different growth rates over the 8-year period. Overall, graduate enrollment of women in S/E fields increased 55 percent between 1977 and 1986; this increase was significantly higher than the 11-percent growth experienced by men. For both men and women, the fastest growth was in those fields that were also experiencing very rapid increases in degree production (i.e., computer science and engineering). Much slower growth rates occurred in the social and life sciences and psychology.

Graduate Degree Attainment Rates

An indicator of the progress made by women in earning advanced S/E degrees is the graduate degree attainment rate (the propensity of men and women to complete graduate degrees). At the master's degree level, this rate is defined as S/E master's degrees expressed as a percentage of S/E bachelor's degrees awarded 2 years earlier. At the doctorate level, it is defined as S/E doctorates expressed as a percentage of S/E baccalaureates granted 7 years earlier.

The graduate degree attainment rate over the 10-year period ending in 1985 rose slightly faster for women than for men at the master's degree level. Nonetheless, the rate for men continues to be higher than that for women: in 1985, the rates were 22 percent versus 16 percent, respectively. The continued differential in attainment rates masks two very different trends in degree production for men and women. First, the rate for men has increased because baccalaureate

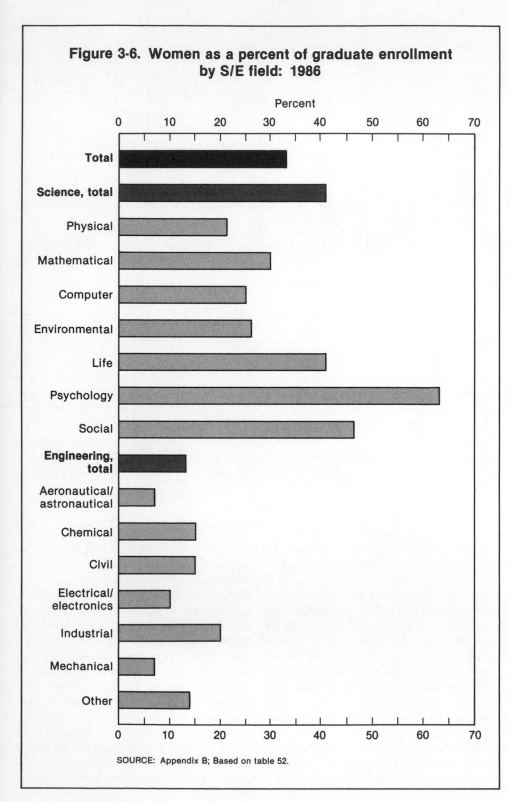

Figure 3-6. Women as a percent of graduate enrollment by S/E field: 1986

SOURCE: Appendix B; Based on table 52.

production fell slightly and master's degree production remained relatively steady. On the other hand, the rate for women has increased only marginally because degree production at both levels has been substantial with master's production outpacing that for baccalaureates.

At the doctorate level, the graduate degree attainment rate is higher for men than women. This gap has narrowed over the decade, however, because of differing growth rates in the number of doctorates awarded. In 1986, the rate for men was 7.5 percent, down from 9.8 percent in 1975. For women, the rates were 4.8 percent (1986) and 5.3 percent (1975). The decline in this rate for men results from the absolute decline in the number of doctorates granted, while for women, increases in S/E baccalaureates outpaced those in S/E doctorates.

Graduate Support Status[27]

Sources of support for graduate education may illuminate potential disparities between men and women: the amount and type of support received may either stimulate or inhibit further study in an S/E field. For those who received a doctorate in a science or engineering field in 1986, both men and women reported universities as their primary source of support more often than other sources (figure 3-7). A substantially larger share of men than women, however, reported this source: 56 percent versus 45 percent.

Although a substantial number of both men and women receive university support, differences exist in actual type of support. Among those receiving university assistance, 47 percent of women and 57 percent of men held research assistantships. The proportions holding teaching assistantships were 40 percent (women) and 32 percent (men).

On a field-specific basis, differences in the type of assistantship reported are narrower (appendix table 54). For example, of those receiving degrees in physical science, men (68 percent) were more likely than women (62 percent) to hold research assistantships. In comparison, one-half of both men and women receiving social science or psychology degrees held teaching assistantships. In 1986, women who had

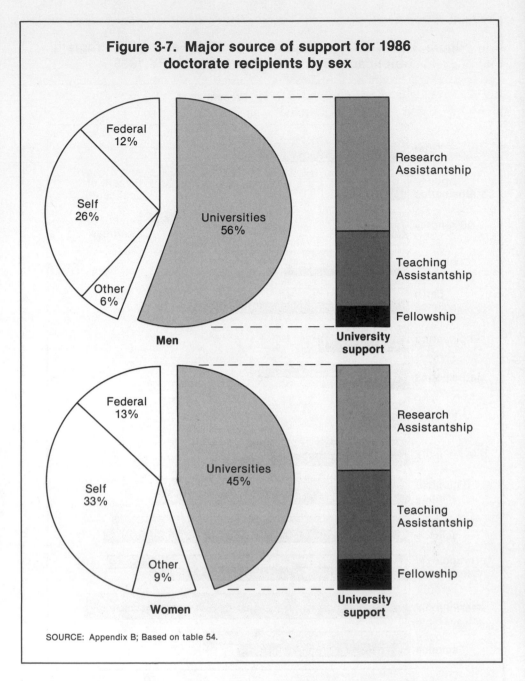

Figure 3-7. Major source of support for 1986 doctorate recipients by sex

Men
- Federal 12%
- Self 26%
- Other 6%
- Universities 56%

University support
- Research Assistantship
- Teaching Assistantship
- Fellowship

Women
- Federal 13%
- Self 33%
- Other 9%
- Universities 45%

University support
- Research Assistantship
- Teaching Assistantship
- Fellowship

SOURCE: Appendix B; Based on table 54.

received university support were twice as likely as men to have earned their S/E doctorates in either psychology or social science (40 percent versus 19 percent). Thus, general variations in type of support received may primarily reflect differences in field distributions.

National Science Foundation Fellowships[28]

Between 1975 and 1985, the representation of women in NSF's Graduate Fellowship Program rose substantially.

In fiscal year (FY) 1985, women accounted for 37 percent (1,614) of all fellowship applicants; this fraction was up from 31 percent (1,778) in FY 1975. In terms of the number of awards offered, women's representation increased from 26 percent (390) to 33 percent (470).[29]

Representation varies considerably by field (figure 3-8): in FY 1985, women accounted for 24 percent of applicants and 19 percent of awards in all engineering, mathematics, and physical science fields combined. However, they represented 52 percent of applicants and

39

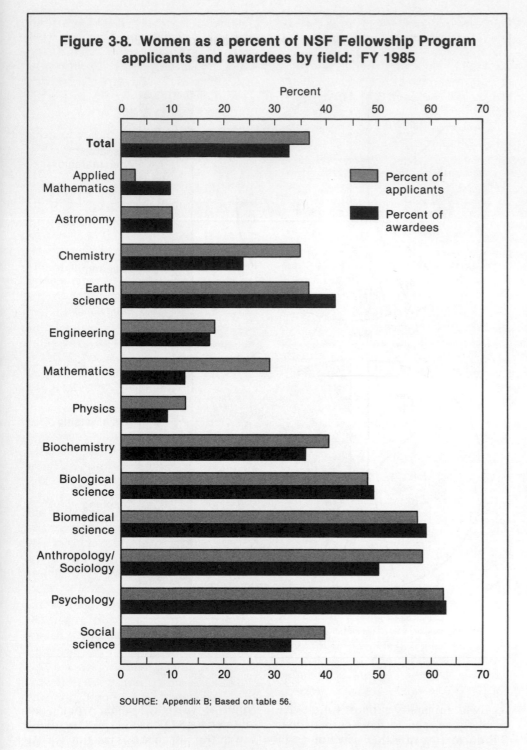

Figure 3-8. Women as a percent of NSF Fellowship Program applicants and awardees by field: FY 1985

SOURCE: Appendix B; Based on table 56.

The number of women holding S/E postdoctoral appointments has risen concurrent with the growth in the number of women earning science and engineering Ph.D.'s. In 1985, about 3,400 postdoctoral appointments in science and engineering were held by women; this number represented 29 percent of all such appointments. In comparison, women accounted for 20 percent of S/E postdoctorates in 1975.

By field, most women (73 percent) held appointments in life science in 1985 while another one-fifth were either in psychology or physical science. The field distribution of men differed somewhat; 59 percent were in life science and 23 percent were in physical science. For engineering, less than 1 percent of women, but 4 percent of men, held appointments in these fields.

Between 1975 and 1985, the number of women holding postdoctorates rose more than three times faster than that of men: 110 percent versus 29 percent. At an almost 230-percent increase, engineering was the fastest growing field for women; however, only 23 women held engineering appointments in 1985. The fastest growing fields for both men and women over the decade were psychology, life science, and environmental science.

RACIAL MINORITIES

Precollege Preparation

Curriculum and Coursework

Curriculum. Historical data on curriculum choice for all high school seniors are available for whites and blacks. This information shows that whites were more likely than blacks to be in an academic curriculum. Among high school seniors, about two-fifths of whites, but only one-third of blacks, were enrolled in these programs.

More recent and detailed data are available for college-bound seniors. These data also show that whites were more inclined than other racial groups to enroll in academic programs. In 1985, 81 percent of whites, compared with 76 percent of Asians, 68 percent of native Americans, and 65 percent of blacks,

48 percent of awards in the behavioral and social science fields. In both life and medical sciences, the proportions of women were 48 percent each of both applicants and awardees.

The representation of women has increased between 1975 and 1985 especially in the number of applicants and awards granted in engineering, mathematics, and physical science fields. For example, in FY 1975, women accounted for 6 percent of both applicants (42) and awardees (12); these figures had risen to 18 percent (143) and 17 percent (44), respectively, by FY 1985.

were in an academic curriculum. These data do not vary substantially when further stratified by sex. Since 1981, proportions in academic programs rose for whites, blacks, and Asians (appendix table 33).

Coursework. Historical data show that blacks and Asians took more years of mathematics in high school than did either whites or native Americans. Two-thirds of Asians, almost one-half of blacks, and approximately two-fifths each of both whites and native Americans had enrolled in four or more mathematics courses in high school. Grade point averages in math, however, were lower for blacks (1.98 on a 4.00-point scale) than for Asians (2.60), whites (2.34), and native Americans (2.19). In addition, there is variation by racial group in terms of types of courses taken. For example, Asians were more likely, and blacks and native Americans were least likely, to have taken advanced mathematics coursework. For example, the proportions of 1982 high school seniors who took calculus were 19 percent for Asians, 8 percent for whites, and 4 percent each for blacks and native Americans.[31]

More recent data for college-bound seniors further indicate that Asians take more years of mathematics coursework than do other racial groups. In 1985, Asians had taken 3.89 years of coursework compared to 3.72 for whites, 3.46 for native Americans, and 3.43 for blacks. Examining number of years of mathematics coursework by sex shows that, regardless of racial group, females take fewer years of mathematics courses. Among females, the average number of years of coursework was highest for Asians (3.81) and lowest for native Americans and blacks (about 3.38 years each).

Historically, Asians also participate to a greater extent in science coursework than do other racial groups. More than 35 percent of Asians had taken four or more science courses while 23 percent of whites and about 19 percent each of blacks and native Americans had done so. The range in grade point average in science was similar to the pattern exhibited for math: the highest average was reported for Asians (2.69) while the lowest was for blacks (2.08). Asians were

more likely than other racial groups to take all types of science courses. For example, almost three-fifths of Asians had taken a chemistry course compared to two-fifths of whites, three-tenths of blacks, and one-quarter of native Americans.[32]

Science coursework patterns are reinforced by the characteristics of college-bound seniors. The average number of years of coursework in both the physical[33] and biological sciences was highest for Asians (appendix table 36). The gap between Asians and all other racial groups was greatest in years of physical science coursework taken: in 1985, Asians had taken 2.12 years of this coursework compared with 1.92 years for whites, 1.72 for native Americans, and 1.68 among blacks. By gender, males (on average) take more years of science coursework than do females across all racial groups. Among females, Asians had the highest rate of participation.

Mathematics and Science Achievement[34]

Mathematics. The results of the latest National Assessment of Educational Progress in mathematics show that blacks continue to score well below their white counterparts.[35] At age 9, the difference was 14 percentage points; at age 13, the gap was 15 points; and by age 17, the difference had increased to 18 points. Because of gains made by blacks at all age levels since 1978, these differences decreased from 15, 18, and 20 points, respectively. Black 13-year-olds exhibited the most statistically significant[36] increases on all components; the largest gain was 8.0 points on the knowledge portion of the assessment. The comparable change for whites was 3.9 percentage points.

Science. On the latest NAEP science assessment, available data are disaggregated by sex between whites and blacks to permit additional analysis.[37] White males and females generally scored higher than blacks at all age levels. The only exceptions to this pattern were the performance of 13- and 17-year-old black males and females on the attitude component: in 1982, blacks scored between 6 and 10 percentage points higher than did whites. Between 1977 and 1982,

changes in scores for blacks were not statistically significant at any age level regardless of component. Scores for whites, however, declined significantly in some cases. For example, there was a significant drop in scores on the attitude section at age 13.

Characteristics of College-Bound Seniors

Scholastic Aptitude Test. In 1985,[38] whites continued to score highest of all racial groups on the verbal component of the SAT; Asians[39] received the highest scores on the mathematics portion. Between 1976 and 1985, however, trends in test scores have varied greatly among racial groups. While scores for blacks have risen substantially on both test components, they have remained unchanged or have dropped for whites and Asians. Scores for native Americans have increased steadily on the mathematics section and have stayed relatively stable on the verbal section.

Minority representation among college-bound seniors has increased dramatically over the decade, especially among blacks and Asians. In 1975, these groups represented 7.9 percent and less than 1.0 percent, respectively, of SAT registrants; by 1985, the proportion accounted for by blacks had increased to 8.9 percent (79,556) while for Asians, it had risen to 5.0 percent (42,637).[40] Black college-bound seniors in 1985 represented 18 percent of all black 18-year-olds; Asian college-bound seniors accounted for 70 percent of all Asian 18-year-olds. The fraction of native American registrants has also increased substantially, almost doubling since 1975. Nonetheless, their proportion of the total college-bound senior population was still very small in 1985—0.5 percent (4,642). Like blacks, native American college-bound seniors accounted for about 18 percent of all native American 18-year-olds.

On the verbal component of the aptitude test, the score for blacks (346) was the lowest among racial groups: 103 points below that for whites (449) in 1985 (figure 3-9). The steady increase in verbal scores for blacks, however, has served to narrow this gap since 1976 when it was 119 points. Verbal scores for Asians and native Americans were

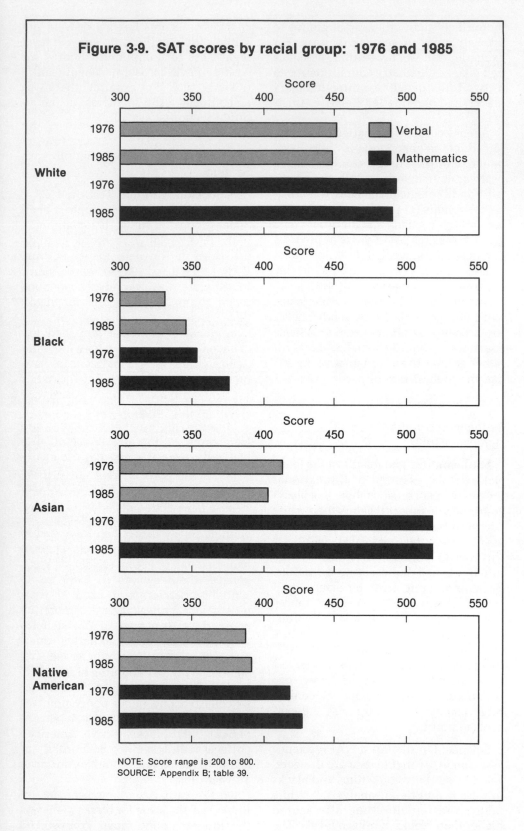

Figure 3-9. SAT scores by racial group: 1976 and 1985

NOTE: Score range is 200 to 800.
SOURCE: Appendix B; table 39.

guage for approximately 3.5 percent each of blacks and native Americans and almost 27 percent of Asians.

Blacks scored lowest among all racial groups on the mathematics portion of the exam. In 1985, their score of 376 was 114 points lower than that of whites (490). As with the verbal component, this score differential has narrowed considerably since 1976 when it was 139 points. Over the 10-year period, scores for blacks rose 22 points compared to a 3-point decline for whites. Asians received the highest scores on this component; in 1985, their score of 518 was 28 points higher than that of whites. The mathematics score for native Americans was 428 in 1985; this score was 62 points lower than that for whites.

Across all racial groups, scores for females were below those for males on both components of the test in 1985 (appendix table 40). These score differences were not as great on the verbal component as on the mathematics section. The differences on the verbal portion ranged from 5 points between Asian males and females to 17 points between native Americans. In contrast, on the mathematics component, the lowest differential (30 points) was for black males and females; the highest (46-47 points) occurred for both whites and native Americans.

Percentile rankings vary by racial group; the largest variation occurs on the mathematics component (appendix table 41). On this component, about 20 percent of Asians scored more than 650 compared to 10 percent of whites and 1 percent each of blacks and native Americans.

Achievement Test Scores. For the five achievement tests related to science and mathematics, Asians scored higher than either whites, blacks, or native Americans on the two mathematics tests and the chemistry exam; whites, however, scored highest on the biology and physics exams (table 3-4). Correspondingly, scores on the SAT mathematics component were much higher for whites and Asians. For example, in 1985, the SAT math scores for those who had taken the mathematics level II achievement test were 655 and 653, respectively, for whites and Asians; in contrast, blacks

404 and 392, respectively, in 1985. Between 1976 and 1985, scores for Asians fell 10 points; native Americans' scores increased by 4 points.

Blacks, native Americans, and Asians were more likely than whites to report that English was not their best language. In 1985, less than 2 percent of whites indicated that English was their second language; English was a second lan-

Table 3-4. Science and mathematics achievement test scores by racial group: 1985

Achievement test	White	Black	Asian	Native American
Mathematics level I	544	478	563	497
Mathematics level II......	660	581	674	614
Chemistry	575	512	587	537
Biology	557	479	548	496
Physics	594	513	593	561

NOTE: Score range is 200 to 800.
SOURCE: Appendix B; table 42.

Among all racial groups, the SAT mathematics scores for those who plan to major either in a physical, mathematical, or biological science or in an engineering field were higher than the average scores for all college-bound seniors in 1985. Consistent with the trend throughout the eighties, however, the scores of those planning majors in agricultural science, social science, psychology, or computer science were generally below the overall averages on the SAT mathematics aptitude test. For example, in 1985, scores for college-bound seniors planning to major in psychology ranged from 362 (blacks) to 481 (Asians); the overall range was from 376 (blacks) to 518 (Asians).

scored 560 and native Americans scored 597.

Asian college-bound seniors are much more inclined than are other racial groups to take one or more achievement tests and to take one or more in a science or mathematics field. In 1985, about 39 percent of Asians took at least one achievement test with more than one-half (54 percent) taking one or more in science and mathematics. In comparison, the proportion taking at least one achievement test ranged from 9 percent for blacks and 12 percent for native Americans to 21 percent for whites. Those who took a science or mathematics test ranged between 43 percent and 48 percent of these groups.

Advanced Placement Examinations. The number of candidates taking AP exams from racial minority groups is small. In 1986, about 6,415 blacks (3.0 percent of the total who took the tests), 18,043 Asians (8.0 percent), and 548 native Americans (0.2 percent) took one or more of these exams.[41] Among those in 1986 who took at least one AP examination, about one-third each of whites, blacks, and native Americans but more than one-half of Asians took at least one test in science and mathematics fields.

Except in physics C - electricity/magnetism, Asians scored higher than did other racial groups on all AP exams offered in science and mathematics with no score falling below 3 points (qualified) in 1986 (table 3-5). The highest grade for Asians (3.64), whites (3.44), and blacks (3.13) was on the mathe-

matics/calculus BC exam; the lowest scores for these three groups (3.00, 2.77, and 1.88, respectively) occurred on the chemistry exam. For native Americans, scores ranged from 2.17 (computer science) to 4.00 (physics C - mechanics).

Intended Undergraduate Major. Asian college-bound seniors are substantially more likely than other racial groups to report an engineering field as their intended undergraduate area of study. In 1985, about 21 percent of Asians choose engineering compared with 11 percent each for whites, blacks, and native Americans. Among science fields, a significant fraction (regardless of racial group) choose computer science or social science (figure 3-10).

Selected Socioeconomic Characteristics of College-Bound Seniors. Data on the characteristics and test scores of college-bound seniors indicate that Asians may be better prepared than other racial groups to pursue study in science and engineering fields. Asians' parents are more likely to have graduate degrees, they themselves are more likely than other seniors to aspire to these degrees, and they are more likely to have a high school grade point average above 3.75. In contrast, blacks and native Americans, whose SAT aptitude test scores are below average, may not have the same access to education in S/E fields. Although they aspire to a higher level of education than that achieved by their

Table 3-5. Science and mathematics advanced placement examination scores by racial group: 1986

Field	White	Black	Asian	Native American
Biology	3.14	2.27	3.49	2.72
Chemistry	2.77	1.88	3.00	2.32
Computer science	2.99	2.05	3.06	2.17
Mathematics/Calculus AB	3.07	2.30	3.39	2.73
Mathematics/Calculus BC	3.44	3.13	3.64	3.00
Physics B.........................	2.76	2.04	3.02	2.87
Physics C - Mechanics	3.45	2.63	3.47	4.00
Physics C - Electricity & Magnetism.....	3.32	2.18	3.25	3.60

NOTE: Score range is from 1 to 5: 1 = no recommendation for credit; 2 = possibly qualified; 3 = qualified; 4 = well qualified; 5 = extremely well qualified.
SOURCE: Appendix B; table 43.

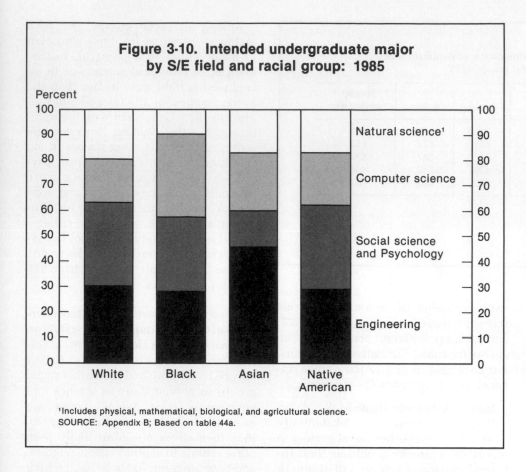

Figure 3-10. Intended undergraduate major by S/E field and racial group: 1985

Percent

Natural science[1]

Computer science

Social science and Psychology

Engineering

White Black Asian Native American

[1]Includes physical, mathematical, biological, and agricultural science.
SOURCE: Appendix B; Based on table 44a.

parents, their grade point averages are in the 2.75 range. In addition, these students' family incomes are lower and students are much more likely to pursue financial aid options. Regardless of socioeconomic variables, however, SAT scores of blacks and native Americans are below those of Asians and whites (appendix table 45).

Parents' Education. The level of education completed by parents was higher for both white and Asian college-bound seniors than for either black or native American seniors. In 1985, about 18 percent each of the fathers of whites and of Asians held a bachelor's degree compared with 9 percent of the fathers of blacks and 13 percent of those of native Americans. For blacks and native Americans, the level of education achieved by their fathers was most often a high school diploma (32 percent and 24 percent, respectively). The parents of Asians, on the other hand, were more likely than parents of other racial group members to hold a graduate or professional degree. About 26 percent of Asian

fathers held an advanced degree compared with 23 percent of whites' fathers, 9 percent of blacks', and 14 percent of native Americans'. The educational level achieved by fathers was generally higher than that for mothers with one exception: mothers of black students had completed some undergraduate or graduate education more often than had black fathers (appendix table 45).

Annual Parental Income. Annual parental income reported by white college-bound seniors was significantly higher than that reported by either blacks, Asians, or native Americans. In 1985, the median yearly income reported by white students was $34,700 compared with $17,100 (blacks), $26,400 (Asians), and $24,700 (native Americans). The largest fraction of both whites (26 percent) and Asians (19 percent) reported incomes exceeding $50,000; for blacks, the largest proportion (21 percent) was in the $6,000 to $11,999 range; and for native Americans, the largest category (16 percent) was the $30,000 to $39,999 range.

Financial Aid Plans. Although most college-bound seniors reported plans to apply for financial aid, a substantially larger proportion of blacks than of other racial groups reported these plans. In 1985, 75 percent of whites, 80 percent of Asians, and 84 percent of native Americans reported financial aid plans, compared with more than 92 percent of blacks.

High School Grade Point Average. Consistent with trends in their SAT aptitude test scores, the average GPA of Asians was higher than that of other groups; the average for blacks was lower. In 1985, the averages were 2.74 (blacks), 2.88 (native Americans), 3.06 (whites), and 3.18 (Asians). Almost 22 percent of Asians reported that their high school GPA was in the 3.75 to 4.00 range, compared with 16 percent of whites, 5 percent of blacks, and 9 percent of native Americans.

Degree-Level Goals. The educational plans of college-bound seniors vary considerably. For example, Asians (31 percent) were much more likely than either whites (18 percent), blacks (20 percent), or native Americans (19 percent) to plan on earning a doctorate or other professional degree. In contrast, the largest proportions of whites, blacks, and native Americans planned a terminal baccalaureate as their highest degree.

Undergraduate Preparation

In 1985, minority representation among GRE test-takers was 12 percent.[42] Of these, 5.5 percent (8,398) were black, 2.3 percent (3,479) were Asian, and 0.6 percent (905) were native American. In comparison, among test-takers who majored in science and engineering fields at the undergraduate level, about 5.7 (5,090) were black, 3.0 percent Asian, and 0.6 percent were native American in 1985. Minority GRE representation has remained relatively unchanged since 1979.[43]

Test-takers who majored in S/E fields regardless of racial group generally scored higher than did all test-takers combined on all GRE components (figure 3-11). Additionally, scores for test-takers who majored in physical science, mathematical science, and engineering were generally higher on all components than scores for biological, behavioral, or social science majors across all racial groups (appendix table 46). Of all those who majored in S/E fields, scores for whites were higher on the verbal and analytical components, while Asian scores outpaced those of other racial groups on the quantitative portion.

On the GRE verbal component in 1985, scores for whites who majored in S/E fields were 137 points higher (524) than those for comparable blacks (387). The differential was not as large between whites and Asians or whites and native Americans: 42 points and 46 points, respectively. Between 1979 and 1985, scores for blacks, however, rose 15 points compared to no change for whites, a 4-point decline for Asians, and a 6-point increase for native Americans.

The score range widens on the quantitative section. Asians had the highest scores, which were more than 200 points greater than those for blacks (in 1985, blacks received the lowest scores). Scores for whites and native Americans were, respectively, 41 points and 100 points lower than those for Asians. The differential between Asians' and blacks' scores has not narrowed since 1979, although it has narrowed slightly between the remaining racial groups. By field, score differences were larger among social and life science majors than among natural science and engineering majors. For example, quantitative scores for engineering majors ranged from 570 for blacks to about 685 for both whites and Asians.

Trends in analytical scores were similar to those on the verbal section. Whites scored 574 in 1985; this score was 166 points higher than blacks' (408), 27 points higher than Asians' (547), and 62 points more than native Americans' (512). Since 1979, scores on this component have increased for all racial groups. The largest increases were registered by blacks and native Americans whose scores increased by more than 40 points each. Scores for whites and Asians rose 27 points and 23 points, respectively.

Earned Degrees[44]

At more advanced levels, the representation of blacks declines and that of Asians increases. For example, in 1985, blacks accounted for 5 percent (16,972)[45] of S/E baccalaureates awarded but only 2 percent (331)[46] of the doctorates. In contrast, about 4 percent (13,266) of the 1985 science and engineering bachelor's degrees and almost 6 percent (798) of the year's S/E doctorates were earned by Asians. The representation of native Americans remained at around 0.4 percent for all degree levels. Since 1979, slower increases in degree production among blacks has resulted in their declining share of degrees granted. In 1979, the proportion of S/E baccalaureates granted to blacks was 6 percent.

Bachelor's Degrees

More than 85 percent each of blacks and native Americans earned their S/E bachelor's degree in a science field in 1985. These degrees were concentrated in three fields: social science, life science, and psychology. In comparison, about one-third of Asians earned engineering baccalaureates. The field distribution of whites was primarily divided between social science (one-quarter) and engineering (one-fifth).

Master's Degrees

In 1985, 1,726 S/E master's degrees (3.4 percent) were awarded to blacks;

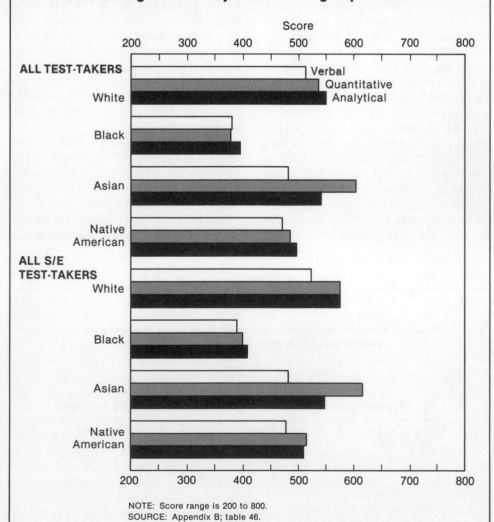

Figure 3-11. Graduate Record Examination scores by undergraduate major and racial group: 1985

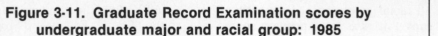

NOTE: Score range is 200 to 800.
SOURCE: Appendix B; table 46.

3,254 (6.4 percent) went to Asians; and another 220 (0.4 percent) were granted to native Americans. By field, blacks were heavily concentrated in social science (24 percent) and psychology (25 percent); also, a relatively large proportion earned degrees in engineering (19 percent). Among Asians, a majority earned degrees in one of two fields: engineering (48 percent) or computer science (19 percent). The field concentrations of both whites and native Americans were more evenly distributed than for other racial groups. For example, the largest fractions of both whites (28 percent) and native Americans (21 percent) earned engineering degrees.

Doctorates

At this level, the largest proportions of both whites and native Americans earned Ph.D.'s in life science in 1985: 30 percent and 43 percent, respectively. The largest share for blacks (32 percent) was in psychology. Similar to the bachelor's and master's degree levels, the largest concentration of Asians was in engineering (35 percent).

Graduate Education

Graduate Enrollment

In 1986, blacks accounted for 3.9 percent (12,316), Asians for 4.5 percent (14,030), and native Americans represented 0.3 percent (897) of all graduate enrollment in science and engineering fields.[47] Since 1982, minority representation has increased substantially for Asians (up from 2.9 percent) and remained unchanged for blacks and native Americans. These changing proportions result from faster increases in the number of minorities enrolling in graduate programs between 1982 and 1984. Enrollment of blacks and native Americans, however, declined between 1984 and 1986. In the 1982-84 period, enrollment of whites in science and engineering fields rose almost 7 percent, while the growth rates for blacks and Asians were 9 percent and 35 percent, respectively. The number of native Americans fluctuated around 1,000 during the 2-year period.

The field distributions of racial groups in graduate programs follow the same patterns as those exhibited in S/E degree production. In 1986, most blacks (87 percent) were enrolled in a graduate science degree program, especially in social science (46 percent) and psychology (17 percent); Asians were most heavily concentrated in graduate engineering programs (39 percent). For whites, the distribution was more even: 24 percent were enrolled in social science programs, 22 percent in engineering, and 17 percent in life science. The 1986 distribution pattern of native Americans was similar to that of blacks.

Graduate Support Status

Among those who received doctorates in science and engineering in 1986, all racial groups most frequently cited universities as their primary source of support but to differing degrees (appendix table 55). The level and type of support received for graduate education can reflect disparities among racial groups. About one-half each of whites, Asians, and native Americans reported receiving university support, compared to less than one-third of blacks.[48] Of those receiving university support, a higher proportion of whites and Asians than of blacks and native Americans held research assistantships (table 3-6). Other frequently cited sources of support were "Federal" and "self": native Americans (33 percent) were more likely to cite self-support than either whites (29 percent),

blacks (26 percent), or Asians (24 percent).

National Science Foundation Fellowships[49]

The National Science Foundation Minority Graduate Fellowship Program was begun as an experimental effort in FY 1978. It was designed as a mechanism to increase the number of scientists and engineers who are members of those racial/ethnic minority groups traditionally underrepresented in the advanced levels of the Nation's science talent pool. In FY 1978, institutional selection was used as the nominating mechanism and in FY 1979, the program was designed as a national competition to carry out the broadened concept of support of graduate study by minorities.

In FY 1985, the number of applicants to the Minority Fellowship Program was 612, up from 404 in FY 1980. By field, about two-fifths of the applicants were in either engineering, mathematics, or physical science fields; one-third were in behavioral and social sciences; the remaining one-quarter were in life and medical sciences. Engineering was the field with the highest number of applicants (112) in FY 1985.

Of the 612 applicants in FY 1985, about one-quarter (159) were offered either new awards or continuations (figure 3-12). An additional one-third (196) received honorable mentions. In FY 1980, the fraction of applicants receiving either new or continuing awards was

Table 3-6. Proportion of doctorate recipients receiving graduate support from universities by type of support and racial group: 1986

(Percent)

Type of support	White	Black	Asian	Native American
Universities, total	53	29	49	52
Fellowship	6	6	5	5
Teaching assistantship	18	11	14	26
Research assistantship	29	12	30	21

SOURCE: Appendix B; Based on table 55.

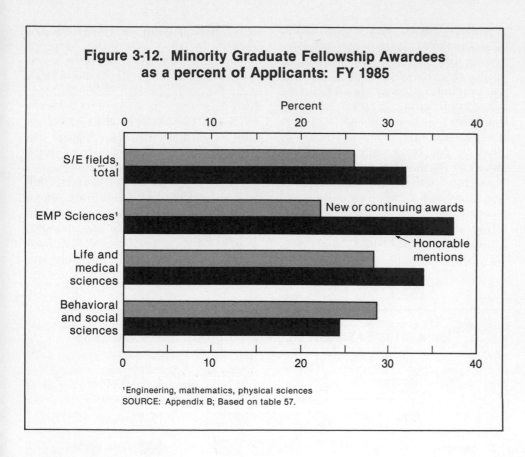

Figure 3-12. Minority Graduate Fellowship Awardees as a percent of Applicants: FY 1985

[1]Engineering, mathematics, physical sciences
SOURCE: Appendix B; Based on table 57.

Coursework. Historically, Hispanics take fewer years of, and different coursework in, mathematics as compared to all high school seniors. About 36 percent of Hispanics and 41 percent of all students had taken 4 or more years of math. Corresponding grade point averages in this subject were 2.04 and 2.27, respectively. Types of courses taken also differ substantially (appendix table 35). For instance, while more than one-half of all seniors had taken geometry, only about two-fifths of Hispanics had done so.

The average number of years of mathematics coursework also differs between Hispanics[51] and all college-bound seniors. In 1985, all seniors had taken an average of 3.68 years of math; for Mexican Americans and Puerto Ricans, the averages were 3.48 and 3.39, respectively.

The same differences that exist in high school mathematics coursework were evident for science coursework. Historical data show that about 15 percent of Hispanic seniors, compared to more than 21 percent of all seniors, took 4 or more years of science. Respective grade point averages in this subject were 2.07 and 2.38. Additionally, types of courses taken varied widely. For example, one-quarter of Hispanics, but one-third of all seniors, had taken chemistry.

Among all college-bound seniors, the average number of years of coursework was 1.90 in physical science and 1.42 in biological science in 1985. The Hispanic averages were lower in number of years for physical science courses— 1.52 for Mexican Americans and 1.69 for Puerto Ricans. In biological science, however, the number of years was below average for Mexican Americans (1.35), but slightly higher than average for Puerto Ricans (1.45).

There are differences between Hispanic males and females in mathematics and science coursetaking. For both Mexican American and Puerto Rican college-bound seniors, males reported a higher average number of years of mathematics and physical science coursework in 1985. In biological science, there was little difference in the averages between Mexican American males and females; Puerto Rican females, however, took more coursework in this subject than did males.

almost one-third (127) of the 404 applicants. One-third (130) of applicants also received honorable mentions.

Postdoctoral Appointments

In 1985, almost 2,000 (17 percent) of the 11,800 postdoctoral appointments in science and engineering fields were held by members of racial minority groups. Specifically, about 2.0 percent (213) were held by blacks, 14.0 percent (1,615) by Asians, and another 0.4 percent (51) by native Americans. While the representation of blacks and native Americans has increased over the 1975-85 period, it has fallen for Asians. In 1975, the numbers of S/E postdoctorates held by racial minorities were 82 (blacks), 1,241 (Asians), and 7 (native Americans).

Field distributions vary by racial group (appendix table 58). Almost all of whites, blacks, and native Americans held postdoctorates in science fields. By field, 66 percent of whites held life science appointments, 87 percent of blacks had postdoctorates in either physical or life

science, and 57 percent of native Americans held appointments in social science. In contrast, the field distribution of Asians showed 49 percent in life science, 29 percent in physical science, and 16 percent with engineering postdoctorates.

HISPANICS

Precollege Preparation

Curriculum and Coursework

Curriculum. Historical data show that a lower proportion of Hispanics than of all high school seniors enroll in an academic curriculum: 27 percent versus 39 percent.[50] This pattern is also exhibited among college-bound seniors. In 1985, almost 79 percent of all college-bound seniors were in academic programs compared with 70 percent of Mexican Americans and 64 percent of Puerto Ricans. Among Hispanic college-bound seniors, males were more likely than females to be in a college-preparatory curriculum.

Mathematics and Science Achievement[52]

Mathematics. Hispanics continue to score below the national average on the mathematics assessment at all three age levels. The differential has narrowed, however, at the 13- and 17-year-old levels. The most recent NAEP assessment reports that Hispanic 9- and 13-year-olds scored 9 percentage points lower than the national average while the gap was 11 points at the 17-year-old level. In 1978, these differences were 9, 15, and 12 points, respectively. The most statistically significant changes occurred at the 13-year-old level (appendix table 37).

Science. Hispanics also scored lower than the national average at all age levels on the NAEP science assessment. Score differentials widen with age from 8.5 percentage points at age 9 to almost 11 points at the 17-year-old level. Regardless of age level, Hispanics scored much lower than the national average on those components that measured understanding and applications of scientific processes.

Characteristics of College-Bound Seniors

Scholastic Aptitude Test. Hispanics continue to score below the national average on both components of the aptitude test, although they have made gains over the last 10 years (figure 3-13). Among Hispanics, scores have increased more for Mexican Americans than for Puerto Ricans on both the verbal and mathematics sections.

An examination of the representation of Hispanics among college-bound seniors in 1985 shows that about 2.2 percent (19,526) of the registrants were Mexican American and another 0.9 percent (8,423) were Puerto Rican.[53] These Hispanic seniors accounted for 11 percent of Mexican American, but 24 percent of Puerto Rican, 18-year-olds. In comparison, total program registrants constituted 28 percent of all 18-year-olds.

Scores for Hispanics on the verbal component were 382 for Mexican Americans and 373 for Puerto Ricans. These scores were, respectively, 49 and 58 points below the average of those for all college-bound seniors. Increases in these scores for Hispanics, however, have caused differences to narrow from 60 points (Mexican Americans) and 67 points (Puerto Ricans) since 1976. One factor contributing to lower scores of Hispanics may be a language barrier. In 1985, for example, about 7 percent of Mexican American college-bound seniors and 9 percent of Puerto Rican seniors reported that English was not their best language; the overall proportion was 4 percent.

On the mathematics component, Hispanics also scored lower than average, with Mexican American scores somewhat higher than those for Puerto Ricans. In 1985, scores for Mexican Americans (426) were 49 points lower than all scores; Puerto Rican scores (405) were 70 points lower. Scores for Mexican Americans rose 16 points between 1976 and 1985; this increase was substantially more than the 4-point increase for Puerto Ricans and the 3-point rise for all college-bound seniors.

Consistent with overall trends, SAT scores for Hispanic males were above those for females; the biggest gap occurred on the mathematics component. Scores on this section for Mexican American males were 50 points higher

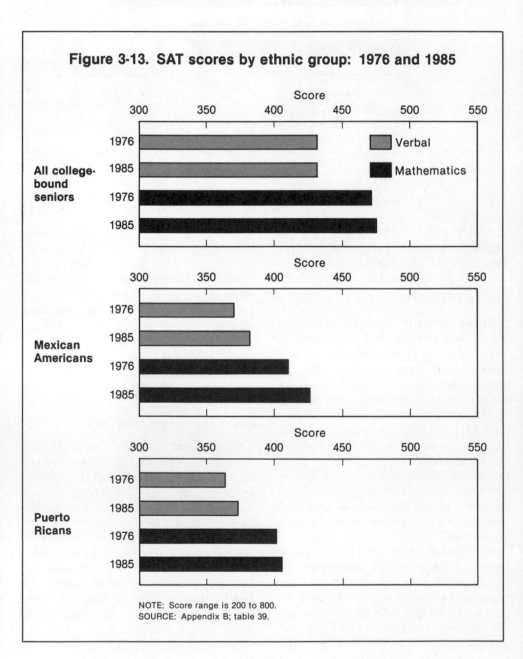

Figure 3-13. SAT scores by ethnic group: 1976 and 1985

NOTE: Score range is 200 to 800.
SOURCE: Appendix B; table 39.

(452 versus 402) than those for females, whereas the difference between Puerto Rican males and females was 54 points (435 versus 381) in 1985. These differentials have not narrowed appreciably during the eighties.

While 3 percent of all college-bound seniors scored in the 650 to 800 range on the verbal test, only about 1 percent of both Hispanic groups did so in 1985. On the mathematics component, the percentage of the total scoring in this range (9 percent) was again three times greater than the percentage of Hispanics (3 percent each).

Achievement Test Scores. Hispanic college-bound seniors scored lower than did all seniors on the five achievement tests administered in science and mathematics (figure 3-14). Unlike the pattern exhibited in scores on the aptitude test, however, scores for Puerto Ricans were higher than those for Mexican Americans on all but the physics exam. In 1985, the highest achievement test score for Hispanics was on the mathematics level II test. Puerto Ricans received a 620 and had a corresponding SAT mathematics score of 610; Mexican Americans obtained a score of 598 on this test and a corresponding mathematics score of 584. Overall, students scored 658 on the mathematics level II test and had SAT math scores of 649.

Mexican American college-bound seniors (19 percent) are more likely than Puerto Ricans (12 percent), but less likely than all seniors (21 percent), to take one or more achievement tests. Additionally, among seniors who take at least one test in this series, about 45 percent of Mexican Americans—compared with 40 percent of Puerto Ricans and 48 percent of all seniors—take one or more of the science and mathematics examinations.

Advanced Placement Examinations. Almost 7,900 Hispanics (3.4 percent) took an AP exam in 1986. Of these test-takers, 3,058 (39 percent) were Mexican American, 1,028 (13 percent) were Puerto Rican, and the remaining 3,790 (almost 49 percent) were classified as "other Hispanic" (primarily Latin American). A smaller proportion of Hispanics than of all AP test-takers took one or more exams in science and mathematics. While more than one-third of all test-

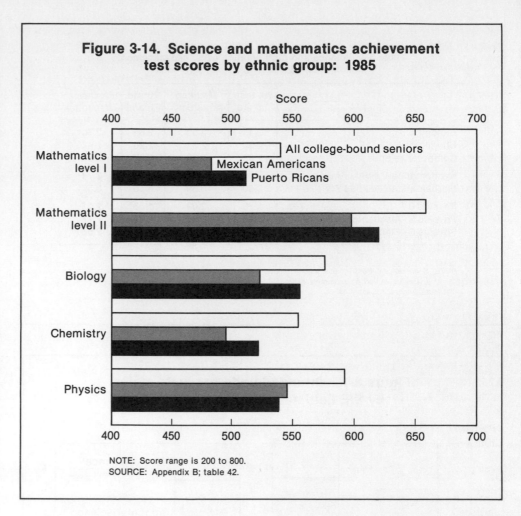

Figure 3-14. Science and mathematics achievement test scores by ethnic group: 1985

NOTE: Score range is 200 to 800.
SOURCE: Appendix B; table 42.

takers took one of these tests, the proportion of Hispanics varied between one-fifth (Mexican American) and one-quarter ("other Hispanic").

Although Hispanics received lower scores than all test-takers on science and mathematics tests, these scores varied considerably by Hispanic subgroup (table 3-7). For example, in 1986, the score range for Mexican Americans was from 2.09 (physics B) to 3.39 (mathematics/calculus BC); for Puerto Ricans, it was 1.63 (physics B) to 3.50 (physics C - electricity/magnetism).

Intended Undergraduate Major. Among college-bound seniors, Mexican Americans were more likely than both Puerto Ricans and all college-bound seniors to choose a science and engineering field as their intended undergraduate major. Within S/E fields, Mexican Americans more often chose engineering as their probable major than did Puerto Ricans: one-third versus one-

quarter (figure 3-15). Within the sciences, both subgroups were more likely to select computer science or social science than a life or physical science field.

The SAT mathematics scores for those Hispanics who chose a physical science or engineering field were higher than the scores received by all Hispanics. In 1985, for example, among Hispanics whose probable major was mathematics, Mexican Americans scored 510 and Puerto Ricans received a 540; the overall averages for Hispanic college-bound seniors on this component were 426 and 405, respectively.

Selected Socioeconomic Characteristics of College-Bound Seniors. Information on the characteristics and scores of Hispanic college-bound seniors reveals a pattern similar to that for blacks and native Americans: Hispanics may not be as well prepared and therefore may not have had the same access to and opportunities for education in S/E

Table 3-7. Science and mathematics advanced placement examination scores by ethnic group: 1986

Field	All test-takers	Mexican Americans	Puerto Ricans	Other Hispanics
Biology.........................	3.15	2.50	2.69	2.70
Chemistry	2.80	2.31	2.26	2.42
Computer science	2.98	2.50	2.57	2.84
Mathematics/Calculus AB	3.09	2.75	2.68	2.73
Mathematics/Calculus BC	3.50	3.39	3.35	3.37
Physics B......................	2.80	2.09	1.63	2.13
Physics C - Mechanics	3.47	3.00	2.67	2.77
Physics C - Electricity & Magnetism	3.33	2.42	3.50	2.65

NOTE: Score range is from 1 to 5: 1 = no recommendation for credit; 2 = possibly qualified; 3 = qualified; 4 = well qualified; 5 = extremely well qualified.
SOURCE: Appendix B; table 43.

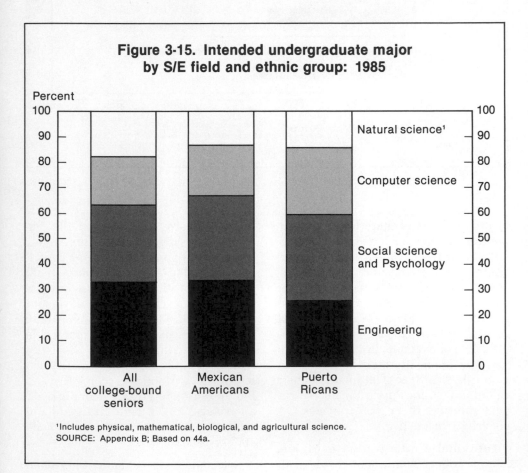

Figure 3-15. Intended undergraduate major by S/E field and ethnic group: 1985

¹Includes physical, mathematical, biological, and agricultural science.
SOURCE: Appendix B; Based on 44a.

Parents' Education. The median number of years of education for both fathers and mothers of Mexican American or Puerto Rican college-bound seniors was slightly more than 12 years in 1985. In contrast, the median number for fathers overall was 14.1 years and for mothers, it was 13.6 years. Further differences arise between Hispanic subgroups. For example, the highest level of education reported for Mexican American parents was more likely than for Puerto Rican parents to be grade school, e.g., 23 percent of Mexican American fathers and 16 percent of Puerto Rican fathers in 1985. In contrast, a higher fraction of Puerto Rican parents had completed high school: 25 percent versus 19 percent of their fathers.

Annual Parental Income. The median income of Hispanic seniors was much lower than that of all college-bound seniors. In 1985, Mexican Americans reported a median income of $20,500 and Puerto Ricans indicated their parents' income to be around $17,000. The median for all college-bound seniors was $32,200 in 1985.

Financial Aid Plans. Reflecting the much lower median annual incomes of their parents, a much higher fraction of Hispanic than all college-bound seniors planned to apply for financial assistance in 1985. While about 77 percent of all seniors reported plans to apply for aid, about 90 percent of both Mexican Americans and Puerto Ricans did so.

High School Grade Point Average. The average GPA for Hispanic college-bound seniors was lower than the national average. In 1985, 2.97 and 2.84 were the averages for Mexican Americans and Puerto Ricans, respectively, compared to 3.03 overall.

Degree-Level Goals. About the same fractions (one-third each) of Mexican American and Puerto Rican college-bound seniors as of all college-bound seniors reported a baccalaureate as their educational goal. At advanced levels, however, Mexican Americans (48 percent) were more likely than either Puerto Ricans (42 percent) or all seniors (46 percent) to report some type of graduate degree as their goal.

fields as did all college-bound seniors. Additionally, while Hispanics plan to achieve higher degree goals than did their parents, the economic means reported by Hispanic college-bound seniors are well below the average; lower economic means may negatively affect attainment of their educational goals. Regardless of socioeconomic variables, however, Hispanics score below all college-bound seniors on both components of the aptitude examination.

Undergraduate Preparation

About 3.3 percent (5,146) of GRE test-takers were Hispanic in 1985, up from 2.8 percent in 1979. Specifically, 1.3 percent (2,069) were Mexican American, 0.9 percent (1,486) were Puerto Rican, and 1.0 percent (1,591) were classified as Latin American or "other Hispanic." The representation of Hispanic GRE test-takers who majored in an S/E field at the undergraduate level was similar to their overall representation—3.5 percent.

Although Hispanic test-takers who majored in S/E fields scored lower than did all S/E test-takers on the three GRE components, there was wide variation among ethnic subgroups (figure 3-16). Scores for Latin Americans were generally higher than those for Mexican Americans or Puerto Ricans among all S/E fields, regardless of component. On the verbal component, for example, scores for Latin Americans (474) were only 15 points lower than the overall average; scores for Mexican Americans (448) and Puerto Ricans (390) were, respectively, 41 points and 99 points lower than average in 1985. Score differences were greatest on the analytical section; they ranged from 422 for Puerto Ricans (120 points lower than the score for all test-takers) to 502 for Latin Americans (40 points lower). All Hispanics who majored in either physical science, mathematical science, or engineering fields received higher scores on the GRE than did social or life science majors.

Earned Degrees

Hispanics account for a larger fraction of degrees awarded at the undergraduate than at graduate levels. In 1985, about 3.1 percent (10,017) of science and engineering baccalaureates, 2.7 percent (1,351) of S/E master's degrees, and 2.1 percent (279) of S/E doctorates were awarded to Hispanics in 1985.[54] Hispanic representation declined slightly from 3.2 percent at the bachelor's level in 1979 but increased from 1.9 percent and 1.7 percent, respectively, at the master's and doctorate degree levels.

At the baccalaureate level, a large fraction of the degrees granted to Hispanics (32 percent) were in social science; another 18 percent were in engineering in 1985. More than two-thirds of Hispanics who earned master's degrees graduated in either engineering, social science, or psychology. At the doctorate level, more than 200 of the 279 degrees granted to Hispanics were in either life science, psychology, or social science.

Graduate Education[55]

Graduate Enrollment

Hispanics represented 3.3 percent (10,312) of graduate enrollment in science and engineering fields in 1986, up from 2.9 percent 4 years earlier. By field, Hispanics accounted for a larger share of enrollment in science fields (3.6 percent) than in engineering (2.3 percent). Driving this proportional increase was a 26-percent growth rate in the number of Hispanics enrolled in S/E programs between 1982 and 1984. In comparison, overall graduate enrollment rose 6 percent during this 2-year period. Graduate enrollment in S/E programs, however, declined about 3 percent for Hispanics and increased about 2 percent overall between 1984 and 1986.

Hispanics were more likely than all graduate students to be enrolled in science rather than engineering programs.

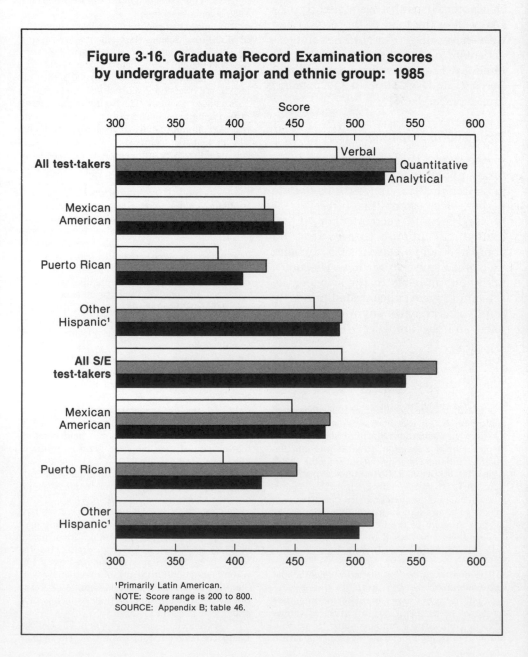

Figure 3-16. Graduate Record Examination scores by undergraduate major and ethnic group: 1985

[1]Primarily Latin American.
NOTE: Score range is 200 to 800.
SOURCE: Appendix B; table 46.

Within science, Hispanics were concentrated in social science and psychology (appendix table 53): for example, 33 percent of Hispanics were in social science and 16 percent were in an engineering field. Among all graduate students, these fields accounted for 25 percent (social science) and 23 percent (engineering) of their enrollment.

Graduate Support Status

Of those who earned S/E doctorates in 1986, Hispanics did not report universities as their primary source of support as often as all new degree holders (41 percent versus 53 percent). Furthermore, Hispanics were slightly less likely than the total of those receiving university support to hold research assistantships. Other sources of support cited by Hispanics were Federal (20 percent) and self-support (27 percent) (appendix table 55).

Postdoctoral Appointments

About 249 Hispanics held postdoctoral appointments in science and engineering in 1985, up from 83 a decade earlier. Because of this threefold increase, Hispanics accounted for 2.1 percent of S/E postdoctorates in 1985 compared to 1 percent in 1975. By field, more than one-half of these Hispanics held appointments in life science; the remainder were concentrated primarily in physical science, environmental science, and psychology.

ENDNOTES

1. Data in this chapter on either 1980 high school seniors or 1980 high school sophomores in 1982 are from the Center for Education Statistics, U.S. Department of Education, *High School and Beyond: A National Longitudinal Study for the 1980's* (Washington, DC: U.S. Government Printing Office, 1984).

2. All data in this chapter on the characteristics of college-bound seniors are from the Admissions Testing Program of the College Board, *Profiles, College-Bound Seniors* (New York: College Entrance Examination Board, annual series, 1981-85).

3. Center for Education Statistics, *High School and Beyond*.

4. The national assessment of mathematics measures achievement in four areas: (a) knowledge of mathematics fundamentals; (b) computational skills; (c) understanding of mathematical methods; and (d) applications—problem-solving ability in mathematics.

5. Data on the mathematics assessment by sex for 1978 and 1982 are from National Assessment of Educational Progress, *The Third National Mathematics Assessment: Results, Trends, and Issues*, Report No. 13-MA-01 (Denver: Education Commission of the States, April 1983), pp. 37-40.

6. Changes are significant at the 0.05 level.

7. The national assessment of science contains four components: (a) knowledge and skills in areas such as biology, physical science, and earth science (science content); (b) understanding of scientific processes (science inquiry); (c) implications of science and technology for society (science-technology-society); and (d) students' orientation toward science (attitudes). The most recent science assessment was conducted in the spring of 1987; results will be available in the fall of 1988. This section depicts the results of the 1982 science assessment.

8. Science assessment data are from University of Minnesota, Science Assessment and Research Project, *Images of Science* (Minneapolis: Minnesota Research and Evaluation Center, June 1983).

9. The Admissions Testing Program of the College Board offers the Scholastic Aptitude Test to college-bound seniors. The examination consists of two components. The verbal component tests reading comprehension and vocabulary skills and the mathematics component assesses problem-solving ability using arithmetic reasoning and basic algebra and geometry skills. The score range is 200 to 800.

10. The Student Descriptive Questionnaire distributed to college-bound seniors as part of the SAT application package was revised in 1986. One-half of the sample of college-bound seniors received the new questionnaire; the remainder completed the older version. In 1987, the entire sample will receive the new questionnaire. Because of this change, comparable time-series data (with the exception of overall scores by gender) are not available after 1985.

11. In addition to the SAT, the Admissions Testing Program offers an achievement test series to college-bound seniors. The series includes 1-hour multiple choice exams in 14 academic areas. About one in five of those students who take the SAT also take one or more of the achievement tests. The score range is 200 to 800.

12. Of the 14 academic subjects in which achievement tests were administered in 1985, 5 were in science and mathematics fields: mathematics level I, mathematics level II, biology, chemistry, and physics.

13. The College Board also administers the Advanced Placement (AP) Program. In this program, a series of exams are offered in 24 areas, 8 of which are in science and mathematics. A student who does well on one or more of these exams may be granted college credit or appropriate placement by participating higher education institutions. The AP grading scale ranges from 1 (no recommendation for credit) to 5 (extremely well qualified in the subject area). About 15 percent of college-bound seniors participate in this program.

14. Advanced Placement Program, The College Board, *AP Yearbook 1986* (New York: The College Entrance Examination Board, 1986), p. 5.

15. The physics C - electricity/magnetism AP exam and the physics C - mechanics exam allow a student the opportunity to earn placement or credit in only one of these respective areas of physics. In contrast, the physics B exam covers all aspects of physics and a student who scores well on this exam may earn as much as a semester's course credit in this field.

16. Two AP exams are offered in mathematics/calculus. The mathematics/calculus AB exam is not as rigorous as the mathematics/calculus BC exam. While up to a full year of college credit may be earned by those who score well on the BC test, scores on the AB test are used primarily for appropriately placing students in courses.

17. The intended undergraduate major of college-bound seniors is determined by answers to question #61 on the Student Descriptive Questionnaire (1985). The question asks students to choose their first choice of college curriculum from a list of 29 major categories of which 7 are in science and 1 is in engineering.

18. On the Student Descriptive Questionnaire for 1985, these variables appeared as questions #39 and #40 (parents' education), question #27 (financial aid plans), questions #12 to #17 (grade point average—calculated based on self-reported grades in six major subjects including English, mathematics, foreign languages, biological sciences, physical sciences, and social sciences), and question #24 (degree-level goals).

19. The GRE contains a general aptitude test and offers advanced tests in 20 subject areas. The aptitude test is comprised of three components. The verbal component assesses the ability to use words in solving problems; the quantitative portion requires an ability to apply elementary mathematical skills and concepts to solve problems in quantitative settings; and the analytical component, a relatively new addition to the test (1979), measures deductive and inductive reasoning skills. The score range on the GRE is 200 to 800.

20. Henry Roy Smith III, *A Summary of Data Collected from Graduate Record Examination Test-Takers During 1984-85*, Data Summary Report #10 (Princeton: Educational Testing Service, 1986), p. 68.

21. For purposes of this analysis, S/E fields include physical science, mathematical science, engineering, biological science, behavioral science, and social science. See Henry Roy Smith III, *Data Summary Report #10*, for an example of field classifications.

22. Total enrollment is projected datum from the U.S. Department of Education, Center for Education Statistics, *Projections of Education Statistics to 1990-91, Volume 1* (Washington, DC: U.S. Government Printing Office, 1982), p. 18.

23. Data for bachelor's and master's degrees in science and engineering are from the U.S. Department of Education, Center for Education Statistics' Annual Survey of Earned Degrees; these have been adapted to National Science Foundation field classifications.

24. Ibid.

25. Data on science and engineering doctorates granted in the United States are from the National Science Foundation's Survey of Earned Doctorates, conducted annually for NSF by the National Academy of Sciences.

26. Data presented in this section are from the National Science Foundation's Survey of Graduate Science and Engineering Students and Postdoctorates. This survey has been conducted annually since 1966.

27. Data for this section are from unpublished tabulations from the National Science Foundation's Survey of Earned Doctorates.

28. Data on this topic are from the National Science Foundation's Fellowship Program. These data are collected by the National Academy of Sciences in support of NSF programs.

29. National Science Foundation, Directorate for Science and Engineering Education, Division of Research Career Development, unpublished tabulations.

30. Data for this section are from the National Science Foundation's Survey of Doctorate Recipients. This survey is conducted biennially for NSF by the National Academy of Sciences.

31. Center for Education Statistics, *High School and Beyond.*

32. Ibid.

33. Includes earth science, chemistry, and physics.

34. See "Mathematics and Science Achievement" in the Women's section of this chapter for an explanation of the NAEP achievement measures.

35. Because of insufficient sample size, the National Assessment of Educational Progress does not include data on racial/ethnic groups other than whites, blacks, and Hispanics. In 1982, with little variation among age groups, about 80 percent of the sample were white, approximately 13 percent black, another 5 percent were classified as Hispanic, and the remaining 2 percent were defined as "other minorities." See National Assessment of Educational Progress, *The Third National Mathematics Assessment: Results, Trends, and Issues,* p. 33.

36. At the 0.05 level.

37. Data are from Science Assessment and Research Project, *Images of Science,* pp. 101-119.

38. Given the 1986 change in the Student Descriptive Questionnaire, no data are available on the racial/ethnic background of college-bound seniors for that year. Data will be available for future years; they will not, however, be comparable with historical data because of changes in the racial/ethnic classification.

39. Question #37 on the 1985 Student Descriptive Questionnaire asked students to describe their racial/ethnic background using the following categories: (a) American Indian or Alaskan Native, (b) black or Afro-American or Negro, (c) Mexican American or Chicano, (d) Oriental or Asian American or Pacific Islander, (e) Puerto Rican, (f) white or Caucasian, and (g) other.

40. Data on minority representation are from Admissions Testing Program of the College Board, *Profiles, College-Bound Seniors, 1985,* pp. xviii - xxiii.

41. Advanced Placement Program, *1986 Advanced Placement Program, National Summary Report,* p. 3.

42. The racial/ethnic classification includes (a) American Indian, Eskimo, or Aleut; (b) black or Afro-American; (c) Mexican American or Chicano; (d) Oriental or Asian American; (e) Puerto Rican; (f) other Hispanic or Latin American; (g) white; and (h) other. Henry Roy Smith III, *Data Summary Report #10,* p. 16.

43. Cheryl L. Wild, *A Summary of Data Collected from Graduate Record Examination Test-Takers During 1978-79, Data Summary Report #4* (Princeton: Educational Testing Service, 1980), p. 16.

44. Earned degree data are for U.S. citizens and permanent residents only.

45. Center for Education Statistics, unpublished data.

46. National Science Foundation, Survey of Earned Doctorates (includes U.S. citizens only).

47. Includes U.S. citizens only.

48. National Science Foundation, Survey of Earned Doctorates, unpublished tabulations (includes data for U.S. citizens only).

49. Data for this section are from the National Science Foundation's Minority Graduate Fellowship Program administered by the Division of Research Career Development in the Directorate for Science and Engineering Education. Minority data are only collected in the aggregate and include both racial and ethnic minorities. Information presented in this section is from unpublished data sources.

50. Center for Education Statistics, *High School and Beyond.*

51. Data on Hispanic college-bound seniors are only available for Mexican Americans and Puerto Ricans.

52. See "Mathematics and Science Achievement" in Women's section for an explanation of NAEP achievement measures.

53. Includes Puerto Ricans from the 50 States and the District of Columbia only.

54. Data for science and engineering bachelor's and master's degrees are from the Center for Education Statistics, unpublished tabulations.

55. Data on NSF Minority Graduate Fellowships define "minority" to include both racial and ethnic groups and cannot be disaggregated. Since these data have already been presented above in the "Racial Minorities" section, they will not be repeated for Hispanics.

Technical Notes

CONCEPTS AND DEFINITIONS

The National Science Foundation (NSF) publishes a variety of data relating to scientists and engineers. These data—which include estimates of graduate enrollments and degree production as well as the number, work activities, sector of employment, and other economic and demographic characteristics of scientists and engineers—are developed by the Division of Science Resources Studies as part of its ongoing programs. This section presents a brief examination of the major NSF data resources used in this report.

SCIENCE AND ENGINEERING PERSONNEL

Estimates of the characteristics of scientists and engineers in the United States were produced by NSF's Scientific and Technical Personnel Data System (STPDS). Broadly speaking, a person is considered a scientist or engineer if at least two of the following criteria are met:

(1) Degree in science (including social science) or engineering;

(2) Employed in a science or engineering occupation; and/or

(3) Professional identification as a scientist or engineer based on total education and experience.

National Estimates

The STPDS is comprised of three subsystems, each designed to measure the characteristics of a particular subpopulation:

- **The Experienced Sample of Scientists and Engineers** is the biennial followup survey to the 1982 Postcensal Survey of Scientists and Engineers. The Postcensal Survey sample was drawn from those individuals who were in the science and engineering (S/E) population at the time of the 1980 census. The Postcensal Survey and both the 1984 and 1986 Experienced Sample surveys were conducted for NSF by the Bureau of the Census. The 1986 survey, the most recent in this series, was based on a sample of 64,000 individuals.

- **The Survey of Recent Science and Engineering Graduates** is designed to measure the magnitude and characteristics of those who earned S/E degrees after the 1980 decennial census was completed. During the eighties, the Institute for Survey Research, Temple University, has conducted this survey series for NSF. The most recent survey, conducted in 1986, focuses on the graduating classes of 1984 and 1985 and is based on a sample of 36,000 individuals.

- **The Survey of Doctorate Recipients** provides information on scientists and engineers granted doctorates in the United States over a 42-year period. The most recent survey, conducted in 1985, covered those individuals who received their doctorates between 1942 and 1984. The sample size for the 1985 survey was 57,000. Since 1973, this survey series has been conducted biennially for NSF by the Office of Scientific and Engineering Personnel, National Academy of Sciences.

In order to produce national estimates, data from the Experienced Sample and Recent Graduate surveys are integrated using a computer-based model. The Science and Engineering Tabulating Model, developed for NSF by Mathematica Policy Research, Inc., was used to generate national estimates for 1982, 1984, and 1986; it may also be employed as a projection model to generate preliminary estimates for future years.

Selected Variable Definitions

Field of Science and Engineering

Data on field of employment are derived from responses to questions asking the name of the specialty most closely related to the respondent's principal employment. The specialty is chosen from a list provided in each questionnaire. Fields are classified as follows:

- **Physical science:** chemistry, physics, astronomy, and other physical sciences, including metallurgy

- **Mathematical science:** mathematics and statistics

- **Computer specialties**

- **Environmental science:** earth, atmospheric, and oceanographic sciences, including geophysics, seismology, and meteorology

- **Life science:** biological, agricultural, and medical sciences (excluding those engaged in patient care)

- **Psychology**

- **Social science:** economics, including agricultural economics; sociology; anthropology; and all other social sciences

- **Engineering:** aeronautical/astronautical, chemical, civil, electrical/electronics, materials science, mechanical, nuclear, petroleum, and other engineering

Data on field of employment are derived from responses to questions that request, based on employment specialties lists included with the questionnaire, the name of the specialty most closely related to the respondent's principal employment.

Work Activities

Data on work activities of scientists and engineers represent their primary work activities. These data are derived from responses to survey questions that ask individuals to select, from a list of 10 to 15 choices, their primary and secondary work activities and to indicate the percentage of time devoted to these activities. Work activities are classified as follows:

- **Research and development (R&D):** basic research; applied research; development; and design of equipment, processes, and models
- **Management of R&D:** management or administration of research and development
- **General management:** management or administration of activities other than research and development
- **Teaching:** teaching and training
- **Production/inspection:** quality control, testing, evaluation, or inspection; and operations including production, maintenance, construction, installation, and exploration
- **Reporting, statistical work, and computing:** report and technical writing, editing, and information retrieval; statistical work including survey work, forecasting, and statistical analysis; computer applications

Additional work activities for which information is collected include distribution (sales, traffic, purchasing, customer and public relations), consulting, and other activities.

Sector of Employment

Information on type of employer is also derived from individual survey respondents. Respondents are asked to choose the category which best describes the type of organization of their principal employment. Data on employment sector are classified as follows:

- **Industry:** business or industry as well as self-employed individuals
- **Educational institutions:** 4-year colleges or universities, medical schools, junior colleges, 2-year colleges, technical institutes, and elementary or secondary school systems
- **Federal Government:** civilian employment only

Other sectors of employment for which information has been collected include hospitals or clinics; nonprofit organizations, other than hospitals, clinics, or educational institutions; U.S. military service, active duty or Commissioned Corps; State and local governments; and other employers.

Statistical Measures

Labor Force Participation Rate

The labor force is defined as those employed and those seeking employment. The labor force participation rate ($Rate_L$) is the ratio of those employed (E) and those unemployed (U) to the population (P).

S/E Employment Rate

The S/E employment rate ($Rate_{SE}$) measures the ratio of those holding jobs in science or engineering (SE) to the total employment (E) of scientists and engineers, which includes those holding nonscience or nonengineering jobs.

Unemployment Rate

The unemployment rate ($Rate_U$) shows the ratio of those who are unemployed but seeking employment (U) to the total labor force (E + U).

S/E Underemployment Rate

The S/E underemployment rate ($Rate_{UE}$) shows the ratio of those who are working part-time but seeking full-time jobs (PTS) or who are working in a non-S/E job when an S/E job would be preferred (NSE) to total employment (E).

S/E Underutilization Rate

The S/E underutilization rate ($Rate_{UZ}$) shows the proportion of those in the total labor force who are unemployed but seeking employment (U), working part-time but seeking full-time jobs (PTS), or working in a non-S/E job when an S/E job would be preferred (NSE).

Reliability of Science and Engineering Estimates

Estimates of scientists and engineers are derived from sample surveys and thus are subject to both sampling and nonsampling errors.

Sampling Errors

The sample used for a particular survey is only one of many possible samples of the same size that could have been selected using the same sample design. Even if the same questionnaire and instructions were used, the estimates from each of the samples would differ. The deviation of the estimated sample from the average of all possible samples is defined as "sampling error." The standard error of a survey estimate attempts to provide a measure of this variation. Standard errors are thus indicators of the degree of precision with which a sample estimate approximates the average results for all possible samples.

The standard error may be used to construct a confidence interval about a given estimate. Thus, when the reported standard error is added to and subtracted from an estimate, the resulting range of values reflects an interval within which about 68 percent of all sample estimates, surveyed under the same conditions, will fall. Intervals reflecting a higher confidence level may be constructed by increasing the number of standard errors for a given estimate. Thus, ± 1.6 standard errors define a 90-percent confidence interval; ± 2 standard errors, a 95-percent confidence interval. The standard errors for the 1986 national data are estimated using the "Method of Random Groups."

Selected tables of standard errors for the various surveys are contained in the tables listed below:

Survey	Table
1986 National estimates of scientists and engineers	1-6
1985 Doctoral scientists and engineers	7

The sampling errors shown here were generated based on approximations and must, therefore, be considered estimates rather than precise measurements.

Nonsampling Errors

Nonsampling errors may be attributed to many sources: inability to obtain information about all cases; definitional difficulties; differences in the interpretation of questions; respondents' inability or unwillingness to provide correct information; mistakes in recording or coding the information; and other errors in collection, response, processing, coverage, and imputation.

Nonsampling errors are not unique to samples; they can occur in complete canvasses as well. No systematic attempt has been made to identify or approximate the magnitude of nonsampling errors associated with the estimates of scientists and engineers presented in this report.

GRADUATE ENROLLMENT

National estimates of graduate S/E enrollments are from the Annual Survey of Graduate Science and Engineering Students and Postdoctorates, currently conducted for NSF by Quantum Research Corporation. The survey universe is composed of all 618 institutions in the United States with departments or programs offering courses of study at the postbaccalaureate level in any S/E field. Included are medical schools and other specialized institutions offering first-professional doctorates in health-related fields. The most recent sample consisted of 414 graduate institutions and 18 historically black universities and colleges.

EARNED DEGREES

Bachelor's and Master's Degrees

Data on earned degrees in science and engineering at the bachelor's and master's level are collected by the Center for Education Statistics of the U.S. Department of Education. These data cover earned degrees conferred in the aggregate United States, which includes the 50 States, the District of Columbia, and outlying areas. Degree data are compiled for the 12-month period from July through the following June.

Doctorates

Data on doctorates granted in science and engineering are developed from Survey of Earned Doctorates, conducted for NSF by the National Academy of Sciences. These data cover all types of doctoral degrees with the exception of such first-professional degrees as the J.D. or M.D. Data are collected for the aggregate United States and cover the period from July to the following June.

ADDITIONAL INFORMATION ON NSF DATA SOURCES

A brief description of each survey and copies of the survey instruments may be found in *A Guide to NSF Science Resources Data*. The *Guide* is available from the Office of the Division Director, Division of Science Resources Studies, 1800 G Street N.W., Room L-602, National Science Foundation, Washington, DC 20550.

Table 1. Standard errors for estimates of total scientists and engineers: 1986

Size of estimate	Physical scientists			Mathematical scientists		Computer Specialists	Environmental scientists		
	Chemists	Physicists/ Astronomers	Other Physical Scientists	Mathematicians	Statisticians		Earth Scientists	Ocean-ographers	Atmospheric Scientists
100	250	110	50	180	50	560	130	40	30
200	260	130	80	200	70	570	140	80	50
500	290	180	150	260	140	590	170	190	130
700	310	210	200	290	180	610	190	260	180
1,000	340	250	270	350	230	630	220	370	250
2,500	480	480	600	600	450	750	370	730	570
5,000	720	830	1,000	990	650	940	600		980
10,000	1,200	1,400	1,600	1,600	880	1,300	970		1,400
25,000	2,300	2,400	2,500	2,300		2,300	1,600		
50,000	3,600	3,000		2,100		3,600	1,800		
75,000	4,400	4,800		3,500		4,600	2,400		
80,000	4,500	5,500		4,400		4,700	2,700		
100,000	5,000					5,200			
125,000	5,600					5,600			
150,000	6,500					5,800			
175,000	7,900					5,900			
200,000						6,000			
225,000						6,000			
250,000						6,200			
275,000						6,400			
300,000						6,900			
400,000									
500,000									

Table 1. (cont.)

Size of estimate	Life Scientists			Psychologists	Social Scientists			Engineers	
	Biologists	Agricultural Scientists	Medical Scientists		Economists	Sociologists/ Anthro-pologists	Other Social Scientists	Chemical Engineers	Aeronautical/ Astronautical Engineers
100	350	180	60	440	300	170	340	150	110
200	360	190	90	450	320	190	360	160	120
500	390	230	190	490	360	260	400	190	160
700	410	260	250	520	390	310	440	210	180
1,000	440	290	330	550	440	370	480	250	220
2,500	590	470	730	740	650	690	710	410	380
5,000	830	750	1,200	1,000	990	1,200	1,100	660	630
10,000	1,300	1,200	1,800	1,500	1,600	1,900	1,700	1,100	1,100
25,000	2,300	2,000	2,500	2,600	2,900	3,000	2,900	2,300	1,900
50,000	3,400	2,300		3,400	3,900	4,400	3,500	3,400	2,200
75,000	3,800	3,200		3,500	4,000	10,800	3,300	3,900	2,300
80,000	3,800	3,600		3,500	4,000	13,300	3,200	3,900	2,400
100,000	3,900			3,700	4,100		3,400	4,200	3,200
125,000	4,100			4,700	4,900		5,000	4,900	
150,000	4,800			7,400	7,300			6,200	
175,000	6,200			12,400					
200,000	8,800			20,500					
225,000									
250,000									
275,000									
300,000									
400,000									
500,000									

Table 1. (cont.)

Size of estimate	Engineers								
	Civil Engineers	Electrical/ Electronics Engineers	Mechanical Engineers	Materials Engineers	Mining Engineers	Nuclear Engineers	Petroleum Engineers	Industrial Engineers	Other Engineers
100	160	300	220	50	30	40	50	120	330
200	170	300	230	60	60	70	80	130	340
500	190	320	240	110	130	140	150	170	360
700	200	330	260	150	170	190	190	200	370
1,000	220	340	270	190	240	270	250	230	390
2,500	320	410	360	420	530	570	540	420	480
5,000	480	540	510	760	870	890	890	720	620
10,000	790	770	800	1,300	1,200	1,100	1,200	1,300	910
25,000	1,600	1,500	1,600	2,000			1,600	2,600	1,700
50,000	2,700	2,500	2,800	2,300				3,900	2,800
75,000	3,600	3,300	3,800					4,600	3,700
80,000	3,700	3,500	4,000					4,700	3,900
100,000	4,100	4,000	4,600					5,300	4,500
125,000	4,400	4,700	5,300					6,600	5,000
150,000	4,600	5,200	5,900						5,400
175,000	4,700	5,600	6,300						5,700
200,000	4,600	5,900	6,600						5,900
225,000	4,500	6,200	6,900						6,000
250,000	4,500	6,500	7,200						6,100
275,000	4,500	6,700	7,400						6,200
300,000	4,500	6,900	7,500						6,300
400,000		7,900	8,600						7,300
500,000		9,800	11,000						10,600

SOURCE: Mathematica Policy Research, Inc.

Size of estimate	Physical scientists			Mathematical scientists		Computer Specialists	Environmental scientists		
	Chemists	Physicists/Astronomers	Other Physical Scientists	Mathematicians	Statisticians		Earth Scientists	Oceanographer	Atmospheric Scientists
100	400	140	90	230	70	680	210	50	40
200	410	160	110	250	90	690	220	80	70
500	440	200	180	310	160	710	250	190	140
700	460	230	230	340	190	730	270	260	190
1,000	490	280	300	400	250	750	300	370	260
2,500	620	500	620	650	460	870	440	730	570
5,000	840	840	1,100	1,000	670	1,100	650		970
10,000	1,300	1,400	1,600	1,600	900	1,400	1,000		1,400
25,000	2,300	2,400	2,500	2,400		2,400	1,600		
50,000	3,600	3,000		2,100		3,700	1,800		
75,000	4,400			3,500		4,600	2,400		
80,000	4,500			4,300		4,800	2,700		
100,000	5,000					5,300			
125,000	5,600					5,700			
150,000	6,500					5,900			
175,000	7,800					6,000			
200,000						6,100			
225,000						6,200			
250,000						6,300			
275,000						6,500			
300,000						7,000			
400,000						11,700			
500,000									

Table 2. (cont.)

Size of estimate	Life Scientists			Psychologists	Social Scientists			Engineers	
	Biologists	Agricultural Scientists	Medical Scientists		Economists	Sociologists/Anthropologists	Other Social Scientists	Chemical Engineers	Aeronautical/Astronautical Engineers
100	430	300	60	350	270	90	430	320	200
200	440	310	90	370	290	110	450	330	210
500	470	350	180	400	330	180	490	360	250
700	490	370	240	430	360	230	520	380	270
1,000	520	410	330	470	410	300	570	410	300
2,500	670	580	720	650	630	620	790	550	450
5,000	910	850	1,200	940	970	1,100	1,100	780	680
10,000	1,300	1,300	1,800	1,500	1,600	1,800	1,800	1,200	1,100
25,000	2,400	2,000	2,500	2,600	2,900	2,900	3,000	2,200	1,900
50,000	3,400	2,300		3,300	3,900	4,500	3,600	3,300	2,200
75,000	3,800	3,200		3,400	4,000		3,400	3,800	2,300
80,000	3,900	3,600		3,400	4,000		3,300	3,900	2,400
100,000	4,000			3,600	4,100		3,400	4,200	3,200
125,000	4,200			4,700	4,900			4,900	
150,000	4,800							6,200	
175,000	6,200								
200,000	8,700								
225,000									
250,000									
275,000									
300,000									
400,000									
500,000									

Table 2. (cont.)

	Engineers								
Size of estimate	Civil Engineers	Electrical/ Electronics Engineer	Mechanical Engineers	Materials Engineers	Mining Engineers	Nuclear Engineers	Petroleum Engineers	Industrial Engineers	Other Engineers
100	340	510	430	100	60	60	120	220	450
200	340	510	440	110	80	80	140	230	450
500	360	530	450	160	150	160	210	270	470
700	370	540	470	190	190	210	250	290	480
1,000	390	550	480	230	250	280	300	330	500
2,500	480	620	560	450	530	570	560	500	580
5,000	620	730	700	770	860	880	880	780	720
10,000	900	940	960	1,300	1,200	1,100	1,200	1,300	1,000
25,000	1,700	1,600	1,700	2,000		3,000	1,700	2,500	1,800
50,000	2,700	2,500	2,800	2,300				3,800	2,800
75,000	3,500	3,300	3,700					4,600	3,700
80,000	3,600	3,400	3,900					4,700	3,900
100,000	4,000	4,000	4,500					5,400	4,400
125,000	4,000	4,600	5,200					6,600	5,000
150,000	4,600	5,100	5,700						5,400
175,000	4,700	5,500	6,200						5,700
200,000	4,700	5,900	6,500						5,900
225,000	4,600	6,200	6,900						6,000
250,000	4,600	6,400	7,100						6,100
275,000	4,500	6,700	7,300						6,200
300,000	4,500	6,900	7,600						6,300
400,000		8,000	8,600						7,300
500,000		9,800	10,900						

Table 2. (cont.)

Females

	Physical scientists			Mathematical scientists			Environmental scientists		
Size of estimate	Chemists	Physicists/ Astronomers	Other Physical Scientists	Mathe- maticians	Statis- ticians	Computer Specialists	Earth Scientists	Ocean- ographers	Atmospheric Scientists
100	170	90	30	150	30	470	80	30	20
200	180	110	50	170	50	480	90	70	40
500	200	160	130	220	120	500	120	180	120
700	220	190	180	260	160	520	140	250	160
1,000	250	230	240	310	210	540	170	350	230
2,500	390	460	560	570	430	660	310	710	550
5,000	610	800	1,000	940	630	840	520		950
10,000	1,000	1,400	1,600	1,500	860	1,200	870		1,400
25,000	2,100	2,400	2,500	2,300		2,200	1,500		
50,000	3,300	3,000		2,100		3,500	1,700		
75,000	4,200			3,400		4,400	2,300		
80,000	4,300			4,300		4,600	2,600		
100,000	4,800					5,100			
125,000	5,400					5,500			
150,000	6,300					5,700			
175,000	7,600					5,800			
200,000						5,900			
225,000						6,000			
250,000						6,100			
275,000						6,300			
300,000						6,800			
400,000						11,500			
500,000									

Table 2. (cont.)

Size of estimate	Life Scientists			Psychologists	Social Scientists			Engineers	
	Biologists	Agricultural Scientists	Medical Scientists		Economists	Sociologists/ Anthropologists	Other Social Scientists	Chemical Engineers	Aeronautical/ Astronautical Engineers
100	280	90	70	530	320	230	280	60	70
200	290	110	100	540	340	260	290	70	80
500	330	140	190	580	380	330	340	100	110
700	350	170	250	600	410	370	370	120	130
1,000	380	200	340	640	460	440	410	150	160
2,500	520	380	730	820	670	760	640	300	310
5,000	760	640	1,200	1,100	1,000	1,200	990	530	540
10,000	1,200	1,100	1,900	1,600	1,600	2,000	1,600	950	950
25,000	2,200	1,800	2,500	2,700	3,000	3,100	2,800	2,000	1,700
50,000	3,300	2,100		3,500	4,000	4,600	3,400	3,000	2,100
75,000	3,700	3,000		3,600	4,100		3,200	3,600	2,200
80,000	3,700	3,400		3,600	4,000		3,200	3,700	2,300
100,000	3,800			3,800	4,100		3,300	4,000	3,000
125,000	4,000			4,800	5,000			4,600	
150,000	4,700							5,900	
175,000	6,100								
200,000	8,600								
225,000									
250,000									
275,000									
300,000									
400,000									
500,000									

Table 2. (cont.)

Size of estimate	Engineers								
	Civil Engineers	Electrical/ Electronics Engineers	Mechanical Engineers	Materials Engineers	Mining Engineers	Nuclear Engineers	Petroleum Engineers	Industrial Engineers	Other Engineers
100	80	190	110	20	20	30	10	60	280
200	90	200	110	30	40	50	30	70	280
500	100	210	130	80	110	130	90	110	300
700	120	220	140	110	150	180	130	130	310
1,000	130	240	160	160	210	250	190	170	330
2,500	220	300	240	370	490	540	450	340	410
5,000	370	410	370	690	820	850	760	620	550
10,000	650	630	640	1,200	1,200	1,100	1,100	1,100	830
25,000	1,400	1,200	1,400	1,900		3,000	1,500	2,400	1,600
50,000	2,400	2,200	2,500	2,300				3,700	2,700
75,000	3,200	3,000	3,400					4,400	3,600
80,000	3,300	3,100	3,600					4,600	3,700
100,000	3,800	3,700	4,200					5,200	4,300
125,000	4,100	4,200	4,900					6,400	4,800
150,000	4,300	4,700	5,400						5,200
175,000	4,400	5,200	5,900						5,500
200,000	4,400	5,500	6,200						5,700
225,000	4,400	5,900	6,500						5,800
250,000	4,300	6,100	6,800						5,900
275,000	4,300	6,400	7,000						6,000
300,000	4,300	6,600	7,200						6,200
400,000		7,700	8,300						7,200
500,000		9,500	10,600						

SOURCE: Mathematica Policy Research, Inc.

Table 3. Standard errors for estimates of scientists and engineers by racial/ethnic group: 1986

White, Non-Hispanic

Size of estimate	Physical scientists			Mathematical scientists		Computer Specialists	Environmental scientists		
	Chemists	Physicists/ Astronomers	Other Physical Scientists	Mathematicians	Statisticians		Earth Scientists	Oceanographers	Atmospheric Scientists
100	270	160	100	150	100	500	120	50	50
200	280	170	120	170	120	510	130	90	70
500	310	220	190	230	170	530	160	200	150
700	330	250	240	260	210	550	180	270	200
1,000	360	290	300	320	260	570	210	370	270
2,500	500	510	610	580	460	690	370	730	580
5,000	730	850	1,000	970	650	880	590		970
10,000	1,200	1,400	1,600	1,600	890	1,300	970		1,400
25,000	2,300	2,400	2,600	2,300		2,300	1,600		
50,000	3,600	3,100		2,100		3,600	1,800		
75,000	4,400	4,700		3,500		4,600	2,400		
80,000	4,500			4,400		4,700	2,700		
100,000	5,000					5,200			
125,000	5,600					5,600			
150,000	6,500					5,800			
175,000	7,900					5,900			
200,000						6,000			
225,000						6,000			
250,000						6,200			
275,000						6,400			
300,000						6,900			
400,000						12,000			
500,000									

Table 3. (cont.)

Size of estimate	Life Scientists			Social Scientists				Engineers	
	Biologists	Agricultural Scientists	Medical Scientists	Psychologists	Economists	Sociologists/ Anthropologists	Other Social Scientists	Chemical Engineers	Aeronautical/ Astronautical Engineers
100	380	130	180	180	300	210	380	120	120
200	390	140	210	200	310	230	390	140	130
500	420	180	290	240	360	300	440	170	160
700	440	210	340	270	390	340	470	190	190
1,000	470	250	410	310	430	410	520	220	220
2,500	620	440	760	510	650	720	740	390	390
5,000	850	730	1,200	830	990	1,200	1,100	650	640
10,000	1,300	1,200	1,800	1,400	1,600	1,900	1,700	1,100	1,100
25,000	2,300	2,000	2,500	2,600	2,900	3,000	2,900	2,300	1,900
50,000	3,300	2,300		3,500	3,900	4,400	3,500	3,400	2,200
75,000	3,800	3,200		3,500	4,000	10,500	3,300	3,900	2,300
80,000	3,800	3,600		3,500	4,000		3,300	3,900	2,400
100,000	3,900	7,000		3,600	4,100		3,400	4,200	3,200
125,000	4,100			4,700	4,900		5,000	4,900	
150,000	4,800			7,500	7,300			6,200	
175,000	6,200			12,900					
200,000	8,700			21,800					
225,000	12,700								
250,000									
275,000									
300,000									
400,000									
500,000									

Table 3. (cont.)

Size of estimate	Engineers								
	Civil Engineers	Electrical/ Electronics Engineers	Mechanical Engineers	Materials Engineers	Mining Engineers	Nuclear Engineers	Petroleum Engineers	Industrial Engineers	Other Engineers
100	190	370	270	70	50	70	20	180	320
200	190	380	280	90	70	90	40	190	320
500	210	390	290	130	140	170	110	230	340
700	230	400	310	170	180	220	160	250	350
1,000	250	420	320	210	250	290	220	290	370
2,500	340	490	410	440	530	580	520	470	460
5,000	500	610	560	770	860	890	890	750	610
10,000	810	840	840	1,300	1,200	1,100	1,200	1,300	900
25,000	1,600	1,500	1,600	2,000			1,600	2,500	1,700
50,000	2,700	2,500	2,800	2,300				3,800	2,800
75,000	3,600	3,300	3,800					4,600	3,700
80,000	3,700	3,500	4,000					4,700	3,900
100,000	4,100	4,100	4,600					5,300	4,500
125,000	4,400	4,700	5,300					6,600	5,000
150,000	4,600	5,200	5,800						5,400
175,000	4,700	5,600	6,300						5,700
200,000	4,600	5,900	6,600						5,900
225,000	4,500	6,200	6,900						6,000
250,000	4,500	6,500	7,100						6,100
275,000	4,500	6,700	7,400						6,200
300,000	4,500	6,900	7,500						6,300
400,000		7,900	8,600						7,300
500,000		9,800	11,000						

Table 3. (cont.)

Minorities

Size of estimate	Physical scientists			Mathematical scientists			Environmental scientists		
	Chemists	Physicists/ Astronomers	Other Physical Scientists	Mathe- maticians	Statis- ticians	Computer Specialists	Earth Scientists	Ocean- ographers	Atmospheric Scientists
100	240	90	30	200	30	590	130	30	10
200	250	100	60	220	50	590	140	70	40
500	280	150	130	270	100	620	180	180	110
700	300	180	170	310	140	630	200	250	160
1,000	330	220	240	360	190	660	230	350	230
2,500	480	440	540	630	390	780	380	710	540
5,000	710	780	970	1,000	580	970	610		940
10,000	1,100	1,300	1,600	1,600	820	1,300	990		1,400
25,000	2,300	2,300	2,500	2,400		2,300	1,600		3,000
50,000	3,600	3,000		2,100		3,700	1,800		
75,000	4,400	4,700		3,600		4,600	2,400		
80,000	4,500			4,400		4,800	2,700		
100,000	5,000					5,300			
125,000	5,600					5,700			
150,000	6,500					5,900			
175,000	7,800					6,000			
200,000						6,100			
225,000						6,100			
250,000						6,200			
275,000						6,500			
300,000						7,000			
400,000						12,100			
500,000									

Table 3. (cont.)

	Life Scientists				Social Scientists			Engineers	
Size of estimate	Biologists	Agricultural Scientists	Medical Scientists	Psychologists	Economists	Sociologists/ Anthro- pologists	Other Social Scientists	Chemical Engineers	Aeronautical/ Astronautical Engineers
100	340	200	10	510	300	160	330	160	110
200	350	210	40	520	320	180	350	170	120
500	380	250	120	570	360	250	390	210	160
700	400	280	170	600	390	290	420	230	180
1,000	430	320	250	640	440	360	470	260	210
2,500	580	510	590	840	660	670	690	420	380
5,000	810	790	1,100	1,200	1,000	1,100	1,000	680	630
10,000	1,200	1,300	1,700	1,700	1,600	1,900	1,600	1,200	1,100
25,000	2,300	2,100	2,300	3,000	3,000	3,000	2,900	2,300	1,900
50,000	3,300	2,300		3,800	3,900	4,300	3,500	3,400	2,200
75,000	3,700	3,200		3,900	4,000	10,500	3,300	3,900	2,300
80,000	3,800	3,700		3,800	4,000		3,200	4,000	2,300
100,000	3,900	7,100		4,000	4,100		3,400	4,300	3,200
125,000	4,100			5,000	4,900		4,900	4,900	
150,000	4,800			7,800	7,300			6,300	
175,000	6,200			13,200					
200,000	8,700			22,100					
225,000									
250,000									
275,000									
300,000									
400,000									
500,000									

Table 3. (cont.)

	Engineers								
Size of estimate	Civil Engineers	Electrical/ Electronics Engineers	Mechanical Engineers	Materials Engineers	Mining Engineers	Nuclear Engineers	Petroleum Engineers	Industrial Engineers	Other Engineers
100	150	240	190	30	20	20	80	90	340
200	160	250	190	50	50	50	100	100	350
500	180	260	210	100	110	120	170	130	370
700	190	270	220	130	160	170	220	160	380
1,000	210	290	240	180	220	240	290	200	400
2,500	300	360	330	400	500	530	580	380	490
5,000	460	480	470	730	840	840	950	660	630
10,000	770	710	760	1,200	1,200	1,000	1,300	1,200	920
25,000	1,600	1,400	1,600	1,900			1,700	2,500	1,700
50,000	2,700	2,400	2,700	2,300				3,800	2,900
75,000	3,500	3,200	3,700					4,500	3,800
80,000	3,600	3,400	3,900					4,600	3,900
100,000	4,100	3,900	4,500					5,200	4,500
125,000	4,400	4,500	5,200					6,500	5,000
150,000	4,600	5,000	5,800						5,400
175,000	4,600	5,500	6,200						5,700
200,000	4,600	5,800	6,500						5,900
225,000	4,500	6,100	6,800						6,000
250,000	4,400	6,300	7,100						6,100
275,000	4,400	6,600	7,300						6,200
300,000	4,500	6,800	7,500						6,300
400,000		7,800	8,500						7,300
500,000		9,700	10,900						

SOURCE: Mathematica Policy Research, Inc.

Table 4. Standard errors for estimates of male scientists and engineers by racial/ethnic group: 1986

White, Non-Hispanic Males

Size of estimate	Physical scientists			Mathematical scientists		Computer Specialists	Environmental scientists		
	Chemists	Physicists/ Astronomers	Other Physical Scientists	Mathe- maticians	Statis- ticians		Earth Scientists	Ocean- ographers	Atmospheric Scientists
100	470	220	150	210	120	630	240	60	70
200	480	230	180	220	140	640	250	100	100
500	500	270	240	280	200	670	280	200	170
700	520	300	280	320	230	680	300	270	210
1,000	550	350	350	370	280	700	330	370	280
2,500	680	550	640	630	470	820	460	730	580
5,000	890	870	1,000	1,000	670	1,000	660		970
10,000	1,300	1,400	1,600	1,600	900	1,400	1,000		1,400
25,000	2,300	2,400	2,600	2,400		2,400	1,600		
50,000	3,600	3,100		2,100		3,700	1,800		
75,000	4,400			3,500		4,600	2,400		
80,000	4,500			4,300		4,800	2,700		
100,000	5,000					5,300			
125,000	5,700					5,700			
150,000	6,500					5,900			
175,000	7,800					6,000			
200,000						6,100			
225,000						6,200			
250,000						6,300			
275,000						6,500			
300,000						7,000			
400,000						11,700			
500,000									

Table 4. (cont.)

Size of estimate	Life Scientists			Social Scientists				Engineers	
	Biologists	Agricultural Scientists	Medical Scientists	Psychologists	Economists	Sociologists/ Anthro- pologists	Other Social Scientists	Chemical Engineers	Aeronautical/ Astronautical Engineers
100	490	280	190	90	260	120	490	340	230
200	500	290	210	110	270	140	510	350	240
500	530	330	290	150	320	210	550	380	270
700	550	350	340	180	350	260	580	400	290
1,000	580	390	420	220	390	330	630	430	320
2,500	720	570	770	420	610	640	840	570	470
5,000	950	840	1,200	740	960	1,100	1,200	800	700
10,000	1,400	1,300	1,800	1,300	1,600	1,900	1,800	1,200	1,100
25,000	2,400	2,000	2,500	2,500	2,900	2,900	3,000	2,200	1,900
50,000	3,400	2,300		3,400	3,900	4,500	3,600	3,300	2,200
75,000	3,800	3,200		3,400	4,000		3,400	3,800	2,300
80,000	3,900	3,600		3,400	4,000		3,400	3,900	2,400
100,000	4,000			3,500	4,100		3,500	4,200	3,200
125,000	4,200			4,600	4,900			4,900	
150,000	4,900							6,200	
175,000	6,200								
200,000	8,600								
225,000									
250,000									
275,000									
300,000									
400,000									
500,000									

Table 4. (cont.)

Size of estimate	Engineers								
	Civil Engineers	Electrical/ Electronics Engineers	Mechanical Engineers	Materials Engineers	Mining Engineers	Nuclear Engineers	Petroleum Engineers	Industrial Engineers	Other Engineers
100	410	670	570	140	90	100	90	330	460
200	420	670	570	160	110	120	110	340	460
500	430	690	590	200	170	190	180	380	480
700	440	700	600	230	210	240	220	400	490
1,000	460	710	620	270	270	300	280	430	510
2,500	550	770	690	480	520	580	550	590	590
5,000	690	880	820	780	840	880	880	850	730
10,000	960	1,100	1,100	1,300	1,200	1,100	1,200	1,300	1,000
25,000	1,700	1,700	1,800	1,900		2,900	1,600	2,500	1,800
50,000	2,700	2,600	2,800	2,300				3,800	2,800
75,000	3,500	3,300	3,700					4,600	3,700
80,000	3,600	3,500	3,900					4,700	3,900
100,000	4,000	4,000	4,500					5,400	4,400
125,000	4,400	4,500	5,100					6,600	5,000
150,000	4,600	5,000	5,700						5,400
175,000	4,700	5,500	6,100						5,700
200,000	4,700	5,800	6,500						5,900
225,000	4,600	6,100	6,800						6,000
250,000	4,600	6,400	7,100						6,100
275,000	4,500	6,700	7,300						6,200
300,000	4,500	6,900	7,600						6,300
400,000		8,000	8,700						7,300
500,000		9,800	10,800						

Table 4. (cont.)

Minority Males

Size of estimate	Physical scientists			Mathematical scientists			Environmental scientists		
	Chemists	Physicists/ Astronomers	Other Physical Scientists	Mathematicians	Statisticians	Computer Specialists	Earth Scientists	Oceanographers	Atmospheric Scientists
100	390	120	70	240	50	700	210	40	30
200	400	140	90	260	70	710	220	70	50
500	430	180	160	320	120	730	250	180	120
700	440	210	200	350	160	750	270	240	170
1,000	470	260	260	410	210	770	290	350	230
2,500	600	460	560	660	400	890	430	710	530
5,000	810	780	960	1,000	600	1,100	630		920
10,000	1,200	1,300	1,500	1,600	830	1,400	970		1,400
25,000	2,200	2,300	2,500	2,400		2,400	1,600		
50,000	3,500	3,000		2,200		3,700	1,800		
75,000	4,300			3,600		4,700	2,400		
80,000	4,500			4,400		4,800	2,700		
100,000	5,000					5,300			
125,000	5,600					5,800			
150,000	6,400					6,000			
175,000	7,700					6,100			
200,000						6,200			
225,000						6,200			
250,000						6,300			
275,000						6,600			
300,000						7,000			
400,000						11,800			
500,000									

Table 4. (cont.)

	Life Scientists				Social Scientists			Engineers	
Size of estimate	Biologists	Agricultural Scientists	Medical Scientists	Psychologists	Economists	Sociologists/ Anthro-pologists	Other Social Scientists	Chemical Engineers	Aeronautical/ Astronautical Engineers
100	420	300	20	420	280	80	420	310	190
200	430	320	40	440	290	100	430	320	200
500	460	350	120	480	340	170	480	350	240
700	480	380	180	510	370	220	510	370	260
1,000	510	420	250	550	410	280	550	400	290
2,500	650	590	600	750	630	600	770	540	430
5,000	880	860	1,100	1,100	980	1,100	1,100	770	660
10,000	1,300	1,300	1,700	1,600	1,600	1,800	1,700	1,200	1,100
25,000	2,300	2,000	2,300	2,900	3,000	2,900	2,900	2,200	1,800
50,000	3,300	2,300		3,700	3,900	4,400	3,500	3,200	2,200
75,000	3,700	3,200		3,700	4,000		3,300	3,800	2,300
80,000	3,800	3,700		3,700	4,000		3,300	3,900	2,400
100,000	3,900			3,900	4,100		3,400	4,200	3,100
125,000	4,100			4,900	4,900			4,900	
150,000	4,800							6,100	
175,000	6,100								
200,000	8,600								
225,000									
250,000									
275,000									
300,000									
400,000									
500,000									

Table 4. (cont.)

	Engineers								
Size of estimate	Civil Engineers	Electrical/ Electronics Engineers	Mechanical Engineers	Materials Engineers	Mining Engineers	Nuclear Engineers	Petroleum Engineers	Industrial Engineers	Other Engineers
100	320	460	400	80	50	40	130	190	440
200	320	470	400	100	70	70	160	200	450
500	340	480	420	140	130	140	220	240	460
700	350	490	430	170	170	180	260	260	480
1,000	370	500	450	210	230	250	320	290	490
2,500	450	570	520	420	490	520	590	450	580
5,000	590	670	650	720	810	820	920	710	720
10,000	860	880	900	1,200	1,200	1,000	1,300	1,200	990
25,000	1,600	1,500	1,600	1,900		2,900	1,700	2,400	1,700
50,000	2,600	2,300	2,700	2,300				3,700	2,800
75,000	3,400	3,100	3,600					4,500	3,700
80,000	3,500	3,200	3,700					4,600	3,900
100,000	3,900	3,800	4,300					5,300	4,400
125,000	4,300	4,300	5,000					6,500	4,900
150,000	4,500	4,800	5,500						5,300
175,000	4,600	5,300	6,000						5,600
200,000	4,600	5,600	6,300						5,800
225,000	4,500	5,900	6,600						6,000
250,000	4,500	6,200	6,900						6,100
275,000	4,400	6,500	7,200						6,200
300,000	4,400	6,700	7,400						6,300
400,000		7,800	8,500						7,300
500,000		9,600	10,700						

SOURCE: Mathematica Policy Research, Inc.

White, Non-Hispanic Females

Size of estimate	Physical scientists			Mathematical scientists		Computer Specialists	Environmental scientists		
	Chemists	Physicists/Astronomers	Other Physical Scientists	Mathematicians	Statisticians		Earth Scientists	Oceanographers	Atmospheric Scientists
100	210	140	80	130	80	430	100	40	40
200	220	160	100	150	100	440	110	80	60
500	250	200	170	200	150	460	140	180	130
700	270	230	210	240	190	480	160	250	180
1,000	290	280	280	290	230	500	190	350	240
2,500	430	480	570	550	430	620	320	710	540
5,000	640	800	980	930	620	810	520		930
10,000	1,000	1,300	1,600	1,500	860	1,200	860		1,400
25,000	2,100	2,300	2,500	2,300		2,200	1,400		
50,000	3,300	3,000		2,100		3,500	1,700		
75,000	4,200			3,400		4,400	2,300		
80,000	4,300			4,300		4,600	2,600		
100,000	4,800					5,100			
125,000	5,400					5,500			
150,000	6,300					5,700			
175,000	7,500					5,800			
200,000						5,900			
225,000						6,000			
250,000						6,100			
275,000						6,300			
300,000						6,800			
400,000						11,500			
500,000									

Table 5. (cont.)

Size of estimate	Life Scientists			Social Scientists				Engineers	
	Biologists	Agricultural Scientists	Medical Scientists	Psychologists	Economists	Sociologists/Anthropologists	Other Social Scientists	Chemical Engineers	Aeronautical/Astronautical Engineers
100	340	80	170	270	310	260	330	80	90
200	350	90	200	280	330	290	250	90	100
500	380	130	280	320	370	350	390	120	130
700	390	150	330	350	400	400	420	140	150
1,000	420	190	410	390	450	470	460	170	180
2,500	570	370	750	600	670	790	680	310	330
5,000	800	630	1,200	920	1,000	1,300	1,000	540	560
10,000	1,200	1,100	1,800	1,500	1,600	2,000	1,600	960	950
25,000	2,200	1,800	2,500	2,700	3,000	3,100	2,800	2,000	1,700
50,000	3,200	2,100		3,500	4,000	4,600	3,400	3,000	2,100
75,000	3,700	3,000		3,600	4,100		3,200	3,600	2,200
80,000	3,700	3,400		3,600	4,000		3,200	3,600	2,300
100,000	3,800			3,700	4,100		3,300	4,000	3,000
125,000	4,100			4,800	5,000			4,600	
150,000	4,700							5,900	
175,000	6,100								
200,000	8,500								
225,000									
250,000									
275,000									
300,000									
400,000									
500,000									

Table 5. (cont.)

Size of estimate	Engineers								
	Civil Engineers	Electrical/ Electronics Engineers	Mechanical Engineers	Materials Engineers	Mining Engineers	Nuclear Engineers	Petroleum Engineers	Industrial Engineers	Other Engineers
100	130	300	200	50	40	60	0	140	280
200	140	310	200	60	60	80	10	150	290
500	150	320	220	110	120	150	80	180	310
700	160	330	230	140	160	200	120	200	320
1,000	180	340	240	180	220	260	180	240	340
2,500	270	410	320	390	470	540	440	400	420
5,000	410	510	450	690	790	830	770	660	560
10,000	680	720	700	1,200	1,100	1,000	1,100	1,100	830
25,000	1,400	1,300	1,400	1,900		2,900	1,500	2,300	1,600
50,000	2,400	2,200	2,500	2,300				3,600	2,700
75,000	3,200	2,900	3,400					4,400	3,500
80,000	3,300	3,100	3,500					4,600	3,700
100,000	3,700	3,600	4,100					5,200	4,200
125,000	4,100	4,200	4,800					6,400	4,800
150,000	4,300	4,700	5,300						5,200
175,000	4,400	5,100	5,800						5,500
200,000	4,400	5,500	6,100						5,700
225,000	4,400	5,800	6,400						5,800
250,000	4,300	6,100	6,700						5,900
275,000	4,300	6,300	7,000						6,000
300,000	4,300	6,600	7,200						6,100
400,000		7,700	8,300						7,200
500,000		9,500	10,500						

Table 5. (cont.)

Minority Females

Size of estimate	Physical scientists			Mathematical scientists		Computer Specialists	Environmental scientists		
	Chemists	Physicists/ Astronomers	Other Physical Scientists	Mathe- maticians	Statis- ticians		Earth Scientists	Ocean- ographers	Atmospheric Scientists
100	140	50	0	160	10	500	70	20	0
200	150	70	20	180	20	500	80	50	20
500	170	110	90	240	80	530	110	160	90
700	190	140	130	270	110	540	130	230	130
1,000	220	180	190	330	160	570	150	330	200
2,500	350	390	490	580	360	680	290	690	500
5,000	560	710	890	960	550	870	490		890
10,000	960	1,200	1,500	1,600	790	1,200	830		1,400
25,000	2,000	2,200	2,400	2,300		2,200	1,400		
50,000	3,200	2,900	9,100	2,100		3,500	1,700		
75,000	4,100			3,500		4,500	2,300		
80,000	4,200			4,300		4,600	2,500		
100,000	4,700					5,100			
125,000	5,300					5,600			
150,000	6,200					5,800			
175,000	7,400					5,900			
200,000						6,000			
225,000						6,000			
250,000						6,100			
275,000						6,400			
300,000						6,800			
400,000						11,600			
500,000									

Table 5. (cont.)

Size of estimate	Life Scientists				Social Scientists			Engineers	
	Biologists	Agricultural Scientists	Medical Scientists	Psychologists	Economists	Sociologists/ Anthropologists	Other Social Scientists	Chemical Engineers	Aeronautical/ Astronautical Engineers
100	270	100	0	600	330	220	260	50	50
200	280	120	30	610	340	240	270	60	60
500	300	150	110	650	390	310	320	90	90
700	320	180	160	680	420	360	350	110	110
1,000	350	220	240	720	460	430	390	140	140
2,500	500	390	590	930	680	750	610	280	290
5,000	730	660	1,100	1,200	1,000	1,200	950	510	520
10,000	1,100	1,100	1,600	1,800	1,600	2,000	1,500	930	920
25,000	2,200	1,800	2,300	3,100	3,000	3,000	2,700	1,900	1,700
50,000	3,200	2,100		3,900	4,000	4,600	3,400	3,000	2,100
75,000	3,600	3,000		3,900	4,100		3,200	3,500	2,200
80,000	3,600	3,500		3,900	4,100		3,100	3,600	2,200
100,000	3,800			4,000	4,100		3,200	4,000	3,000
125,000	4,000			5,100	5,000			4,600	
150,000	4,600							5,900	
175,000	6,000								
200,000	8,400								
225,000									
250,000									
275,000									
300,000									
400,000									
500,000									

Table 5. (cont.)

Size of estimate	Engineers								
	Civil Engineers	Electrical/ Electronics Engineers	Mechanical Engineers	Materials Engineers	Mining Engineers	Nuclear Engineers	Petroleum Engineers	Industrial Engineers	Other Engineers
100	40	100	30	0	0	0	30	0	270
200	40	100	30	10	20	30	50	10	270
500	60	110	50	50	80	100	120	40	290
700	70	120	60	80	120	140	160	60	300
1,000	90	130	70	120	180	210	220	100	320
2,500	170	200	150	330	430	480	490	260	410
5,000	310	300	280	630	750	780	820	520	550
10,000	580	510	530	1,100	1,100	990	1,200	1,000	820
25,000	1,300	1,100	1,200	1,800		2,800	1,600	2,200	1,600
50,000	2,300	2,000	2,300	2,200				3,500	2,700
75,000	3,100	2,700	3,200					4,300	3,500
80,000	3,200	2,900	3,400					4,400	3,700
100,000	3,600	3,400	4,000					5,100	4,200
125,000	4,000	4,000	4,600					6,300	4,800
150,000	4,200	4,500	5,100						5,200
175,000	4,300	4,900	5,600						5,500
200,000	4,300	5,200	6,000						5,700
225,000	4,300	5,600	6,300						5,800
250,000	4,200	5,800	6,500						5,900
275,000	4,200	6,100	6,800						6,000
300,000	4,200	6,400	7,000						6,100
400,000		7,400	8,100						7,200
500,000									

SOURCE: Mathematica Policy Research, Inc.

Table 6. Generalized standard errors of statistical rates for male and female scientists and engineers by racial/ethnic group, size of rate, and size of base: 1986

White, Non-Hispanic Males

Size of base	Size of rate										
	0.01	0.02	0.05	0.10	0.25	0.50	0.75	0.90	0.95	0.98	0.99
100	0.0110	0.0127	0.0174	0.0244	0.0391	0.0460	0.0356	0.0236	0.0189	0.0159	0.0149
200	0.0110	0.0127	0.0174	0.0244	0.0391	0.0459	0.0356	0.0236	0.0189	0.0159	0.0149
500	0.0110	0.0126	0.0173	0.0243	0.0391	0.0459	0.0356	0.0235	0.0188	0.0159	0.0149
700	0.0109	0.0126	0.0173	0.0243	0.0391	0.0459	0.0355	0.0235	0.0188	0.0159	0.0149
1,000	0.0109	0.0126	0.0173	0.0243	0.0390	0.0458	0.0355	0.0235	0.0188	0.0158	0.0148
2,500	0.0107	0.0124	0.0171	0.0241	0.0388	0.0457	0.0353	0.0233	0.0186	0.0156	0.0146
5,000	0.0104	0.0121	0.0168	0.0238	0.0385	0.0453	0.0350	0.0230	0.0183	0.0153	0.0143
10,000	0.0098	0.0114	0.0162	0.0231	0.0379	0.0447	0.0344	0.0224	0.0177	0.0147	0.0137
25,000	0.0081	0.0097	0.0145	0.0214	0.0362	0.0430	0.0327	0.0207	0.0160	0.0130	0.0120
50,000	0.0056	0.0073	0.0120	0.0190	0.0337	0.0406	0.0302	0.0182	0.0135	0.0105	0.0095
75,000	0.0036	0.0052	0.0100	0.0169	0.0317	0.0385	0.0282	0.0162	0.0115	0.0085	0.0075
80,000	0.0032	0.0049	0.0096	0.0166	0.0314	0.0382	0.0278	0.0158	0.0111	0.0082	0.0072
100,000	0.0019	0.0036	0.0083	0.0153	0.0301	0.0369	0.0265	0.0145	0.0098	0.0069	0.0059
125,000	0.0007	0.0023	0.0070	0.0140	0.0288	0.0356	0.0253	0.0132	0.0085	0.0056	0.0046
150,000		0.0014	0.0061	0.0131	0.0278	0.0347	0.0243	0.0123	0.0076	0.0046	0.0036
175,000		0.0007	0.0054	0.0124	0.0272	0.0340	0.0236	0.0116	0.0069	0.0040	0.0030

Minority Males

Size of base	Size of rate										
	0.01	0.02	0.05	0.10	0.25	0.50	0.75	0.90	0.95	0.98	0.99
100	0.0173	0.0214	0.0332	0.0511	0.0917	0.1166	0.0905	0.0513	0.0345	0.0235	0.0196
200	0.0171	0.0213	0.0331	0.0510	0.0915	0.1165	0.0903	0.0512	0.0343	0.0233	0.0195
500	0.0167	0.0208	0.0326	0.0505	0.0911	0.1160	0.0899	0.0507	0.0339	0.0229	0.0190
700	0.0164	0.0205	0.0323	0.0502	0.0908	0.1157	0.0896	0.0504	0.0336	0.0226	0.0187
1,000	0.0159	0.0201	0.0319	0.0498	0.0903	0.1153	0.0891	0.0500	0.0331	0.0221	0.0183
2,500	0.0138	0.0179	0.0297	0.0476	0.0882	0.1131	0.0870	0.0478	0.0310	0.0200	0.0162
5,000	0.0106	0.0147	0.0266	0.0445	0.0850	0.1100	0.0838	0.0447	0.0278	0.0168	0.0130
10,000	0.0055	0.0096	0.0214	0.0393	0.0799	0.1048	0.0787	0.0395	0.0227	0.0117	0.0079
25,000		0.0021	0.0139	0.0318	0.0723	0.0973	0.0712	0.0320	0.0151	0.0041	0.0003
50,000		0.0021	0.0139	0.0318	0.0723	0.0973	0.0711	0.0320	0.0151	0.0041	0.0003
75,000			0.0050	0.0229	0.0634	0.0884	0.0622	0.0231	0.0062		

Table 6. (cont.)

White, Non-Hispanic Females

Size of base	Size of rate										
	0.01	0.02	0.05	0.10	0.25	0.50	0.75	0.90	0.95	0.98	0.99
100	0.0165	0.0198	0.0291	0.0429	0.0717	0.0838	0.0630	0.0404	0.0318	0.0264	0.0246
200	0.0163	0.0197	0.0290	0.0428	0.0715	0.0837	0.0629	0.0402	0.0316	0.0263	0.0245
500	0.0160	0.0193	0.0287	0.0425	0.0712	0.0834	0.0626	0.0399	0.0313	0.0260	0.0242
700	0.0158	0.0191	0.0285	0.0423	0.0710	0.0832	0.0624	0.0397	0.0311	0.0258	0.0239
1,000	0.0155	0.0188	0.0281	0.0419	0.0707	0.0828	0.0620	0.0394	0.0308	0.0254	0.0236
2,500	0.0139	0.0172	0.0265	0.0403	0.0691	0.0812	0.0604	0.0378	0.0292	0.0238	0.0220
5,000	0.0113	0.0146	0.0240	0.0378	0.0665	0.0787	0.0579	0.0352	0.0266	0.0213	0.0195
10,000	0.0068	0.0101	0.0194	0.0332	0.0620	0.0741	0.0533	0.0307	0.0221	0.0167	0.0149
25,000			0.0093	0.0231	0.0518	0.0640	0.0432	0.0205	0.0119		
50,000			0.0020	0.0158	0.0445	0.0567	0.0359	0.0132	0.0046		
75,000				0.0163	0.0450	0.0572	0.0364	0.0137	0.0051		
80,000				0.0169	0.0456	0.0578	0.0370	0.0143	0.0057		
100,000					0.0485	0.0606	0.0399	0.0172	0.0086		

Minority Females

Size of base	Size of rate										
	0.01	0.02	0.05	0.10	0.25	0.50	0.75	0.90	0.95	0.98	0.99
100	0.0122	0.0173	0.0317	0.0529	0.0970	0.1163	0.0870	0.0554	0.0435	0.0362	0.0338
200	0.0123	0.0174	0.0318	0.0530	0.0970	0.1163	0.0870	0.0554	0.0436	0.0363	0.0338
500	0.0123	0.0174	0.0318	0.0530	0.0971	0.1164	0.0871	0.0554	0.0436	0.0363	0.0339
700	0.0122	0.0173	0.0317	0.0529	0.0971	0.1164	0.0871	0.0554	0.0436	0.0363	0.0339
1,000	0.0113	0.0164	0.0307	0.0519	0.0970	0.1163	0.0871	0.0554	0.0436	0.0363	0.0338
2,500	0.0073	0.0124	0.0268	0.0480	0.0960	0.1153	0.0861	0.0544	0.0426	0.0353	0.0329
5,000	0.0000	0.0004	0.0148	0.0360	0.0921	0.1114	0.0821	0.0505	0.0387	0.0314	0.0289
10,000	0.0167	0.0218	0.0362	0.0574	0.0801	0.0994	0.0702	0.0385	0.0267	0.0194	0.0169

SOURCE: Mathematica Policy Research, Inc.

Table 7. Standard errors for estimates of doctoral scientists and engineers: 1985

Standard errors of totals		Standard errors of percent						
Size of estimate	Estimated sampling error	Base of percent	Estimated percent					
			1/99	2/98	5/95	10/90	25/75	50/50
100	35	500	1.56	2.19	3.41	4.69	6.78	7.82
200	49	1,000	1.10	1.55	2.41	3.32	4.79	5.53
500	78	2,000	0.78	1.10	1.71	2.35	3.39	3.91
1,000	111	5,000	0.49	0.69	1.08	1.47	2.14	2.47
2,000	156	10,000	0.35	0.49	0.76	1.05	1.52	1.75
5,000	246	15,000	0.28	0.40	0.62	0.86	1.24	1.43
10,000	346	20,000	0.25	0.35	0.54	0.74	1.07	1.24
15,000	420	30,000	0.20	0.28	0.44	0.61	0.87	1.01
20,000	482	40,000	0.17	0.24	0.38	0.52	0.76	0.87
30,000	583	50,000	0.16	0.22	0.34	0.47	0.68	0.78
40,000	664	75,000	0.13	0.18	0.28	0.38	0.55	0.64
50,000	732	100,000	0.11	0.15	0.24	0.33	0.48	0.55
75,000	864	150,000	0.09	0.13	0.20	0.27	0.40	0.45
100,000	958	200,000	0.08	0.11	0.17	0.23	0.34	0.39
150,000	1,072	250,000	0.07	0.10	0.15	0.21	0.30	0.35
200,000	1,107	300,000	0.06	0.09	0.14	0.19	0.28	0.32
250,000	1,072	350,000	0.06	0.08	0.13	0.18	0.26	0.30
300,000	960	375,000	0.06	0.08	0.12	0.17	0.25	0.29

Employed Women

Standard errors of totals		Standard errors of percent						
Size of estimate	Estimated sampling error	Base of percent	Estimated percent					
			1/99	2/98	5/95	10/90	25/75	50/50
100	22	50	1.00	1.41	2.19	3.02	4.35	5.03
200	32	1,000	0.71	1.00	1.55	2.13	3.08	3.56
500	50	2,000	0.50	0.70	1.10	1.51	2.18	2.51
1,000	71	5,000	0.32	0.45	0.69	0.95	1.38	1.59
2,000	99	10,000	0.22	0.31	0.49	0.67	0.97	1.12
5,000	152	15,000	0.18	0.26	0.40	0.55	0.80	0.92
10,000	205	20,000	0.16	0.22	0.35	0.48	0.69	0.80
15,000	237	30,000	0.13	0.18	0.28	0.39	0.56	0.65
20,000	258	40,000	0.11	0.16	0.25	0.34	0.49	0.56
30,000	272	50,000	0.10	0.14	0.22	0.30	0.44	0.50
40,000	253							
50,000	192							

SOURCE: National Science Foundation, SRS

APPENDIX B

Statistical Tables

Appendix table 1. Employed scientists and engineers by field and sex: 1976, 1984, and 1986

Field	1976			1984			1986		
	Total	Men	Women	Total	Men	Women	Total	Men	Women
Total scientists and engineers	2,331,200	2,131,600	199,700	3,995,500	3,482,900	512,600	4,626,500	3,927,800	698,600
Scientists	959,500	781,300	178,200	1,781,400	1,343,300	438,100	2,186,300	1,586,700	599,600
Physical scientists	188,900	172,700	16,200	254,100	225,800	28,300	288,400	250,100	38,300
Chemists	132,800	119,100	13,700	168,600	146,300	22,300	184,700	156,000	28,800
Physicists/astronomers	44,300	42,600	1,700	61,200	58,200	3,000	72,600	67,700	4,900
Other physical scientists	11,800	10,900	800	24,300	21,200	3,100	31,100	26,400	4,700
Mathematical scientists	48,600	37,100	11,500	100,400	78,500	21,900	131,000	97,100	33,900
Mathematicians	43,400	33,700	9,700	83,900	65,900	17,900	110,700	81,500	29,200
Statisticians	5,200	3,400	1,800	16,500	12,500	4,000	20,300	15,600	4,800
Computer specialists	119,000	98,400	20,600	436,800	322,700	114,100	562,600	400,000	162,500
Environmental scientists	54,800	50,900	3,900	98,100	87,800	10,300	111,300	98,400	12,900
Earth scientists	46,500	42,900	3,600	82,300	73,500	8,800	93,700	82,200	11,500
Oceanographers	4,400	4,400	(1)	3,200	2,700	500	4,200	3,500	700
Atmospheric scientists	3,800	3,600	300	12,600	11,600	1,000	13,500	12,800	700
Life scientists	213,500	179,600	33,900	353,300	270,700	82,600	411,800	309,000	102,800
Biological scientists	139,400	115,300	24,100	236,600	176,100	60,500	273,300	199,600	73,600
Agricultural scientists	40,700	39,100	1,600	88,700	72,400	16,300	103,300	81,500	21,800
Medical scientists	33,300	25,100	8,200	27,900	22,200	5,800	35,200	27,900	7,300
Psychologists	112,500	76,900	35,600	209,500	121,100	88,400	253,500	138,400	115,200
Social scientists	222,300	165,700	56,600	329,200	236,800	92,400	427,800	293,800	134,000
Economists	62,500	54,600	8,000	125,600	106,900	18,600	163,600	131,700	31,900
Sociologists/anthropologists	33,900	22,500	11,400	77,700	45,700	32,000	93,600	48,800	44,800
Other social scientists	125,900	88,700	37,200	125,900	84,200	41,800	170,800	113,500	57,300

Appendix table 1. - continued

Field	1976			1984			1986		
	Total	Men	Women	Total	Men	Women	Total	Men	Women
Engineers	1,371,700	1,350,300	21,400	2,214,100	2,139,600	74,500	2,440,100	2,341,100	99,000
Aeronautical/astronautical	56,800	56,400	400	97,200	94,900	2,200	110,500	106,200	4,300
Chemical	77,500	75,000	2,500	140,100	131,300	8,800	149,000	137,800	11,200
Civil	188,200	182,800	5,400	312,700	303,400	9,300	346,300	333,400	12,900
Electrical/electronics	283,000	281,400	1,600	500,700	488,500	12,200	574,500	555,500	18,900
Industrial	NA	NA	NA	131,700	126,400	5,300	137,700	130,600	7,100
Materials	NA	NA	NA	51,300	49,100	2,200	53,100	50,500	2,500
Mechanical	276,200	273,900	2,300	445,600	434,600	11,000	492,600	478,600	14,000
Mining	NA	NA	NA	16,500	15,900	600	17,300	16,600	700
Nuclear	NA	NA	NA	22,100	21,300	800	22,700	21,900	800
Petroleum	NA	NA	NA	33,300	31,300	2,000	30,800	28,900	1,800
Other engineers	490,000	480,900	9,100	463,000	442,900	20,100	505,600	481,000	24,600

(1) Too few cases to estimate.
NA: Not available.

NOTE: Detail may not add to total because of rounding.
SOURCE: National Science Foundation, SRS.

Appendix table 2. Employed scientists and engineers by field and racial/ethnic group: 1976, 1984, and 1986

1976

Field	Total (1)	White	Black	Asian	Native American	Hispanic (2)
Total scientists and engineers	2,331,200	2,141,900	38,100	106,600	NA	NA
Scientists	959,500	870,900	21,400	48,500	NA	NA
Physical scientists	188,900	172,400	3,200	7,600	NA	NA
Chemists	132,800	121,200	2,800	6,800	NA	NA
Physicists/astronomers	44,300	40,500	2,300	600	NA	NA
Other physical scientists	11,800	10,700	100	200	NA	NA
Mathematical scientists	48,600	44,200	2,600	1,600	NA	NA
Mathematicians	43,400	39,700	2,300	1,200	NA	NA
Statisticians	5,200	4,500	200	400	NA	NA
Computer specialists	119,000	110,700	1,600	4,000	NA	NA
Environmental scientists	54,800	48,300	2,000	3,200	NA	NA
Earth scientists	46,500	42,400	1,200	2,700	NA	NA
Oceanographers	4,400	2,600	1,800	100	NA	NA
Atmospheric scientists	3,800	3,400	(3)	400	NA	NA
Life scientists	213,500	200,700	4,900	5,300	NA	NA
Biological scientists	139,400	131,000	3,000	3,700	NA	NA
Agricultural scientists	40,700	38,800	1,500	900	NA	NA
Medical scientists	33,300	30,900	1,400	700	NA	NA
Psychologists	112,500	105,100	3,800	1,000	NA	NA
Social scientists	222,300	189,400	3,300	25,800	NA	NA
Economists	62,500	54,500	800	6,700	NA	NA
Sociologists/anthropologists	33,900	30,200	500	1,100	NA	NA
Other social scientists	125,900	104,700	2,000	18,000	NA	NA

Appendix table 2. - continued

Field	1976						
	Total (1)	White	Black	Asian	Native American	Hispanic (2)
Engineers	1,371,700	1,271,000	16,700	58,100	NA	NA
Aeronautical/astronautical	56,800	54,100	300	1,600	NA	NA
Chemical	77,500	72,200	1,500	2,400	NA	NA
Civil	188,200	165,700	1,600	14,800	NA	NA
Electrical/electronics	283,000	262,500	2,900	13,800	NA	NA
Industrial	NA	NA	NA	NA	NA	NA
Materials	NA	NA	NA	NA	NA	NA
Mechanical	276,200	258,700	2,400	9,700	NA	NA
Mining	NA	NA	NA	NA	NA	NA
Nuclear	NA	NA	NA	NA	NA	NA
Petroleum	NA	NA	NA	NA	NA	NA
Other engineers	490,000	457,800	8,000	15,800	NA	NA

Appendix table 2. - continued

Field	1984					
	Total (1)	White	Black	Asian	Native American	Hispanic (2)
Total scientists and engineers	3,995,500	3,641,200	90,500	186,500	20,400	86,600
Scientists	1,781,400	1,623,800	53,400	69,100	8,600	38,800
Physical scientists	254,100	230,700	6,100	12,500	1,100	4,300
Chemists	168,600	151,500	5,300	8,500	900	3,200
Physicists/astronomers	61,200	56,400	600	2,800	200	800
Other physical scientists	24,300	22,800	200	1,100	(3)	300
Mathematical scientists	100,400	88,900	4,700	4,700	400	2,700
Mathematicians	83,900	74,100	4,300	3,800	200	2,400
Statisticians	16,500	14,800	400	900	200	400
Computer specialists	436,800	392,600	12,100	24,600	1,800	8,200
Environmental scientists	98,100	94,200	600	1,800	300	1,800
Earth scientists	82,300	79,200	400	1,300	200	1,500
Oceanographers	3,200	3,000	(3)	100	(3)	100
Atmospheric scientists	12,600	12,000	100	400	(3)	300
Life scientists	353,300	329,300	6,700	10,400	2,100	7,300
Biological scientists	236,600	218,900	5,600	7,600	900	5,600
Agricultural scientists	88,700	84,200	800	1,700	1,100	1,300
Medical scientists	27,900	26,300	300	1,100	100	400
Psychologists	209,500	196,000	7,300	2,000	1,800	4,200
Social scientists	329,200	292,100	15,900	13,100	1,200	10,200
Economists	125,600	113,000	4,400	5,600	700	2,500
Sociologists/anthropologists	77,700	67,000	4,400	3,600		4,300
Other social scientists	125,900	112,100	6,800	3,900	200	3,400

Appendix table 2. - continued

Field	Total (1)	White	1984				
			Black	Asian	Native American	Hispanic (2)	
Engineers	2,214,100	2,017,400	37,100	117,500	11,700	47,800
Aeronautical/astronautical	97,200	90,200	1,200	4,900	200	1,300
Chemical	140,100	125,100	1,500	10,300	700	2,900
Civil	312,700	275,000	4,800	23,800	1,700	8,100
Electrical/electronics	500,700	447,700	11,400	31,100	3,900	11,300
Industrial	131,700	123,700	3,000	2,800	600	3,400
Materials	51,300	46,600	800	3,100	200	100
Mechanical	445,600	412,100	4,800	21,300	2,500	9,200
Mining	16,500	15,800	100	300	400	100
Nuclear	22,100	20,500	100	1,300	(3)	100
Petroleum	33,300	31,100	300	700	500	1,000
Other engineers	463,000	429,500	9,100	18,000	1,000	10,400

Appendix table 2. - continued

Field	1986					
	Total (1)	White	Black	Asian	Native American	Hispanic (2)
Total scientists and engineers	4,626,500	4,190,400	114,900	226,800	23,600	93,400
Scientists	2,186,300	1,973,100	73,700	94,000	10,300	46,100
Physical scientists	288,400	261,800	6,200	15,400	1,000	4,800
Chemists	184,700	164,700	4,800	11,700	800	2,900
Physicists/astronomers	72,600	67,600	900	3,000	200	1,700
Other physical scientists	31,100	29,500	500	700	(3)	200
Mathematical scientists	131,000	115,500	6,800	5,900	200	3,100
Mathematicians	110,700	97,100	6,200	4,800	200	2,800
Statisticians	20,300	18,400	600	1,100	(3)	300
Computer specialists	562,600	497,100	18,900	36,100	2,200	9,300
Environmental scientists	111,300	105,800	1,000	2,600	400	1,800
Earth scientists	93,700	89,300	800	1,600	300	1,600
Oceanographers	4,200	3,900	(3)	(3)	100	100
Atmospheric scientists	13,500	12,600	100	500	(3)	200
Life scientists	411,800	377,900	8,800	15,000	2,800	9,900
Biological scientists	273,300	249,300	7,300	10,300	1,400	7,300
Agricultural scientists	103,300	96,100	1,100	2,900	1,300	2,300
Medical scientists	35,200	32,500	400	1,900	100	300
Psychologists	253,500	234,100	9,100	5,200	1,900	5,900
Social scientists	427,800	380,800	22,900	14,200	1,700	11,400
Economists	163,600	149,000	5,200	6,100	1,000	3,400
Sociologists/anthropologists	93,400	78,500	7,800	4,300	400	5,000
Other social scientists	170,800	153,300	10,000	3,800	300	3,000

Appendix table 2. - continued

Field	1986					
	Total (1)	White	Black	Asian	Native American	Hispanic (2)
Engineers	2,440,100	2,217,300	41,300	132,800	13,300	47,200
Aeronautical/astronautical	110,500	100,800	1,600	6,600	400	1,500
Chemical	149,000	133,900	2,000	10,100	900	2,700
Civil	346,300	308,600	5,200	24,500	1,100	7,300
Electrical/electronics	574,500	512,100	11,900	37,900	3,300	12,200
Industrial	137,700	129,100	2,500	3,800	700	2,500
Materials	53,100	48,600	600	3,000	300	400
Mechanical	492,600	452,600	6,700	24,600	2,900	9,000
Mining	17,300	16,800	(3)	400	(3)	100
Nuclear	22,700	20,800	400	1,500	(3)	100
Petroleum	30,800	28,700	300	400	700	700
Other engineers	505,600	465,300	10,000	20,200	3,000	10,700

(1) Detail will not add to total because
    a) racial and ethnic categories are not mutually exclusive and
    b) total includes other and no report.
(2) Includes members of all racial groups.
(3) Too few cases to estimate.
NA: Not available.

NOTE: Detail may not add to total because of rounding.
SOURCE: National Science Foundation, SRS.

Appendix table 3. Employed scientists and engineers by field, sex, and racial/ethnic group: 1982, 1984, and 1986

1982

Field	Total (1)	White	Black	Asian	Native American	Hispanic (2)
Total scientists and engineers	3,253,100	2,992,000	71,500	134,600	15,600	70,000
Men	2,864,100	2,652,200	48,500	115,700	13,700	60,500
Women	388,900	339,800	23,000	18,900	1,900	9,500
Scientists	1,405,700	1,294,200	40,000	48,000	6,500	28,100
Men	1,075,100	1,001,400	22,200	33,600	4,900	20,400
Women	330,600	292,900	17,800	14,400	1,600	7,700
Physical scientists	227,400	212,700	3,500	8,200	600	3,600
Men	205,100	193,000	2,700	6,600	600	3,200
Women	22,300	19,800	800	1,600	(3)	500
Mathematical scientists	79,400	72,300	3,600	2,700	100	1,400
Men	54,000	50,600	900	2,100	100	800
Women	25,300	21,800	2,600	700	(3)	600
Computer specialists	299,000	272,300	8,900	13,100	1,100	4,600
Men	220,300	204,400	3,900	8,300	800	3,700
Women	78,700	67,900	5,000	4,700	300	900
Environmental scientists	87,200	80,900	600	3,600	900	1,400
Men	74,800	68,800	500	3,500	800	1,200
Women	12,400	12,100	100	100	(3)	200
Life scientists	337,100	316,900	8,000	7,800	1,300	6,700
Men	268,500	253,300	6,700	5,500	900	4,700
Women	68,600	63,600	1,300	2,300	400	2,000
Psychologists	138,400	130,400	4,500	1,200	1,000	2,300
Men	83,000	78,800	2,200	500	700	1,000
Women	55,400	51,600	2,300	700	300	1,300
Social scientists	237,200	208,700	10,900	11,300	1,500	8,000
Men	169,300	152,500	5,200	7,100	900	5,800
Women	67,900	56,100	5,700	4,200	600	2,200
Engineers	1,847,300	1,697,800	31,500	86,700	9,800	41,900
Men	1,789,000	1,650,900	26,200	82,100	8,800	40,100
Women	58,300	46,900	5,200	4,500	300	1,800

Appendix table 3. - continued

Field	Total (1)	White	Black	Asian	Native American	Hispanic (2)
1984						
Total scientists and engineers						
Men	3,995,500	3,641,200	90,500	186,500	20,400	86,600
Women	3,482,900	3,189,000	67,600	159,500	18,900	71,900
	512,600	452,200	22,900	27,000	1,500	15,200
Scientists	1,781,400	1,623,800	53,400	69,100	8,600	38,800
Men	1,343,300	1,235,000	33,500	48,100	7,400	26,200
Women	438,100	388,800	19,800	20,900	1,300	12,700
Physical scientists	254,100	230,700	6,100	12,500	1,100	4,300
Men	225,800	206,700	4,900	9,700	1,100	3,500
Women	28,300	24,000	1,200	2,800	(3)	800
Mathematical scientists	100,400	88,900	4,700	4,700	400	2,700
Men	78,500	69,600	3,000	4,200	400	2,000
Women	21,900	19,300	1,700	600	(3)	700
Computer specialists	436,800	392,600	12,100	24,600	1,800	8,200
Men	322,700	292,900	6,600	17,400	1,600	5,100
Women	114,100	99,600	5,600	7,200	100	3,100
Environmental scientists	98,100	94,200	600	1,800	300	1,800
Men	87,800	84,300	500	1,700	200	1,600
Women	10,300	9,900	100	100	(3)	200
Life scientists	353,300	329,300	6,700	10,400	2,100	7,300
Men	270,700	255,600	4,500	6,200	1,600	4,600
Women	82,600	73,700	2,100	4,200	500	2,700
Psychologists	209,500	196,000	7,300	2,000	1,800	4,200
Men	121,100	114,400	3,000	800	1,500	2,000
Women	88,400	81,600	4,300	1,200	300	2,200
Social scientists	329,200	292,100	15,900	13,100	1,200	10,200
Men	236,800	211,500	11,000	8,300	1,000	7,300
Women	92,400	80,600	4,800	4,800	200	2,900
Engineers	2,214,100	2,017,400	37,100	117,500	11,700	47,800
Men	2,139,600	1,953,900	34,100	111,400	11,500	45,200
Women	74,500	63,500	3,100	6,100	200	2,600

Appendix table 3. - continued

1986

Field	Total (1)	White	Black	Asian	Native American	Hispanic (2)
Total scientists and engineers						
Men	4,626,500	4,190,400	114,900	226,800	23,600	93,400
Women	3,927,800	3,581,500	80,500	190,500	21,000	73,800
	698,600	608,900	34,500	36,300	2,700	19,600
Scientists						
Men	2,186,300	1,973,100	73,700	94,000	10,300	46,100
Women	1,586,700	1,448,300	43,600	65,000	7,900	29,800
	599,600	524,800	30,100	29,000	2,400	16,400
Physical scientists						
Men	288,400	261,800	6,200	15,400	1,000	4,800
Women	250,100	230,100	4,500	11,200	1,000	3,900
	38,300	31,700	1,700	4,200	(3)	900
Mathematical scientists						
Men	131,000	115,500	6,800	5,900	200	3,100
Women	97,100	85,200	4,500	5,100	100	1,900
	33,900	30,300	2,300	800	100	1,200
Computer specialists						
Men	562,600	497,100	18,900	36,100	2,200	9,300
Women	400,000	354,100	11,700	27,300	1,800	6,400
	162,500	143,000	7,200	8,800	400	2,900
Environmental scientists						
Men	111,300	105,800	1,000	2,100	400	1,800
Women	98,400	93,400	900	2,000	400	1,700
	12,900	12,400	100	200	100	200
Life scientists						
Men	411,800	377,900	8,800	15,000	2,800	9,900
Women	309,000	288,900	5,500	9,400	1,800	5,900
	102,800	89,100	3,300	5,600	1,000	4,100
Psychologists						
Men	253,500	234,100	9,100	5,200	1,900	5,900
Women	138,400	131,700	3,100	800	1,400	2,700
	115,200	102,500	6,000	4,400	500	3,100
Social scientists						
Men	427,800	380,800	22,900	14,200	1,700	11,400
Women	293,800	265,000	13,500	9,200	1,300	7,400
	134,000	115,800	9,400	5,000	400	4,000
Engineers						
Men	2,440,100	2,217,300	41,300	132,800	13,300	47,200
Women	2,341,100	2,133,200	36,900	125,500	13,100	44,000
	99,000	84,100	4,400	7,300	300	3,200

(1) Detail will not add to total because
   a) racial and ethnic categories are not mutually exclusive and
   b) total includes other and no report.
(2) Includes members of all racial groups.
(3) Too few cases to estimate.
NOTE: Detail may not add to total because of rounding.
SOURCE: National Science Foundation, SRS.

Appendix table 4. Employed doctoral scientists and engineers by field and sex: 1975, 1983, and 1985

Field	1975			1983			1985		
	Total	Men	Women	Total	Men	Women	Total	Men	Women
Total scientists and engineers	255,900	233,900	22,100	369,300	320,500	48,800	400,400	341,900	58,500
Scientists	213,500	191,700	21,800	307,800	260,000	47,800	334,500	277,500	57,000
Physical scientists	54,600	52,100	2,500	64,000	59,800	4,200	67,500	62,800	4,700
Chemists	35,800	33,800	2,100	41,300	37,800	3,500	43,700	39,900	3,800
Physicists/astronomers	18,800	18,300	500	22,700	22,000	700	23,700	22,900	900
Mathematical scientists	13,600	12,700	900	16,400	15,000	1,400	16,700	15,200	1,600
Mathematicians	11,900	11,000	800	13,600	12,500	1,100	13,900	12,700	1,200
Statisticians	1,700	1,700	100	2,800	2,500	300	2,800	2,500	300
Computer specialists	3,500	3,400	100	12,200	10,900	1,300	15,000	13,300	1,600
Environmental scientists	12,100	11,800	300	16,500	15,600	900	17,300	16,200	1,100
Earth scientists	9,500	9,300	200	12,500	11,900	600	13,200	12,400	800
Oceanographers	1,300	1,200	100	1,700	1,600	200	2,000	1,700	200
Atmospheric scientists	1,300	1,300	(1)	2,200	2,100	100	2,100	2,000	100
Life scientists	63,300	55,800	7,500	92,800	76,600	16,200	101,800	82,100	19,700
Biological scientists	39,000	33,300	5,800	55,200	44,600	10,600	59,900	47,700	12,600
Agricultural scientists	11,000	10,800		14,500	13,900	700	15,500	14,700	800
Medical scientists	13,300	11,700	1,600	23,100	18,100	4,900	26,500	20,200	6,200
Psychologists	30,000	23,700	6,300	46,600	33,000	13,700	52,200	35,600	16,600
Social scientists	36,300	32,200	4,100	59,300	49,300	10,100	64,000	52,200	11,800
Economists	11,800	11,200	600	17,000	15,500	1,400	17,900	16,200	1,700
Sociologists/anthropologists	7,900	6,300	1,700	12,100	8,600	3,500	12,700	9,100	3,600
Other social scientists	16,600	14,800	1,800	30,300	25,200	5,100	33,400	27,000	6,400

Appendix table 4. - continued

Field	1975			1983			1985		
	Total	Men	Women	Total	Men	Women	Total	Men	Women
Engineers	42,400	42,200	200	61,500	60,500	1,100	65,900	64,400	1,500
Aeronautical/astronautical	2,000	2,000	(1)	3,700	3,600	100	3,800	3,700	100
Chemical	5,400	5,300	(1)	7,000	6,900	100	7,100	7,000	100
Civil	3,800	3,800	(1)	5,300	5,200	100	6,400	6,300	100
Electrical/electronics	8,500	8,500	(1)	12,700	12,500	200	14,300	13,900	300
Materials	4,800	4,700	(1)	7,400	7,300	200	7,300	7,000	200
Mechanical	4,000	4,000	(1)	5,700	5,600	100	6,600	6,500	100
Nuclear	1,700	1,700	(1)	2,300	2,300	(1)	2,400	2,300	(1)
Systems design	2,400	2,400	(1)	3,900	3,800	100	3,700	3,500	200
Other engineers	9,800	9,800	100	13,600	13,300	300	14,300	14,000	400

(1) Too few cases to estimate.

NOTE: Detail may not add to totals because of rounding.

SOURCE: National Science Foundation, SRS.

Appendix table 5. Employed doctoral scientists and engineers by field and racial/ethnic group: 1975, 1983, and 1985

Field	1975					
	Total (1)	White	Black	Asian	Native American	Hispanic (2)
Total scientists and engineers	255,900	232,800	2,500	13,600	200	2,000
Scientists	213,500	195,800	2,400	9,300	200	1,700
Physical scientists	54,600	49,800	500	3,000	(3)	400
Chemists	35,800	32,700	400	1,900	(3)	300
Physicists/astronomers	18,800	17,100	100	1,100	(3)	100
Mathematical scientists	13,600	12,300	100	700	(3)	100
Mathematicians	11,900	10,700	100	700	(3)	100
Statisticians	1,700	1,600	(3)	100	(3)	(3)
Computer specialists	3,500	3,200	(3)	200	(3)	(3)
Environmental scientists	12,100	11,400	(3)	300	(3)	100
Earth scientists	9,500	9,000	(3)	200	(3)	100
Oceanographers	1,300	1,200	(3)	(3)	(3)	(3)
Atmospheric scientists	1,300	1,200	(3)	100	(3)	(3)
Life scientists	63,300	57,800	700	3,400	100	600
Biological scientists	39,000	35,500	600	2,000	(3)	400
Agricultural scientists	11,000	10,300	(3)	400	(3)	100
Medical scientists	13,300	12,000	100	900	(3)	200
Psychologists	30,000	28,300	400	300	(3)	200
Social scientists	36,300	33,100	600	1,400	100	300
Economists	11,800	10,800	100	500	(3)	100
Sociologists/anthropologists	7,900	7,200	100	200	(3)	100
Other social scientists	16,600	15,100	300	600	(3)	100

Appendix table 5. – continued

Field	1975					
	Total (1)	White	Black	Asian	Native American	Hispanic (2)
Engineers	42,400	36,900	100	4,300	(3)	300
Aeronautical/ astronautical	2,000	1,800	(3)	200	(3)	(3)
Chemical	5,400	4,700	(3)	500	(3)	(3)
Civil	3,800	3,100	(3)	600	(3)	100
Electrical/electronics	8,500	7,300	(3)	900	(3)	100
Materials	4,800	4,300	(3)	400	(3)	(3)
Mechanical	4,000	3,400	(3)	600	(3)	(3)
Nuclear	1,700	1,500	(3)	100	(3)	(3)
Systems design	2,400	2,100	(3)	200	(3)	(3)
Other engineers	9,800	8,700	(3)	800	(3)	(3)

Appendix table 5. - continued

Field	1983					
	Total (1)	White	Black	Asian	Native American	Hispanic (2)
Total scientists and engineers	369,300	329,900	5,000	29,900	400	5,400
Scientists	307,800	280,000	4,500	19,300	400	4,500
Physical scientists	64,000	56,800	700	5,700	100	900
Chemists	41,300	36,500	400	3,900	(3)	700
Physicists/astronomers	22,700	20,300	200	1,800	(3)	200
Mathematical scientists	16,400	14,600	200	1,400	(3)	200
Mathematicians	13,600	12,300	200	1,000	(3)	200
Statisticians	2,800	2,300	(3)	400	(3)	(3)
Computer specialists	12,200	11,000	(3)	900	(3)	200
Environmental scientists	16,500	15,500	(3)	800	(3)	200
Earth scientists	12,500	11,800	(3)	600	(3)	200
Oceanographers	1,700	1,700	(3)	100	(3)	(3)
Atmospheric scientists	2,200	2,100	(3)	100	(3)	(3)
Life scientists	92,800	83,700	1,100	6,800	100	1,300
Biological scientists	55,200	49,700	600	4,200	(3)	700
Agricultural scientists	14,500	13,500	100	800	(3)	300
Medical scientists	23,100	20,600	400	1,700	(3)	300
Psychologists	46,600	44,500	1,000	700	100	700
Social scientists	59,300	53,800	1,500	3,100	100	1,000
Economists	17,000	15,100	300	1,300	100	300
Sociologists/ anthropologists	12,100	11,100	400	400	(3)	200
Other social scientists	30,300	27,700	800	1,400	(3)	500

Appendix table 5. - continued

Field	1983						
	Total (1)	White	Black	Asian	Native American	Hispanic (2)
Engineers	61,500	49,900	400	10,500	(3)	1,000
Aeronautical/ astronautical	3,700	3,100	(3)	500	(3)	(3)
Chemical	7,000	5,400	(3)	1,500	(3)	100
Civil	5,300	4,200	(3)	1,100	(3)	100
Electrical/electronics	12,700	10,300	100	2,100	(3)	200
Materials	7,400	6,100	(3)	1,200	(3)	200
Mechanical	5,700	4,400	100	1,200	(3)	100
Nuclear	2,300	1,900	(3)	400	(3)	(3)
Systems design	3,900	3,500	(3)	300	(3)	100
Other engineers	13,600	10,900	100	2,300	(3)	200

Appendix table 5. - continued

Field	1985					
	Total (1)	White	Black	Asian	Native American	Hispanic (2)
Total scientists and engineers	400,400	355,100	5,700	34,500	500	5,900
Scientists	334,500	302,500	5,200	22,700	400	5,100
Physical scientists	67,500	59,600	500	6,600	100	900
Chemists	43,700	38,500	400	4,300	(3)	700
Physicists/astronomers	23,700	21,100	100	2,200	(3)	300
Mathematical scientists	16,700	14,900	200	1,400	(3)	300
Mathematicians	13,900	12,500	100	1,000	(3)	300
Statisticians	2,800	2,400	(3)	300	(3)	(3)
Computer specialists	15,000	13,100	100	1,600	(3)	200
Environmental scientists	17,300	15,800	100	1,100	(3)	300
Earth scientists	13,200	12,000	100	900	(3)	100
Oceanographers	2,000	1,800	(3)	100	(3)	100
Atmospheric scientists	2,100	1,900	(3)	100	(3)	100
Life scientists	101,800	92,000	1,400	7,400	100	1,400
Biological scientists	59,900	53,900	800	4,700	100	800
Agricultural scientists	15,500	14,400	100	900	(3)	200
Medical scientists	26,500	23,700	500	1,900	(3)	400
Psychologists	52,200	49,500	1,200	800	100	1,000
Social scientists	64,000	57,700	1,700	3,800	100	1,100
Economists	17,900	15,800	300	1,500	100	400
Sociologists/anthropologists	12,700	11,700	300	500	(3)	200
Other social scientists	33,400	30,100	1,100	1,800	(3)	500

Appendix table 5. - continued

Field	1985					
	Total (1)	White	Black	Asian	Native American	Hispanic (2)
Engineers	65,900	52,600	500	11,900	100	800
Aeronautical/ astronautical	3,800	3,300	(3)	500	(3)	(3)
Chemical	7,100	5,100	100	1,900	(3)	100
Civil	6,400	5,100	100	1,200	(3)	100
Electrical/electronics	14,300	11,400	100	2,600	(3)	200
Materials	7,300	5,700	(3)	1,500	(3)	100
Mechanical	6,600	5,100	100	1,400	(3)	100
Nuclear	2,400	1,800	(3)	500	(3)	(3)
Systems design	3,700	3,200	(3)	400	(3)	200
Other engineers	14,300	11,900	100	2,000	(3)	100

(1) Detail will not add to total employed because
    a) racial and ethnic categories are not mutually exclusive and
    b) total employed includes other and no report.
(2) Includes members of all racial groups.
(3) Too few cases to estimate.

SOURCE: National Science Foundation, SRS.

Appendix table 6. Employed doctoral scientists and engineers by field,
sex, and racial/ethnic group: 1983 and 1985

Field and sex	1983					
	Total (1)	White	Black	Asian	Native American	Hispanic (2)
Total scientists and engineers	369,300	329,900	5,000	29,900	400	5,400
Men	320,500	286,400	3,600	26,400	400	4,700
Women	48,800	43,500	1,400	3,400	(3)	700
Scientists	307,800	280,000	4,500	19,300	400	4,500
Men	260,000	237,300	3,200	16,200	300	3,800
Women	47,800	42,700	1,300	3,200	(3)	700
Physical scientists	64,000	56,800	700	5,700	100	900
Men	59,800	53,400	600	5,000	100	800
Women	4,200	3,400	100	700	(3)	100
Mathematical scientists	16,400	14,600	200	1,400	(3)	200
Men	15,000	13,400	200	1,200	(3)	200
Women	1,400	1,200	(3)	200	(3)	(3)
Computer specialists	12,200	11,000	(3)	900	(3)	200
Men	10,900	9,900	(3)	800	(3)	200
Women	1,300	1,100	(3)	100	(3)	(3)
Environmental scientists	16,500	15,500	(3)	800	(3)	200
Men	15,600	14,700	(3)	700	(3)	200
Women	900	800	(3)	100	(3)	(3)
Life scientists	92,800	83,700	1,100	6,800	100	1,300
Men	76,600	69,500	700	5,300	100	1,100
Women	16,200	14,200	400	1,500	(3)	200

Appendix table 6. - continued

Field and sex	1983					
	Total (1)	White	Black	Asian	Native American	Hispanic (2)
Psychologists	46,600	44,500	1,000	700	100	700
Men	33,000	31,700	500	400	100	500
Women	13,700	12,800	500	300	(3)	200
Social scientists	59,300	53,800	1,500	3,100	100	1,000
Men	49,300	44,600	1,100	2,700	100	800
Women	10,100	9,200	400	400	(3)	200
Engineers	61,500	49,900	400	10,500	(3)	1,000
Men	60,500	49,100	400	10,300	(3)	900
Women	1,100	800	(3)	300	(3)	(3)

Field and sex	1985					
	Total (1)	White	Black	Asian	Native American	Hispanic (2)
Total scientists and engineers	400,400	355,100	5,700	34,500	500	5,900
Men	341,900	303,100	4,000	30,400	400	4,900
Women	58,500	52,000	1,700	4,100	100	1,000
Scientists	334,500	302,500	5,200	22,700	400	5,100
Men	277,500	251,600	3,500	18,800	400	4,200
Women	57,000	50,900	1,700	3,800	100	900
Physical scientists	67,500	59,600	500	6,600	100	900
Men	62,800	55,800	500	5,800	100	800
Women	4,700	3,800	(3)	800	(3)	100
Mathematical scientists	16,700	14,900	200	1,400	(3)	300
Men	15,200	13,600	100	1,200	(3)	200
Women	1,600	1,300	(3)	200	(3)	(3)
Computer specialists	15,000	13,100	100	1,600	(3)	200
Men	13,300	11,600	100	1,500	(3)	200
Women	1,600	1,400	(3)	200	(3)	(3)
Environmental scientists	17,300	15,800	100	1,100	(3)	300
Men	16,200	14,800	100	1,100	(3)	200
Women	1,100	1,000	(3)	100	(3)	(3)
Life scientists	101,800	92,000	1,400	7,400	100	1,400
Men	82,100	74,700	900	5,700	100	1,100
Women	19,700	17,300	500	1,800	(3)	300
Psychologists	52,200	49,500	1,200	800	100	1,000
Men	35,600	34,100	600	400	100	700
Women	16,600	15,400	600	400	(3)	300

Appendix table 6. - continued

Field and sex	1985					
	Total (1)	White	Black	Asian	Native American	Hispanic (2)
Social scientists	64,000	57,700	1,700	3,800	100	1,100
Men	52,200	47,000	1,300	3,300	100	900
Women	11,800	10,700	500	500	(3)	200
Engineers	65,900	52,600	500	11,900	100	800
Men	64,400	51,500	500	11,600	100	800
Women	1,500	1,100	(3)	300	(3)	(3)

(1) Detail will not add to total employed because
    a) racial and ethnic categories are not mutually exclusive and
    b) total employed includes other and no report.
(2) Includes members of all racial groups.
(3) Too few cases to estimate.

SOURCE: National Science Foundation, SRS.

Appendix table 7. Selected characteristics of physically disabled scientists and engineers: 1986

Field	Total population	Visual	Auditory	Ambulatory	Other
Total scientists and engineers	94,200	21,100	16,500	20,500	36,100
Scientists	40,400	9,700	7,600	9,800	13,400
Physical scientists	7,600	2,500	1,100	1,400	2,600
Mathematical scientists	1,600	300	400	500	500
Computer specialists	9,200	1,800	2,700	3,000	1,700
Environmental scientists	3,000	200	400	1,300	1,100
Life scientists	6,300	1,300	1,200	1,700	2,100
Psychologists	6,100	1,100	1,400	1,200	2,400
Social scientists	6,600	2,600	400	700	2,900
Engineers	53,800	11,400	8,900	10,800	22,700

Appendix table 7. - continued

Field	Total population	Labor force status			
		Labor Force	Total Employed	Employed in S/E	Unemployed, seeking
Total scientists and engineers	94,200	71,400	70,300	63,400	1,100
Scientists	40,400	34,500	34,200	29,400	300
Physical scientists	7,600	5,300	5,300	5,100	(1)
Mathematical scientists	1,600	1,600	1,500	1,300	100
Computer specialists	9,200	9,100	9,100	7,800	(1)
Environmental scientists	3,000	2,000	2,000	1,900	(1)
Life scientists	6,300	5,700	5,600	5,100	100
Psychologists	6,100	5,400	5,400	3,600	(1)
Social scientists	6,600	5,500	5,300	4,500	100
Engineers	53,800	36,900	36,100	34,000	800

103

Appendix table 7. – continued

Field	Total Outside Labor Force	Reason Outside Labor Force		
		Retired	Illness	Other
Total scientists and engineers	22,900	16,400	5,300	1,200
Scientists	5,900	4,100	1,000	800
Physical scientists	2,400	1,600	800	(1)
Mathematical scientists	100	(1)	(1)	100
Computer specialists	100	(1)	100	(1)
Environmental scientists	1,000	900	100	(1)
Life scientists	600	400	100	100
Psychologists	700	400	(1)	300
Social scientists	1,200	1,000	(1)	200
Engineers	16,900	12,300	4,300	400

(1) Too few cases to estimate.

NOTE: Detail may not add to totals because of rounding.

SOURCE: National Science Foundation, SRS.

Appendix table 8. Employed scientists and engineers by field, racial/ethnic group, and years of professional experience: 1986

Field and racial/ethnic group	Total Employed (1)	Professional Experience								
		1 or less	2-4	5-9	10-14	15-19	20-24	25-29	30-34	35 and over
Total scientists and engineers (1)	4,626,500	104,200	584,200	726,700	680,900	625,800	526,500	459,600	359,200	417,400
White	4,190,400	91,600	522,800	646,500	607,200	564,900	469,300	419,700	338,100	402,100
Black	114,900	2,600	18,800	21,700	23,400	14,100	12,600	7,600	5,600	3,100
Asian	226,800	7,500	25,800	38,200	38,400	35,000	32,300	24,500	12,500	7,300
Native American	23,600	1,300	1,600	2,700	2,500	2,500	5,600	2,900	1,500	3,300
Hispanic (2)	93,400	3,000	18,900	19,500	13,900	13,200	7,800	6,400	3,900	3,800
Scientists	2,186,300	73,600	367,700	412,600	354,300	307,400	227,600	155,900	117,200	111,400
White	1,973,100	65,600	328,300	366,400	317,600	280,900	205,500	139,700	109,300	107,100
Black	73,700	1,800	14,400	14,900	15,100	8,800	7,000	4,800	3,200	800
Asian	94,000	4,500	15,100	19,800	15,900	12,400	9,800	9,000	3,800	2,100
Native American	10,300	(3)	1,200	1,600	600	400	3,200	1,200	700	1,200
Hispanic	46,100	2,000	13,100	10,000	6,400	7,300	2,900	1,500	1,500	600
Physical scientists	288,400	7,400	29,500	33,400	36,700	39,100	40,900	37,500	25,300	31,100
White	261,800	6,800	26,900	29,700	32,400	34,500	36,800	33,700	23,900	30,200
Black	6,200	200	1,200	700	500	1,000	800	900	600	100
Asian	15,400	300	900	2,200	2,200	3,100	2,800	2,300	700	500
Native American	1,000	(3)	(3)	100	(3)	(3)	400	300	(3)	200
Hispanic	4,800	(3)	700	300	700	1,000	600	700	500	200
Mathematical scientists	131,000	2,400	17,100	18,200	17,300	23,100	20,200	13,300	9,000	6,200
White	115,500	2,000	15,400	17,000	14,900	21,200	17,200	10,800	7,000	5,900
Black	6,800	200	300	600	1,300	600	1,300	1,700	600	200
Asian	5,900	200	900	400	500	500	1,300	600	1,300	(3)
Native American	200	(3)	100	(3)	(3)	(3)	(3)	100	(3)	(3)
Hispanic	3,100	(3)	800	500	400	1,200	100	100	(3)	(3)
Computer specialists	562,600	13,300	105,400	123,900	115,500	86,500	53,700	29,000	15,800	6,300
White	497,100	11,100	91,400	109,900	102,000	77,700	47,000	26,100	14,900	6,200
Black	18,900	400	3,600	3,500	3,900	2,900	1,900	500	700	100
Asian	36,100	1,500	7,400	8,100	8,900	4,600	2,900	1,900	200	(3)
Native American	2,200	(3)	200	200	100	100	1,400	(3)	(3)	(3)
Hispanic	9,300	400	3,000	2,600	1,000	900	900	100	200	(3)

Appendix table 8. - continued

Field and racial/ethnic group	Total Employed (1)	Professional Experience								
		1 or less	2-4	5-9	10-14	15-19	20-24	25-29	30-34	35 and over
Environmental scientists	111,300	3,600	16,500	21,500	18,200	10,100	8,200	11,700	8,100	10,300
White	105,800	3,400	15,800	20,200	16,600	9,600	7,800	11,300	7,700	10,200
Black	1,000	(3)	100	100	700	100	(3)	100	(3)	(3)
Asian	2,100	100	100	200	800	300	300	100	200	(3)
Native American	400	(3)	100	100	200	(3)	(3)	100	100	100
Hispanic	1,800	100	300	700	100	100	200	200	200	(3)
Life scientists	411,800	13,800	68,800	81,400	61,400	51,700	38,400	26,800	28,700	28,300
White	377,900	12,200	63,400	72,000	56,100	47,300	36,400	24,200	27,400	27,300
Black	8,800	1,000	1,000	2,400	2,300	1,200	500	400	400	200
Asian	15,000	1,000	2,400	3,500	2,200	2,400	1,300	1,600	300	200
Native American	2,800	(3)	200	700	200	(3)	100	500	500	600
Hispanic	9,900	700	2,900	2,400	1,200	1,200	300	300	500	400
Psychologists	253,500	8,800	38,300	50,100	44,900	39,000	28,500	16,500	12,600	8,200
White	234,100	8,200	36,100	43,600	40,600	36,900	27,100	15,400	12,200	7,900
Black	9,100	200	1,200	1,700	3,600	600	500	1,000	200	100
Asian	5,200	100	200	3,600	300	500	100	100	200	(3)
Native American	1,900	(3)	100	300	300	200	700	100	(3)	300
Hispanic	5,900	200	2,000	1,600	700	1,100	200	(3)	(3)	(3)
Social scientists	427,800	24,300	92,200	84,100	60,400	58,000	37,600	21,100	17,700	20,900
White	380,800	21,800	79,400	74,000	55,100	53,700	33,300	18,300	16,100	19,400
Black	22,900	700	6,900	5,900	2,800	2,500	2,100	200	600	100
Asian	14,200	1,400	3,100	1,700	1,000	1,000	1,100	2,400	900	1,300
Native American	1,700	(3)	500	400	100	(3)	700	100	100	(3)
Hispanic	11,400	600	3,200	1,900	2,200	1,900	600	100	100	(3)
Engineers	2,440,100	30,600	216,500	314,100	326,600	318,400	298,800	303,700	242,000	306,000
White	2,217,300	26,000	194,400	280,100	289,600	284,000	263,800	280,000	228,800	295,000
Black	41,300	3,800	4,700	6,800	8,500	5,300	5,700	2,800	2,400	2,300
Asian	132,800	3,000	10,700	18,400	22,500	22,600	22,500	15,600	8,700	5,200
Native American	13,300	200	400	1,100	1,800	2,100	2,500	1,700	800	2,100
Hispanic	47,200	1,100	5,800	9,500	7,500	5,900	4,900	4,900	2,400	3,200

(1) Detail will not add to total employed because
    a) racial and ethnic categories are not mutually exclusive and
    b) total employed includes other and no report.
(2) Includes members of all racial groups.
(3) Too few cases to estimate.

SOURCE: National Science Foundation, SRS.

Appendix table 9. Employed men scientists and engineers by field, racial/ethnic group, and years of professional experience: 1986

Field and racial/ethnic group	Total Employed (1)	Professional Experience								
		1 or less	2-4	5-9	10-14	15-19	20-24	25-29	30-34	35 and over
Total scientists and engineers (1)	3,927,800	72,000	396,200	541,700	561,300	557,900	491,100	441,600	346,300	403,800
White	3,581,500	63,200	358,300	487,200	502,700	504,300	437,900	404,600	326,400	389,800
Black	80,500	1,400	10,900	12,900	15,600	12,000	10,600	6,900	4,600	2,900
Asian	190,500	5,800	17,600	26,900	32,700	31,500	30,700	22,800	12,300	6,100
Native American	21,000	200	900	1,700	2,300	2,300	5,600	2,300	1,400	3,300
Hispanic (2)	73,800	2,300	10,700	14,000	11,600	11,800	7,200	6,200	3,900	3,800
Scientists	1,586,700	44,600	212,100	258,900	246,800	244,800	195,100	139,900	107,100	99,900
White	1,448,300	39,900	192,000	234,000	223,200	224,800	176,500	126,100	100,100	97,000
Black	43,600	800	7,400	7,400	7,500	7,000	4,900	4,100	2,400	600
Asian	65,000	3,100	8,700	10,400	11,600	9,200	8,600	7,700	3,600	900
Native American	7,900	(3)	600	700	600	200	3,200	700	700	1,200
Hispanic	29,800	1,300	6,000	5,700	4,500	6,000	2,400	1,400	1,500	500
Physical scientists	250,100	5,200	21,000	24,300	30,800	35,100	38,000	35,700	24,600	29,100
White	230,100	4,900	19,600	22,200	27,500	31,500	34,700	32,200	23,400	28,300
Black	4,500	100	600	600	300	800	500	900	600	100
Asian	11,200	200	500	1,000	1,400	2,400	2,300	2,000	600	500
Native American	1,000	(3)	(3)	100	(3)	(3)	400	300	(3)	200
Hispanic	3,900	(3)	500	200	600	800	400	700	500	200
Mathematical scientists	97,100	1,300	9,300	10,900	11,000	18,800	18,300	11,800	7,900	5,300
White	85,200	1,100	8,000	10,300	9,400	17,200	15,700	9,600	6,600	5,100
Black	4,500	(3)	600	300	700	400	1,100	1,500	600	(3)
Asian	5,100	200	800	200	400	300	1,200	600	1,300	(3)
Native American	1,000	(3)	(3)	(3)	(3)	(3)	(3)	100	(3)	(3)
Hispanic	1,900	(3)	200	200	100	1,200	100	100	(3)	(3)
Computer specialists	400,000	8,500	64,700	80,700	76,700	64,500	47,800	27,400	14,600	5,500
White	354,100	6,900	56,300	71,300	67,000	58,800	42,300	24,600	13,700	5,400
Black	11,700	200	2,100	1,900	2,300	2,000	800	500	700	100
Asian	27,300	1,200	5,000	5,800	7,100	3,200	2,700	1,700	200	(3)
Native American	1,800	(3)	(3)	100	100	100	1,400	(3)	(3)	(3)
Hispanic	6,400	300	1,600	2,000	1,000	200	900	100	200	(3)

Appendix table 9. - continued

Field and racial/ethnic group	Total Employed (1)	Professional Experience								
		1 or less	2-4	5-9	10-14	15-19	20-24	25-29	30-34	35 and over
Environmental scientists	98,400	2,800	12,600	17,800	15,900	9,200	7,800	11,600	7,900	10,200
White	93,400	2,700	12,100	16,700	14,300	8,800	7,400	11,200	7,600	10,200
Black	900	(3)	100	100	600	100	(3)	(3)	(3)	(3)
Asian	2,000	100	100	(3)	800	300	300	100	200	(3)
Native American	400	(3)	100	(3)	100	(3)	(3)	100	100	(3)
Hispanic	1,700	100	200	700	100	100	100	200	200	(3)
Life scientists	309,000	8,300	36,400	54,800	48,400	43,900	33,400	22,200	26,600	26,400
White	288,900	7,200	34,600	50,000	45,200	40,600	31,700	20,700	25,300	25,300
Black	5,500	100	300	1,200	1,500	1,000	400	300	300	200
Asian	9,400	800	800	1,800	1,300	2,000	1,100	1,100	300	200
Native American	1,800	(3)	(3)	300	100	(3)	100	100	500	600
Hispanic	5,900	300	1,000	1,400	800	1,000	200	300	500	400
Psychologists	138,400	3,700	13,700	20,000	24,900	25,900	18,800	12,900	9,600	6,200
White	131,700	3,600	13,000	18,900	23,700	24,600	17,800	12,100	9,300	5,900
Black	3,100	(3)	400	700	800	300	200	700	100	(3)
Asian	800	(3)	(3)	100	100	200	(3)	100	200	(3)
Native American	1,400	(3)	100	(3)	300	(3)	700	100	(3)	300
Hispanic	2,700	(3)	800	500	500	800	200	(3)	(3)	(3)
Social scientists	293,800	15,000	54,400	50,400	39,100	47,400	31,000	18,300	15,700	17,200
White	265,000	13,600	48,500	44,600	36,200	43,300	26,900	15,700	14,200	16,800
Black	13,500	400	3,800	2,600	1,400	2,400	2,000	300	600	100
Asian	9,200	600	1,500	1,400	1,600	800	1,000	2,300	900	100
Native American	1,300	(3)	1,300	200	100	(3)	400	100	100	100
Hispanic	7,400	600	1,700	700	1,400	1,900	500	100	100	(3)
Engineers	2,341,100	27,300	184,100	282,700	314,500	313,100	296,000	301,600	239,300	303,800
White	2,133,200	23,300	166,300	253,200	279,500	279,500	261,400	278,500	226,300	292,800
Black	36,900	600	3,500	5,500	8,000	5,000	5,700	2,800	2,200	2,300
Asian	125,500	2,700	8,900	16,500	21,100	22,200	22,100	14,900	8,600	5,200
Native American	13,100	200	300	1,000	1,700	2,100	2,500	1,700	800	2,100
Hispanic	44,000	1,000	4,700	8,300	7,000	5,800	4,800	4,900	2,400	3,200

(1) Detail will not add to total employed because
   a) racial and ethnic categories are not mutually exclusive and
   b) total employed includes other and no report.
(2) Includes members of all racial groups.
(3) Too few cases to estimate.

SOURCE: National Science Foundation, SRS.

Appendix table 10. Employed women scientists and engineers by field, racial/ethnic group, and years of professional experience: 1986

Field and racial/ethnic group	Total Employed (1)	Professional Experience								
		1 or less	2-4	5-9	10-14	15-19	20-24	25-29	30-34	35 and over
Total scientists and engineers (1)	698,600	32,200	188,000	185,000	119,600	67,900	35,400	18,000	12,900	13,600
White	608,900	28,400	164,500	159,300	104,500	60,600	31,400	15,000	11,700	12,200
Black	34,500	1,200	7,900	8,700	7,900	2,100	2,100	1,700	1,000	200
Asian	36,300	1,800	8,200	11,300	5,700	3,500	1,700	1,700	200	1,200
Native American	2,700	100	700	1,000	100	200	(3)	500	(3)	(3)
Hispanic (2)	19,600	700	8,200	5,600	2,300	1,400	600	100	(3)	100
Scientists	599,600	29,000	155,600	153,700	107,500	62,600	32,500	15,900	10,100	11,500
White	524,800	25,700	136,300	132,400	94,400	56,000	29,000	13,600	9,200	10,100
Black	30,100	1,000	6,900	7,400	7,500	1,800	2,100	700	800	200
Asian	29,000	1,400	6,400	9,400	4,300	3,100	1,300	1,000	100	1,200
Native American	2,400	(3)	600	900	100	200	(3)	500	(3)	(3)
Hispanic	16,400	600	7,100	4,400	1,900	1,300	500	100	(3)	100
Physical scientists	38,300	2,200	8,400	9,100	5,900	3,900	2,900	1,700	700	2,000
White	31,700	2,000	7,300	7,500	4,900	2,900	2,100	1,400	500	1,900
Black	1,700	100	600	200	200	200	300	(3)	100	(3)
Asian	4,200	100	400	1,200	800	700	600	300	100	(3)
Native American	(3)	(3)	(3)	(3)	(3)	(3)	(3)	(3)	(3)	(3)
Hispanic	900	(3)	200	100	200	200	200	(3)	(3)	(3)
Mathematical scientists	33,900	1,100	7,800	7,200	6,300	4,300	1,900	1,500	1,000	900
White	30,300	900	7,300	6,700	5,500	4,000	1,600	1,200	400	700
Black	2,300	200	100	200	600	100	200	200	500	100
Asian	800	(3)	100	200	200	200	100	(3)	(3)	(3)
Native American	100	(3)	100	(3)	(3)	(3)	(3)	(3)	(3)	(3)
Hispanic	1,200	(3)	600	300	300	(3)	(3)	(3)	(3)	(3)
Computer specialists	162,500	4,900	40,600	43,200	38,800	22,000	5,900	1,600	1,200	800
White	143,000	4,200	35,100	38,600	35,000	18,900	4,600	1,500	1,200	800
Black	7,200	200	1,500	1,600	1,700	900	1,100	(3)	(3)	(3)
Asian	8,800	300	2,500	2,300	1,800	1,400	200	(3)	(3)	(3)
Native American	400	(3)	200	100	(3)	(3)	(3)	100	(3)	(3)
Hispanic	2,900	100	1,400	600	(3)	700	(3)	100	(3)	(3)

Appendix table 10. – continued

Field and racial/ethnic group	Total Employed (1)	Professional Experience								
		1 or less	2-4	5-9	10-14	15-19	20-24	25-29	30-34	35 and over
Environmental scientists	12,900	800	3,900	3,700	2,400	900	400	100	200	100
White	12,400	800	3,800	3,500	2,300	900	400	100	200	100
Black	100	(3)	(3)	(3)	100	(3)	(3)	(3)	(3)	(3)
Asian	200	(3)	(3)	100	(3)	(3)	(3)	(3)	(3)	(3)
Native American	100	(3)	(3)	(3)	(3)	(3)	(3)	(3)	(3)	(3)
Hispanic	200	(3)	100	(3)	(3)	(3)	100	(3)	(3)	(3)
Life scientists	102,800	5,600	32,400	26,600	13,000	7,800	5,000	4,500	2,100	2,000
White	89,100	5,000	28,800	22,100	10,900	6,700	4,700	3,500	2,000	2,000
Black	3,300	(3)	700	1,200	800	200	(3)	100	100	(3)
Asian	5,600	200	1,600	1,700	1,000	400	200	500	(3)	(3)
Native American	1,000	(3)	100	400	(3)	(3)	(3)	400	(3)	(3)
Hispanic	4,100	400	2,000	1,000	400	100	100	(3)	(3)	100
Psychologists	115,200	5,100	24,600	30,200	20,000	13,100	9,800	3,700	3,000	2,000
White	102,500	4,600	23,200	24,700	16,900	12,300	9,300	3,300	2,900	1,900
Black	6,000	200	800	1,000	2,800	300	400	300	100	100
Asian	4,400	100	200	3,600	200	300	100	(3)	(3)	(3)
Native American	500	(3)	(3)	300	(3)	200	(3)	(3)	(3)	(3)
Hispanic	3,100	100	1,200	1,200	300	300	100	(3)	(3)	(3)
Social scientists	134,000	9,400	37,700	33,700	21,200	10,600	6,600	2,800	2,000	3,800
White	115,800	8,200	30,900	29,400	19,000	10,400	6,300	2,600	1,900	2,600
Black	9,400	300	3,100	3,300	1,400	200	100	100	100	(3)
Asian	5,000	800	1,700	300	400	200	100	100	(3)	1,200
Native American	400	(3)	1,200	100	(3)	(3)	(3)	100	(3)	(3)
Hispanic	4,000	(3)	1,600	1,200	800	300	100	(3)	(3)	(3)
Engineers	99,000	3,300	32,500	31,300	12,100	5,300	2,900	2,100	2,800	2,200
White	84,100	2,700	28,200	26,900	10,100	4,600	2,400	1,400	2,500	2,200
Black	4,400	100	1,000	1,300	300	300	(3)	(3)	100	(3)
Asian	7,300	300	1,900	1,900	1,400	400	400	700	100	(3)
Native American	300	(3)	100	100	100	(3)	(3)	(3)	(3)	(3)
Hispanic	3,200	100	1,100	1,200	400	100	100	(3)	(3)	(3)

(1) Detail will not add to total employed because
    a) racial and ethnic categories are not mutually exclusive and
    b) total employed includes other and no report.
(2) Includes members of all racial groups.
(3) Too few cases to estimate.

SOURCE: National Science Foundation, SRS.

Appendix table 11. Employed doctoral scientists and engineers by field, racial/ethnic group, and years of professional experience: 1985

Field and racial/ethnic group	Total Employed (1)	Years of professional experience								
		1 or less	2-4	5-9	10-14	15-19	20-24	25-29	30-34	35 and over
Total scientists and engineers (1)	400,400	10,700	46,800	70,400	71,400	58,400	34,400	20,800	17,300	7,600
White	355,100	9,500	40,400	61,100	63,700	53,700	31,700	19,500	16,600	7,500
Black	5,700	200	900	1,500	1,000	400	400	200	400	(3)
Asian	34,500	1,000	5,100	7,300	6,300	4,100	2,500	900	500	100
Native American	500	(3)	100	100	100	100	100	(3)	(3)	(3)
Hispanic (2)	5,900	300	900	1,500	1,000	700	300	100	100	(3)
Scientists	334,500	9,400	40,400	60,300	58,900	46,600	28,300	18,000	14,600	6,400
White	302,500	8,500	35,900	54,100	53,700	43,100	26,300	16,900	14,100	6,300
Black	5,200	200	800	1,300	1,000	400	200	200	100	(3)
Asian	22,700	700	3,400	4,500	3,900	3,000	1,700	800	400	100
Native American	400	(3)	100	100	(3)	100	100	(3)	(3)	(3)
Hispanic	5,100	300	800	1,300	900	500	300	100	100	(3)
Physical scientists	67,500	1,100	6,600	9,400	10,300	11,300	7,600	5,000	4,300	2,300
White	59,600	900	5,200	8,200	9,100	10,200	7,000	4,700	4,100	2,300
Black	(3)	(3)	100	(3)	100	(3)	(3)	(3)	(3)	(3)
Asian	6,600	200	1,200	1,100	1,000	1,100	600	200	100	(3)
Native American	100	(3)	(3)	(3)	(3)	(3)	(3)	(3)	(3)	(3)
Hispanic	900	(3)	100	200	200	200	100	(3)	(3)	(3)
Mathematical scientists	16,700	300	1,400	2,400	2,800	3,200	1,900	800	600	400
White	14,900	200	1,300	2,100	2,500	2,900	1,700	800	600	400
Black	1,200	(3)	(3)	(3)	(3)	(3)	(3)	(3)	(3)	(3)
Asian	1,400	(3)	100	200	300	200	100	(3)	(3)	(3)
Native American	(3)	(3)	(3)	(3)	(3)	(3)	(3)	(3)	(3)	(3)
Hispanic	300	(3)	100	(3)	200	(3)	(3)	(3)	(3)	(3)

Appendix table 11. - continued

Field and racial/ethnic group	Total Employed (1)	Years of professional experience								
		1 or less	2-4	5-9	10-14	15-19	20-24	25-29	30-34	35 and over
Computer specialists	15,000	500	1,900	2,900	3,400	2,000	1,100	300	300	100
White	13,100	500	1,600	2,600	2,900	1,900	1,000	300	300	100
Black	100	(3)	(3)	(3)	(3)	(3)	(3)	(3)	(3)	(3)
Asian	1,600	(3)	300	200	400	200	100	(3)	(3)	(3)
Native American	(3)	(3)	(3)	(3)	(3)	(3)	(3)	(3)	(3)	(3)
Hispanic	200	(3)	(3)	100	(3)	(3)	(3)	(3)	(3)	(3)
Environmental scientists	17,300	500	1,800	3,100	3,400	2,600	1,500	900	600	500
White	15,800	500	1,600	2,800	3,100	2,500	1,500	800	600	500
Black	100	(3)	(3)	(3)	(3)	(3)	(3)	(3)	(3)	(3)
Asian	1,100	(3)	100	300	200	100	(3)	(3)	(3)	(3)
Native American	(3)	(3)	(3)	(3)	(3)	(3)	(3)	(3)	(3)	(3)
Hispanic	300	(3)	100	(3)	100	(3)	(3)	(3)	(3)	(3)
Life scientists	101,800	3,100	13,200	18,300	18,200	13,100	8,300	5,700	4,500	1,800
White	92,000	2,800	12,000	16,500	16,300	12,100	7,600	5,200	4,300	1,700
Black	1,400	(3)	200	200	300	(3)	(3)	(3)	(3)	(3)
Asian	7,400	200	900	1,500	1,400	900	600	100	200	(3)
Native American	100	(3)	(3)	(3)	(3)	(3)	(3)	(3)	(3)	(3)
Hispanic	1,400	100	200	300	300	100	100	(3)	(3)	(3)
Psychologists	52,200	1,800	7,800	10,900	8,300	6,100	3,400	2,600	2,100	400
White	49,500	1,700	7,400	10,200	8,000	5,900	3,300	2,600	2,000	400
Black	1,200	100	200	300	100	100	(3)	(3)	(3)	(3)
Asian	800	100	100	200	100	100	(3)	(3)	(3)	(3)
Native American	100	(3)	(3)	(3)	(3)	(3)	(3)	(3)	(3)	(3)
Hispanic	1,000	100	200	200	100	(3)	(3)	(3)	(3)	(3)

Appendix table 11. - continued

Field and racial/ethnic group	Total Employed (1)	Years of professional experience								
		1 or less	2-4	5-9	10-14	15-19	20-24	25-29	30-34	35 and over
Social scientists	64,000	2,200	7,700	13,300	12,600	8,300	4,600	2,700	2,100	1,000
White	57,700	1,900	6,900	11,700	11,700	7,600	4,200	2,500	2,000	900
Black	1,700	(3)	200	500	300	100	100	(3)	(3)	(3)
Asian	3,800	200	600	900	500	500	300	200	(3)	(3)
Native American	100	(3)	(3)	(3)	(3)	(3)	100	(3)	(3)	(3)
Hispanic	1,100	100	200	400	100	100	(3)	(3)	(3)	(3)
Engineers	65,900	1,300	6,400	10,100	12,500	11,800	6,100	2,800	2,600	1,200
White	52,600	1,100	4,500	7,000	9,900	10,600	5,300	2,600	2,500	1,200
Black	500	(3)	100	200	100	(3)	(3)	(3)	(3)	(3)
Asian	11,900	200	1,700	2,800	2,400	1,100	800	100	100	(3)
Native American	100	(3)	(3)	(3)	100	(3)	(3)	(3)	(3)	(3)
Hispanic	800	(3)	100	200	100	100	(3)	(3)	(3)	(3)

(1) Detail will not add to total employed because
   a) racial and ethnic categories are not mutually exclusive and
   b) total employed includes other and no report.
(2) Includes members of all racial groups.
(3) Too few cases to estimate.

SOURCE: National Science Foundation, SRS.

Appendix table 12. Employed doctoral men scientists and engineers by field, racial/ethnic group, and years of professional experience: 1985

Field and racial/ethnic group	Total Employed (1)	Years of professional experience								
		1 or less	2-4	5-9	10-14	15-19	20-24	25-29	30-34	35 and over
Total scientists and engineers (1)	341,900	7,300	34,100	55,100	61,400	53,900	32,100	19,700	16,500	7,300
White	303,100	6,400	28,900	47,500	54,600	49,600	29,600	18,500	15,900	7,200
Black	4,000	100	500	1,000	800	300	100	200	100	(3)
Asian	30,400	700	4,300	6,200	5,600	3,800	2,300	900	500	100
Native American	(3)	(3)	(3)	100	100	100	(3)	(3)	(3)	(3)
Hispanic (2)	4,900	200	700	1,200	900	600	300	100	100	(3)
Scientists	277,500	6,100	28,100	45,500	49,100	42,200	26,000	16,900	13,900	6,100
White	251,600	5,500	24,700	40,800	44,900	39,000	24,300	15,800	13,400	6,000
Black	3,500	100	400	800	800	300	100	200	100	(3)
Asian	18,800	500	2,600	3,500	3,200	2,700	1,500	800	400	100
Native American	400	(3)	(3)	100	(3)	100	100	(3)	(3)	(3)
Hispanic	4,200	200	600	1,000	700	500	300	100	100	(3)
Physical scientists	62,800	900	5,600	8,400	9,500	10,900	7,300	4,800	4,200	2,300
White	55,800	800	4,400	7,300	8,400	9,800	6,800	4,600	4,000	2,300
Black	500	(3)	100	100	100	(3)	(3)	(3)	(3)	(3)
Asian	5,800	100	1,100	900	900	1,000	500	200	100	(3)
Native American	100	(3)	(3)	(3)	(3)	(3)	(3)	(3)	(3)	(3)
Hispanic	800	(3)	100	100	200	200	100	(3)	(3)	(3)
Mathematical scientists	15,200	200	1,200	2,000	2,500	3,000	1,800	800	600	400
White	13,600	200	1,000	1,800	2,200	2,800	1,600	800	600	400
Black	1,100	(3)	(3)	(3)	(3)	(3)	(3)	(3)	(3)	(3)
Asian	(3)	(3)	(3)	200	200	200	100	(3)	(3)	(3)
Native American	(3)	(3)	(3)	(3)	(3)	(3)	(3)	(3)	(3)	(3)
Hispanic	200	(3)	(3)	(3)	(3)	(3)	(3)	(3)	(3)	(3)

Appendix table 12. - continued

Field and racial/ethnic group	Total Employed (1)	Years of professional experience								
		1 or less	2-4	5-9	10-14	15-19	20-24	25-29	30-34	35 and over
Computer specialists	13,300	400	1,600	2,500	3,000	1,900	1,000	300	300	100
White	11,600	400	1,300	2,300	2,600	1,800	1,000	300	300	100
Black	100	(3)	(3)	(3)	(3)	(3)	(3)	(3)	(3)	(3)
Asian	1,500	(3)	300	200	300	200	100	(3)	(3)	(3)
Native American	(3)	(3)	(3)	(3)	(3)	(3)	(3)	(3)	(3)	(3)
Hispanic	200	(3)	(3)	100	(3)	(3)	(3)	(3)	(3)	(3)
Environmental scientists	16,200	400	1,500	2,800	3,200	2,500	1,500	900	600	500
White	14,800	400	1,300	2,500	3,000	2,400	1,500	800	600	400
Black	100	(3)	(3)	(3)	(3)	(3)	(3)	(3)	(3)	(3)
Asian	1,100	(3)	100	200	200	100	(3)	(3)	(3)	(3)
Native American	(3)	(3)	(3)	(3)	(3)	(3)	(3)	(3)	(3)	(3)
Hispanic	200	(3)	(3)	(3)	100	(3)	(3)	(3)	(3)	(3)
Life scientists	82,100	2,000	8,800	13,300	14,800	11,700	7,400	5,300	4,300	1,700
White	74,700	1,800	8,000	12,100	13,300	10,800	6,900	4,900	4,100	1,600
Black	900	(3)	100	100	300	100	(3)	100	(3)	(3)
Asian	5,700	200	600	1,100	1,100	800	500	300	100	(3)
Native American	100	(3)	(3)	(3)	(3)	(3)	(3)	(3)	(3)	(3)
Hispanic	1,100	100	100	300	300	100	100	(3)	(3)	(3)
Psychologists	35,600	800	4,100	6,200	5,800	4,800	2,700	2,300	1,900	400
White	34,100	800	3,900	5,900	5,700	4,700	2,700	2,300	1,800	400
Black	600	(3)	100	100	100	(3)	(3)	(3)	(3)	(3)
Asian	400	(3)	100	100	100	(3)	(3)	(3)	(3)	(3)
Native American	100	(3)	(3)	(3)	(3)	(3)	(3)	(3)	(3)	(3)
Hispanic	700	100	100	200	100	(3)	(3)	(3)	(3)	(3)

Appendix table 12. - continued

Field and racial/ethnic group	Total Employed (1)	Years of professional experience								
		1 or less	2-4	5-9	10-14	15-19	20-24	25-29	30-34	35 and over
Social scientists	52,200	1,300	5,300	10,200	10,300	7,400	4,200	2,500	2,000	900
White	47,000	1,100	4,700	8,900	9,600	6,800	3,900	2,300	1,900	900
Black	1,300	(3)	100	400	300	100	100	200	(3)	(3)
Asian	3,300	200	500	800	400	500	300	200	(3)	(3)
Native American	100	(3)	(3)	(3)	(3)	(3)	100	(3)	(3)	(3)
Hispanic	900	100	200	400	100	100	(3)	(3)	(3)	(3)
Engineers	64,400	1,200	6,000	9,600	12,300	11,700	6,100	2,800	2,600	1,200
White	51,500	1,000	4,300	6,700	9,800	10,600	5,300	2,600	2,500	1,200
Black	500	(3)	100	200	100	(3)	(3)	(3)	(3)	(3)
Asian	11,600	200	1,700	2,700	2,400	1,100	800	100	100	(3)
Native American	100	(3)	(3)	(3)	100	(3)	(3)	(3)	(3)	(3)
Hispanic	800	(3)	100	200	100	100	(3)	(3)	(3)	(3)

(1) Detail will not add to total employed because
 a) racial and ethnic categories are not mutually exclusive and
 b) total employed includes other and no report.
(2) Includes members of all racial groups.
(3) Too few cases to estimate.

SOURCE: National Science Foundation, SRS.

Appendix table 13. Employed doctoral women scientists and engineers
by field, racial/ethnic group, and years of
professional experience: 1985

Field and racial/ethnic group	Total Employed (1)	Years of professional experience								
		1 or less	2-4	5-9	10-14	15-19	20-24	25-29	30-34	35 and over
Total scientists and engineers (1)	58,500	3,400	12,700	15,300	10,000	4,500	2,300	1,100	800	300
White	52,000	3,100	11,500	13,600	9,000	4,100	2,100	1,100	700	300
Black	1,700	100	400	500	200	100	(3)	(3)	(3)	(3)
Asian	4,100	200	800	1,100	700	300	200	(3)	(3)	(3)
Native American	100	(3)	(3)	(3)	(3)	(3)	(3)	(3)	(3)	(3)
Hispanic (2)	1,000	100	200	200	100	100	(3)	(3)	(3)	(3)
Scientists	57,000	3,300	12,400	14,900	9,700	4,400	2,300	1,100	700	300
White	50,900	3,000	11,200	13,300	8,800	4,000	2,100	1,100	700	300
Black	1,700	100	300	500	200	100	(3)	(3)	(3)	(3)
Asian	3,800	200	700	1,000	600	300	200	(3)	(3)	(3)
Native American	(3)	(3)	(3)	(3)	(3)	(3)	(3)	(3)	(3)	(3)
Hispanic	900	100	200	200	100	100	(3)	(3)	(3)	(3)
Physical scientists	4,700	200	900	1,000	800	500	300	200	100	100
White	3,800	200	800	800	700	400	200	200	100	100
Black	(3)	(3)	(3)	(3)	(3)	(3)	(3)	(3)	(3)	(3)
Asian	800	(3)	200	200	100	100	(3)	(3)	(3)	(3)
Native American	(3)	(3)	(3)	(3)	(3)	(3)	(3)	(3)	(3)	(3)
Hispanic	100	(3)	(3)	(3)	(3)	(3)	(3)	(3)	(3)	(3)
Mathematical scientists	1,600	100	300	300	300	200	100	(3)	(3)	(3)
White	1,300	100	200	300	300	200	100	(3)	(3)	(3)
Black	(3)	(3)	(3)	(3)	(3)	(3)	(3)	(3)	(3)	(3)
Asian	200	(3)	(3)	(3)	(3)	(3)	(3)	(3)	(3)	(3)
Native American	(3)	(3)	(3)	(3)	(3)	(3)	(3)	(3)	(3)	(3)
Hispanic	(3)	(3)	(3)	(3)	(3)	(3)	(3)	(3)	(3)	(3)

Appendix table 13. - continued

Field and racial/ethnic group	Total Employed (1)	Years of professional experience								
		1 or less	2-4	5-9	10-14	15-19	20-24	25-29	30-34	35 and over
Computer specialists	1,600	100	300	400	300	100	(3)	(3)	(3)	(3)
White	1,400	100	300	400	300	100	(3)	(3)	(3)	(3)
Black	(3)	(3)	(3)	(3)	(3)	(3)	(3)	(3)	(3)	(3)
Asian	200	(3)	(3)	100	(3)	(3)	(3)	(3)	(3)	(3)
Native American	(3)	(3)	(3)	(3)	(3)	(3)	(3)	(3)	(3)	(3)
Hispanic	(3)	(3)	(3)	(3)	(3)	(3)	(3)	(3)	(3)	(3)
Environmental scientists	1,100	100	300	300	200	100	(3)	(3)	(3)	(3)
White	1,000	100	300	300	200	100	(3)	(3)	(3)	(3)
Black	(3)	(3)	(3)	(3)	(3)	(3)	(3)	(3)	(3)	(3)
Asian	100	(3)	(3)	(3)	(3)	(3)	(3)	(3)	(3)	(3)
Native American	(3)	(3)	(3)	(3)	(3)	(3)	(3)	(3)	(3)	(3)
Hispanic	(3)	(3)	(3)	(3)	(3)	(3)	(3)	(3)	(3)	(3)
Life scientists	19,700	1,100	4,400	5,000	3,400	1,500	800	400	300	100
White	17,300	1,000	4,000	4,400	3,000	1,300	700	400	200	100
Black	500	(3)	100	100	100	(3)	(3)	(3)	(3)	(3)
Asian	1,800	100	300	500	300	100	100	(3)	(3)	(3)
Native American	(3)	(3)	(3)	(3)	(3)	(3)	(3)	(3)	(3)	(3)
Hispanic	300	(3)	100	100	(3)	(3)	(3)	(3)	(3)	(3)
Psychologists	16,600	900	3,700	4,600	2,500	1,300	700	300	200	(3)
White	15,400	900	3,500	4,300	2,300	1,200	700	300	200	(3)
Black	600	100	100	200	100	(3)	(3)	(3)	(3)	(3)
Asian	400	(3)	100	100	100	(3)	(3)	(3)	(3)	(3)
Native American	(3)	(3)	(3)	(3)	(3)	(3)	(3)	(3)	(3)	(3)
Hispanic	300	(3)	100	100	(3)	(3)	(3)	(3)	(3)	(3)

Appendix table 13. - continued

Field and racial/ethnic group	Total Employed (1)	Years of professional experience								
		1 or less	2-4	5-9	10-14	15-19	20-24	25-29	30-34	35 and over
Social scientists	11,800	800	2,400	3,100	2,200	900	400	200	100	100
White	10,700	800	2,200	2,800	2,100	900	400	200	100	(3)
Black	500	(3)	100	100	100	(3)	(3)	(3)	(3)	(3)
Asian	500	(3)	100	200	100	(3)	(3)	(3)	(3)	(3)
Native American	(3)	(3)	(3)	(3)	(3)	(3)	(3)	(3)	(3)	(3)
Hispanic	200	(3)	(3)	100	(3)	(3)	(3)	(3)	(3)	(3)
Engineers	1,500	100	300	500	300	100	(3)	(3)	(3)	(3)
White	1,100	100	300	300	200	(3)	(3)	(3)	(3)	(3)
Black	300	(3)	(3)	(3)	(3)	(3)	(3)	(3)	(3)	(3)
Asian	300	(3)	100	100	100	(3)	(3)	(3)	(3)	(3)
Native American	(3)	(3)	(3)	(3)	(3)	(3)	(3)	(3)	(3)	(3)
Hispanic	(3)	(3)	(3)	(3)	(3)	(3)	(3)	(3)	(3)	(3)

(1) Detail will not add to total employed because
   a) racial and ethnic categories are not mutually exclusive and
   b) total employed includes other and no report.
(2) Includes members of all racial groups.
(3) Too few cases to estimate.

SOURCE: National Science Foundation, SRS.

Appendix table 14. Employed scientists and engineers by field,
racial/ethnic group, and selected sector
of employment: 1986

Field and racial/ethnic group	Total Employed (1)	Sector of Employment		
		Business and industry	Educational institutions	Federal Government
Total scientists and engineers (2)	4,626,500	3,134,500	627,000	354,100
White	4,190,400	2,857,300	568,600	315,800
Black	114,900	62,800	17,400	15,300
Asian	226,800	151,900	30,500	14,600
Native American	23,600	17,300	1,800	2,200
Hispanic (3)	93,400	58,200	11,200	8,200
Scientists	2,186,300	1,193,700	526,200	167,900
White	1,973,100	1,082,500	479,400	149,600
Black	73,700	33,000	15,600	10,100
Asian	94,000	52,900	22,600	4,500
Native American	10,300	5,600	1,800	1,300
Hispanic	46,100	23,700	9,000	3,300
Physical scientists	288,400	163,700	71,100	29,700
White	261,800	147,900	65,700	26,600
Black	6,200	3,000	1,100	1,400
Asian	15,400	9,400	3,700	1,300
Native American	1,000	800	(4)	300
Hispanic	4,800	2,600	800	600
Mathematical scientists	131,000	54,700	58,700	11,100
White	115,500	50,100	50,500	9,800
Black	6,800	1,900	3,400	800
Asian	5,900	1,400	3,700	300
Native American	200	1,100	(4)	(4)
Hispanic	3,100	1,300	1,500	200
Computer specialists	562,600	439,700	37,700	38,500
White	497,100	392,600	33,500	32,500
Black	18,900	11,000	2,800	4,100
Asian	36,100	27,900	(4)	900
Native American	2,200	1,900	(4)	300
Hispanic	9,300	7,400	200	700

120

Appendix table 14. — continued

Field and racial/ethnic group	Total Employed (1)	Sector of Employment		
		Business and industry	Educational institutions	Federal Government
Environmental scientists	111,300	65,100	18,200	17,600
White	105,800	62,300	17,000	16,600
Black	1,000	700	(4)	200
Asian	2,100	700	800	600
Native American	400	100	100	100
Hispanic	1,800	800	400	400
Life scientists	411,800	153,100	147,900	42,400
White	377,900	141,000	136,600	38,100
Black	8,800	2,800	2,500	1,800
Asian	15,000	5,900	5,500	1,000
Native American	2,800	900	1,200	600
Hispanic	9,900	4,300	3,100	700
Psychologists	253,500	101,800	79,400	6,900
White	234,100	93,800	74,600	6,000
Black	9,100	2,400	3,400	400
Asian	5,200	3,800	600	(4)
Native American	1,900	2,800	300	(4)
Hispanic	5,900	2,900	600	100
Social scientists	427,800	215,500	113,100	21,800
White	380,800	194,800	101,600	20,100
Black	22,900	11,400	4,400	1,400
Asian	14,200	4,000	5,600	300
Native American	1,700	1,000	200	(4)
Hispanic	11,400	4,500	2,400	600
Engineers	2,440,100	1,940,800	100,900	186,200
White	2,217,300	1,774,800	89,100	166,200
Black	41,300	29,800	1,800	5,200
Asian	132,800	99,000	7,900	10,200
Native American	13,300	11,700	(4)	1,000
Hispanic	47,200	34,500	2,200	4,900

(1) Includes state/local/other governments, military, nonprofit organizations, hospitals/clinics, other, and no report.
(2) Detail will not add to total employed because
   a) racial and ethnic categories are not mutually exclusive and
   b) total employed includes other and no report.
(3) Includes members of all racial groups.
(4) Too few cases to estimate.

SOURCE: National Science Foundation, SRS.

121

Appendix table 15. Employed men scientists and engineers by field, racial/ethnic group, and selected sector of employment: 1986

Field and racial/ethnic group	Total Employed (1)	Sector of Employment		
		Business and industry	Educational institutions	Federal Government
Total scientists and engineers (2)	3,927,800	2,741,700	479,200	310,400
White	3,581,500	2,514,500	436,700	279,000
Black	80,500	45,200	11,400	11,500
Asian	190,500	129,700	24,500	13,100
Native American	21,000	16,500	1,100	1,800
Hispanic (3)	73,800	47,600	7,300	7,000
Scientists	1,586,700	876,200	385,000	131,800
White	1,448,300	803,500	353,200	119,600
Black	43,600	19,300	9,700	6,400
Asian	65,000	36,000	17,400	3,400
Native American	7,900	5,000	1,000	900
Hispanic	29,800	15,400	5,300	2,500
Physical scientists	250,100	142,700	61,500	27,000
White	230,100	131,400	57,000	24,400
Black	4,500	1,900	900	1,200
Asian	11,200	6,300	3,100	1,100
Native American	1,000	800	(4)	300
Hispanic	3,900	2,100	600	500
Mathematical scientists	97,100	41,900	43,400	8,100
White	85,200	38,300	36,500	7,100
Black	4,500	1,200	2,700	500
Asian	5,100	1,200	3,300	300
Native American	100	(4)	100	(4)
Hispanic	1,900	1,000	800	100
Computer specialists	400,000	315,700	24,900	27,000
White	354,100	281,800	22,100	23,400
Black	11,700	6,900	2,100	2,400
Asian	27,300	21,500	2,200	700
Native American	1,800	1,500	(4)	300
Hispanic	6,400	5,000	100	300

Appendix table 15. - continued

Field and racial/ethnic group	Total Employed (1)	Sector of Employment		
		Business and industry	Educational institutions	Federal Government
Environmental scientists	98,400	58,400	15,800	15,500
White	93,400	55,700	14,700	14,500
Black	900	600	(4)	100
Asian	2,000	700	700	500
Native American	400	100	100	100
Hispanic	1,700	700	400	400
Life scientists	309,000	117,600	111,000	33,100
White	288,900	110,400	104,000	30,300
Black	5,500	1,900	1,600	1,200
Asian	9,400	3,900	3,700	500
Native American	1,800	800	700	200
Hispanic	5,900	2,400	1,800	700
Psychologists	138,400	51,300	47,900	3,700
White	131,700	48,800	46,100	3,500
Black	3,100	800	1,500	100
Asian	800	100	200	(4)
Native American	1,400	800	100	(4)
Hispanic	2,700	1,600	100	(4)
Social scientists	293,800	148,600	80,600	17,500
White	265,000	137,100	72,700	16,300
Black	13,500	6,100	2,900	900
Asian	9,200	2,300	4,200	200
Native American	1,300	1,000	1,100	(4)
Hispanic	7,400	2,500	1,400	600
Engineers	2,341,100	1,865,500	94,100	178,500
White	2,133,200	1,711,000	83,500	159,400
Black	36,900	25,900	1,800	5,000
Asian	125,500	93,600	7,100	9,800
Native American	13,100	11,500	(4)	900
Hispanic	44,000	32,200	2,000	4,500

(1) Includes state/local/other governments, military, nonprofit organizations, hospitals/clinics, other, and no report.
(2) Detail will not add to total employed because
   a) racial and ethnic categories are not mutually exclusive and
   b) total employed includes other and no report.
(3) Includes members of all racial groups.
(4) Too few cases to estimate.

SOURCE: National Science Foundation, SRS.

123

Appendix table 16. Employed women scientists and engineers by
field, racial/ethnic group, and selected
sector of employment: 1986

| | | Sector of Employment | | |
Field and racial/ethnic group	Total Employed (1)	Business and industry	Educational institutions	Federal Government
Total scientists and engineers (2)	698,600	392,800	147,800	43,700
White	608,900	342,800	131,900	36,900
Black	34,500	17,500	6,000	3,900
Asian	36,300	22,200	6,000	1,500
Native American	2,700	800	700	400
Hispanic (3)	19,600	10,600	3,900	1,200
Scientists	599,600	317,500	141,100	36,100
White	524,800	279,000	126,200	30,000
Black	30,100	13,700	6,000	3,700
Asian	29,000	16,900	5,100	1,100
Native American	2,400	600	700	400
Hispanic	16,400	8,300	3,700	800
Physical scientists	38,300	20,900	9,600	2,700
White	31,700	16,500	8,700	2,200
Black	1,700	1,100	100	200
Asian	4,200	3,000	600	200
Native American	(4)	(4)	(4)	(4)
Hispanic	900	500	200	100
Mathematical scientists	33,900	12,800	15,300	3,000
White	30,300	11,800	14,000	2,700
Black	2,300	700	700	300
Asian	800	200	400	(4)
Native American	100	100	(4)	(4)
Hispanic	1,200	300	700	100
Computer specialists	162,500	124,000	12,800	11,500
White	143,000	110,900	11,300	9,100
Black	7,200	4,100	700	1,700
Asian	8,800	6,200	600	1,300
Native American	400	400	(4)	(4)
Hispanic	2,900	2,400	100	400

Appendix table 16. - continued

Field and racial/ethnic group	Total Employed (1)	Sector of Employment		
		Business and industry	Educational institutions	Federal Government
Environmental scientists	12,900	6,800	2,400	2,200
White	12,400	6,600	2,300	2,000
Black	100	(4)	(4)	100
Asian	200	100	(4)	(4)
Native American	100	(4)	(4)	(4)
Hispanic	200	100	(4)	(4)
Life scientists	102,800	35,500	37,000	9,300
White	89,100	30,500	32,600	7,800
Black	3,300	800	900	600
Asian	5,600	2,100	1,800	500
Native American	1,000	1,100	1,400	400
Hispanic	4,100	1,900	1,200	(4)
Psychologists	115,200	50,500	31,500	3,200
White	102,500	45,000	28,500	2,500
Black	6,000	1,600	1,900	300
Asian	4,400	3,700	400	(4)
Native American	500	(4)	200	(4)
Hispanic	3,100	1,200	500	100
Social scientists	134,000	66,900	32,500	4,200
White	115,800	57,700	28,800	3,700
Black	9,400	5,300	1,500	400
Asian	5,000	1,700	1,400	100
Native American	400	(4)	100	(4)
Hispanic	4,000	2,000	900	(4)
Engineers	99,000	75,300	6,700	7,600
White	84,100	63,800	5,600	6,800
Black	4,400	3,800	100	200
Asian	7,300	5,300	800	400
Native American	300	200	(4)	(4)
Hispanic	3,200	2,300	200	400

(1) Includes state/local/other governments, military, nonprofit organizations, hospitals/clinics, other, and no report.
(2) Detail will not add to total employed because
    a) racial and ethnic categories are not mutually exclusive and
    b) total employed includes other and no report.
(3) Includes members of all racial groups.
(4) Too few cases to estimate.

SOURCE: National Science Foundation, SRS.

125

Appendix table 17. Employed scientists and engineers by field, racial/ethnic group, and selected primary work activity: 1986

Field and racial/ethnic group	Total Employed (1)	Research	Development	Management of R&D	General management
Total scientists and engineers (2)	4,626,500	393,500	875,500	398,600	883,600
White	4,190,900	355,000	780,800	366,800	810,600
Black	114,900	6,800	15,400	7,300	25,700
Asian	226,800	23,300	60,800	17,500	32,100
Native American	23,600	1,200	3,700	2,500	4,600
Hispanic (3)	93,400	8,100	15,300	6,300	17,700
Scientists	2,186,300	291,500	182,200	162,600	383,000
White	1,973,100	263,900	161,400	148,200	345,300
Black	73,700	5,700	3,800	3,800	18,600
Asian	94,000	15,900	13,400	6,200	12,800
Native American	10,300	900	200	1,700	1,800
Hispanic	46,100	5,700	3,300	3,100	8,800
Physical scientists	288,400	70,500	44,700	43,000	30,500
White	261,800	62,600	39,800	39,400	28,800
Black	6,200	1,500	1,000	600	900
Asian	15,400	4,900	3,400	1,400	400
Native American	1,000	400	(4)	700	(4)
Hispanic	4,800	1,700	900	500	700
Mathematical scientists	131,000	12,000	6,000	14,700	21,000
White	115,500	11,200	5,500	13,500	18,800
Black	6,800	200	300	700	900
Asian	5,900	400	100	200	300
Native American	5,200	(4)	(4)	(4)	100
Hispanic	3,100	100	100	(4)	800
Computer specialists	562,600	15,000	97,800	32,800	54,000
White	497,100	12,400	85,500	29,800	47,000
Black	18,900	200	1,800	700	3,600
Asian	36,100	2,200	8,500	1,900	2,600
Native American	2,200	(4)	(4)	200	400
Hispanic	9,300	100	1,300	300	800

Appendix table 17. – continued

Field and racial/ethnic group	Total Employed (1)	Research	Development	Management of R&D	General management
Environmental scientists	111,300	29,900	6,400	7,500	14,300
White	105,800	28,300	6,200	7,200	13,400
Black	1,000	100	(4)	(4)	600
Asian	2,100	1,100	200	100	100
Native American	400	100	(4)	100	(4)
Hispanic	1,800	300	100	(4)	200
Life scientists	411,800	112,700	15,700	30,100	80,100
White	377,900	101,700	14,000	27,100	74,500
Black	8,800	2,700	300	600	2,200
Asian	15,000	5,700	1,000	1,700	1,500
Native American	2,800	200	(4)	700	1,000
Hispanic	9,900	3,100	300	600	1,700
Psychologists	253,500	17,400	3,200	9,500	56,500
White	234,100	16,300	3,000	8,800	50,400
Black	9,100	500	(4)	500	2,300
Asian	5,200	300	(4)	200	3,500
Native American	1,900	(4)	(4)	(4)	(4)
Hispanic	5,900	300	(4)	(4)	1,100
Social scientists	427,800	33,800	8,500	25,200	126,600
White	380,800	31,300	7,400	22,400	112,300
Black	22,900	1,300	300	900	8,100
Asian	14,200	900	100	800	4,300
Native American	1,700	200	(4)	(4)	200
Hispanic	11,400	100	400	1,700	3,400
Engineers	2,440,100	102,000	693,200	236,000	500,600
White	2,217,300	91,100	619,400	218,700	465,400
Black	41,300	1,100	11,700	3,500	7,100
Asian	132,800	7,500	47,400	11,400	19,300
Native American	13,300	200	3,500	800	2,800
Hispanic	47,200	2,400	12,000	3,200	9,000

Appendix table 17. - continued

Field and racial/ethnic group	Teaching	Production/ inspection	Reporting, statistical work, and computing
Total scientists and engineers (2)	357,800	582,600	472,800
White	325,100	526,000	422,900
Black	10,800	15,000	15,200
Asian	16,900	27,700	25,400
Native American	700	3,900	1,800
Hispanic (3)	7,400	13,700	10,300
Scientists	300,800	159,000	359,600
White	274,300	140,200	322,000
Black	10,200	5,300	12,100
Asian	12,300	8,200	19,000
Native American	700	1,500	1,200
Hispanic	6,200	3,300	7,400
Physical scientists	45,800	32,200	6,900
White	43,700	27,300	6,500
Black	400	1,200	200
Asian	1,400	3,400	100
Native American	(4)	(4)	(4)
Hispanic	300	300	300
Mathematical scientists	46,600	5,100	16,500
White	38,900	4,200	14,800
Black	3,400	400	700
Asian	3,300	500	800
Native American	100	(4)	(4)
Hispanic	1,400	(4)	300
Computer specialists	19,600	20,500	271,300
White	17,600	16,800	241,400
Black	1,200	1,400	9,000
Asian	1,200	1,900	15,900
Native American	(4)	(4)	1,200
Hispanic	400	200	5,100

Appendix table 17. - continued

Field and racial/ethnic group	Teaching	Production/ inspection	Reporting, statistical work, and computing
Environmental scientists	9,200	23,800	6,800
White	8,800	22,300	6,500
Black	(4)	100	100
Asian	200	300	200
Native American	100	100	(4)
Hispanic	400	400	100
Life scientists	61,500	44,000	13,300
White	57,900	40,700	12,000
Black	1,400	500	400
Asian	1,600	1,600	100
Native American	200	300	(4)
Hispanic	800	1,200	200
Psychologists	39,100	11,000	5,300
White	37,200	9,000	4,900
Black	1,100	500	200
Asian	200	(4)	200
Native American	300	600	(4)
Hispanic	600	1,000	200
Social scientists	79,000	22,500	39,500
White	70,200	19,900	36,000
Black	3,800	1,200	1,400
Asian	4,300	600	1,700
Native American	100	600	(4)
Hispanic	2,300	200	1,200
Engineers	56,900	423,600	113,200
White	50,800	385,700	100,800
Black	600	9,700	3,200
Asian	4,600	19,500	6,400
Native American	(4)	2,500	600
Hispanic	1,100	10,400	2,900

(1) Includes consulting, other, and no report.
(2) Detail will not add to total employed because
    a) racial and ethnic categories are not mutually exclusive and
    b) total employed includes other and no report.
(3) Includes members of all racial groups.
(4) Too few cases to estimate.

SOURCE: National Science Foundation, SRS.

Appendix table 18. Employed men scientists and engineers by field,
racial/ethnic group, and selected primary
work activity: 1986

Field and racial/ethnic group	Total Employed (1)	Research	Development	Management of R&D	General management
Total scientists and engineers (2)	3,927,800	314,400	802,300	367,200	781,100
White	3,581,500	285,200	717,800	339,300	724,000
Black	80,500	4,200	13,500	5,300	19,300
Asian	190,000	18,600	55,600	15,800	25,800
Native American	21,000	1,000	3,600	2,500	3,700
Hispanic (3)	73,800	5,800	13,200	6,100	14,800
Scientists	1,586,700	221,300	141,300	135,500	289,400
White	1,448,300	202,200	126,200	124,000	266,200
Black	43,600	3,100	2,600	1,900	12,700
Asian	65,000	11,600	10,400	5,200	7,100
Native American	7,900	800	100	1,700	1,000
Hispanic	29,800	3,700	2,200	3,000	6,200
Physical scientists	250,100	60,900	39,700	40,900	27,300
White	230,100	54,400	36,000	37,500	25,900
Black	4,500	1,200	600	500	900
Asian	11,200	4,000	2,600	1,300	200
Native American	1,000	400	(4)	700	(4)
Hispanic	3,900	1,500	700	400	700
Mathematical scientists	97,100	10,400	4,700	12,200	16,300
White	85,200	9,700	4,400	11,600	14,300
Black	4,500	100	200	100	800
Asian	5,100	300	100	100	300
Native American	1,100	(4)	(4)	(4)	(4)
Hispanic	1,900	100	100	(4)	800
Computer specialists	400,000	11,200	72,400	27,200	43,300
White	354,100	8,900	63,600	24,700	37,800
Black	11,700	100	1,200	500	2,600
Asian	27,300	2,000	6,900	1,700	2,500
Native American	1,800	(4)	(4)	200	400
Hispanic	6,400	100	600	200	700

Appendix table 18. - continued

Field and racial/ethnic group	Total Employed (1)	Research	Development	Management of R&D	General management
Environmental scientists	98,400	25,600	5,600	7,000	13,000
White	93,400	24,100	5,500	6,700	12,000
Black	900	100	(4)	(4)	600
Asian	2,000	1,000	100	(4)	100
Native American	400	100	(4)	100	(4)
Hispanic	1,700	200	100	(4)	200
Life scientists	309,000	80,400	10,600	26,100	67,200
White	288,900	74,100	9,500	23,300	63,600
Black	5,500	1,300	300	400	1,600
Asian	9,400	3,300	600	1,700	1,000
Native American	1,800	1,200	(4)	500	500
Hispanic	5,900	1,700	300	500	1,200
Psychologists	138,400	9,900	1,500	5,100	32,100
White	131,700	9,600	1,500	4,800	30,700
Black	3,100	100	(4)	200	1,200
Asian	800	(4)	(4)	100	200
Native American	1,400	(4)	(4)	(4)	(4)
Hispanic	2,700	100	(4)	600	600
Social scientists	293,800	23,000	6,700	17,100	90,200
White	265,000	21,200	5,900	15,400	81,800
Black	13,500	300	300	300	5,100
Asian	9,200	900	100	300	2,800
Native American	1,300	100	(4)	(4)	100
Hispanic	7,400	100	400	1,700	2,100
Engineers	2,341,100	93,100	661,000	231,700	491,700
White	2,133,200	83,000	591,500	215,300	457,800
Black	36,900	1,000	10,800	3,400	6,600
Asian	125,500	6,900	45,200	10,600	18,700
Native American	13,100	6,200	3,500	800	2,700
Hispanic	44,000	2,100	11,000	3,200	8,600

Appendix table 18. - continued

Field and racial/ethnic group	Teaching	Production/ inspection	Reporting, statistical work, and computing
Total scientists and engineers (2)	276,300	529,000	341,100
White	251,500	480,900	308,500
Black	8,000	11,600	8,100
Asian	14,300	24,000	17,200
Native American	500	3,900	1,600
Hispanic (3)	3,900	12,200	7,900
Scientists	223,300	124,400	237,200
White	203,900	111,500	214,800
Black	7,400	3,000	6,300
Asian	10,200	5,600	11,500
Native American	400	1,400	1,100
Hispanic	2,800	2,500	5,200
Physical scientists	39,000	24,100	5,700
White	37,300	21,600	5,500
Black	300	700	200
Asian	1,300	1,500	(4)
Native American	(4)	(4)	(4)
Hispanic	100	200	300
Mathematical scientists	33,800	3,500	10,900
White	27,300	3,100	9,800
Black	2,700	(4)	400
Asian	3,100	400	600
Native American	100	(4)	(4)
Hispanic	700	(4)	100
Computer specialists	12,800	15,900	180,700
White	11,500	12,700	161,900
Black	(4)	1,100	4,500
Asian	1,100	1,700	10,300
Native American	(4)	(4)	1,100
Hispanic	100	200	3,800

Appendix table 18. - continued

Field and racial/ethnic group	Teaching	Production/ inspection	Reporting, statistical work, and computing
Environmental scientists	8,300	21,900	5,700
White	8,000	20,600	5,500
Black	(4)	100	100
Asian	200	300	200
Native American	100	100	(4)
Hispanic	400	300	100
Life scientists	46,700	34,700	8,800
White	44,400	32,500	8,200
Black	1,000	1,200	300
Asian	1,000	1,200	100
Native American	200	200	(4)
Hispanic	400	700	100
Psychologists	25,900	7,600	2,000
White	25,100	5,900	2,000
Black	600	300	(4)
Asian	200	(4)	(4)
Native American	(4)	600	(4)
Hispanic	200	800	(4)
Social scientists	56,800	16,700	23,500
White	50,300	15,100	21,900
Black	2,800	600	900
Asian	3,500	500	400
Native American	100	600	(4)
Hispanic	900	200	800
Engineers	53,000	404,600	103,900
White	47,600	369,400	93,700
Black	600	8,600	1,800
Asian	4,100	18,400	5,700
Native American	(4)	2,500	400
Hispanic	1,100	9,700	2,700

(1) Includes consulting, other, and no report.
(2) Detail will not add to total employed because
    a) racial and ethnic categories are not mutually exclusive and
    b) total employed includes other and no report.
(3) Includes members of all racial groups.
(4) Too few cases to estimate.

SOURCE: National Science Foundation, SRS.

Appendix table 19. Employed women scientists and engineers by field, racial/ethnic group, and selected primary work activity: 1986

Field and racial/ethnic group	Total Employed (1)	Research	Development	Management of R&D	General management
Total scientists and engineers (2)	698,600	79,000	73,200	31,400	102,500
White	608,900	69,900	63,000	27,500	86,600
Black	34,500	2,600	2,000	2,000	6,400
Asian	36,300	4,800	5,200	1,700	6,300
Native American	2,700	2,200	(4)	(4)	900
Hispanic (3)	19,600	2,200	2,100	200	2,900
Scientists	599,600	70,200	41,000	27,000	93,600
White	524,800	61,800	35,200	24,100	79,100
Black	30,100	2,600	1,100	1,900	5,800
Asian	29,000	4,200	3,000	1,000	5,800
Native American	2,400	2,000	(4)	(4)	900
Hispanic	16,400	2,000	1,100	100	2,600
Physical scientists	38,300	9,700	5,100	2,100	3,100
White	31,700	8,200	3,800	1,900	2,900
Black	1,700	400	400	100	100
Asian	4,200	900	800	100	200
Native American	(4)	(4)	(4)	(4)	(4)
Hispanic	900	200	200	100	(4)
Mathematical scientists	33,900	1,600	1,300	2,500	4,700
White	30,300	1,500	1,200	1,900	4,500
Black	2,300	100	100	500	100
Asian	800	100	(4)	(4)	(4)
Native American	100	(4)	(4)	(4)	100
Hispanic	1,200	(4)	(4)	(4)	(4)
Computer specialists	162,500	3,800	25,400	5,600	10,600
White	143,000	3,500	21,900	5,100	9,300
Black	7,200	(4)	600	200	1,000
Asian	8,800	200	1,600	200	300
Native American	400	(4)	(4)	(4)	(4)
Hispanic	2,900	(4)	800	(4)	100

Appendix table 19. - continued

Field and racial/ethnic group	Total Employed (1)	Research	Development	Management of R&D	General management
Environmental scientists	12,900	4,400	800	500	1,400
White	12,400	4,200	700	500	1,400
Black	100	(4)	(4)	(4)	(4)
Asian	200	100	100	(4)	(4)
Native American	100	(4)	(4)	(4)	(4)
Hispanic	200	100	(4)	(4)	(4)
Life scientists	102,800	32,300	5,100	4,000	13,000
White	89,100	27,600	4,600	3,800	10,900
Black	3,300	1,400	(4)	600	600
Asian	5,600	2,400	500	100	500
Native American	1,000	(4)	(4)	(4)	600
Hispanic	4,100	1,400	(4)	(4)	500
Psychologists	115,200	7,600	1,700	4,300	24,400
White	102,500	6,700	1,500	4,000	19,700
Black	6,000	400	(4)	300	1,100
Asian	4,400	200	(4)	(4)	3,300
Native American	500	(4)	(4)	(4)	(4)
Hispanic	3,100	300	(4)	(4)	600
Social scientists	134,000	10,800	1,700	8,100	36,400
White	115,800	10,100	1,500	7,000	30,500
Black	9,400	200	100	700	3,000
Asian	5,000	400	(4)	500	1,400
Native American	400	200	(4)	(4)	200
Hispanic	4,000	(4)	(4)	(4)	1,400
Engineers	99,000	8,900	32,200	4,300	8,900
White	84,100	8,100	27,900	3,400	7,500
Black	4,400	(4)	800	100	500
Asian	7,300	500	2,300	700	600
Native American	300	(4)	1,100	(4)	(4)
Hispanic	3,200	200	1,100	(4)	400

Appendix table 19. — continued

Field and racial/ethnic group	Teaching	Production/ inspection	Reporting, statistical work, and computing
Total scientists and engineers (2)	81,500	53,600	131,700
White	73,600	45,000	114,400
Black	2,800	3,400	7,100
Asian	2,600	3,700	8,200
Native American	200	100	300
Hispanic (3)	3,500	1,500	2,400
Scientists	77,500	34,600	122,400
White	70,400	28,700	107,300
Black	2,800	2,300	5,800
Asian	2,100	2,600	7,500
Native American	200	100	100
Hispanic	3,400	800	2,200
Physical scientists	6,800	8,000	1,200
White	6,400	5,700	1,100
Black	100	400	(4)
Asian	100	1,900	(4)
Native American	(4)	(4)	
Hispanic	200	100	(4)
Mathematical scientists	12,800	1,600	5,600
White	11,600	1,100	4,900
Black	700	400	400
Asian	200	(4)	300
Native American	(4)	(4)	(4)
Hispanic	700	100	200
Computer specialists	6,800	4,500	90,600
White	6,000	4,000	79,400
Black	100	300	4,500
Asian	200	200	5,600
Native American	(4)	(4)	1,100
Hispanic	400	(4)	1,300

Appendix table 19. - continued

Field and racial/ethnic group	Teaching	Production/ inspection	Reporting, statistical work, and computing
Environmental scientists	900	1,800	1,100
White	900	1,700	1,100
Black	(4)	(4)	(4)
Asian	(4)	(4)	(4)
Native American	(4)	(4)	(4)
Hispanic	(4)	100	(4)
Life scientists	14,700	9,300	4,500
White	13,500	8,200	3,800
Black	300	200	100
Asian	600	400	(4)
Native American	(4)	100	(4)
Hispanic	400	500	100
Psychologists	13,200	3,400	3,300
White	12,100	3,100	2,900
Black	500	300	200
Asian	100	(4)	(4)
Native American	200	(4)	(4)
Hispanic	400	100	200
Social scientists	22,300	5,900	16,000
White	19,800	4,800	14,000
Black	1,000	600	500
Asian	800	100	1,400
Native American	(4)	(4)	(4)
Hispanic	1,300	(4)	400
Engineers	3,900	19,000	9,400
White	3,200	16,300	7,100
Black	(4)	1,100	1,300
Asian	500	1,100	700
Native American	(4)	(4)	100
Hispanic	100	800	200

(1) Includes consulting, other, and no report.
(2) Detail will not add to total employed because
    a) racial and ethnic categories are not mutually exclusive and
    b) total employed includes other and no report.
(3) Includes members of all racial groups.
(4) Too few cases to estimate.

SOURCE: National Science Foundation, SRS.

Appendix table 20. Doctoral scientists and engineers in four-year colleges and universities by field, racial/ethnic group, and tenure status: 1985

Field and racial/ethnic group	Total, four-year colleges & universities (1)	Tenure-track: Tenured	Tenure-track: Not tenured	Non-tenure track
Total scientists and engineers (2)	202,000	119,300	34,400	33,400
White	181,100	108,200	30,300	29,400
Black	3,500	1,900	700	600
Asian	14,800	7,600	3,100	3,100
Native American	2,300	1,200	100	(4)
Hispanic (3)	2,900	1,300	600	700
Scientists	180,500	106,200	30,000	31,300
White	163,100	96,700	26,900	27,800
Black	3,400	1,900	600	600
Asian	11,900	6,100	2,200	2,800
Native American	200	200	(4)	(4)
Hispanic	2,600	1,200	600	700
Physical scientists	28,200	16,500	3,000	5,000
White	25,100	14,900	2,700	4,200
Black	300	100	(4)	100
Asian	2,300	1,100	200	700
Native American	100	100	(4)	(4)
Hispanic	400	300	(4)	(4)
Mathematical scientists	13,000	9,500	2,100	800
White	11,600	8,500	1,800	600
Black	100	100	(4)	(4)
Asian	1,100	700	200	100
Native American	(4)	(4)	(4)	(4)
Hispanic	200	100	100	(4)

Appendix table 20. - continued

Field and racial/ethnic group	Total, four-year colleges & universities (1)	Tenure-track: Tenured	Tenure-track: Not tenured	Non-tenure track
Computer specialists	5,100	2,200	1,400	1,100
White	4,400	2,000	1,100	1,000
Black	(4)	(4)	(4)	(4)
Asian	600	200	200	100
Native American	(4)	(4)	(4)	(4)
Hispanic	100	100	(4)	(4)
Environmental scientists	7,100	4,000	1,100	1,400
White	6,600	3,800	1,100	1,200
Black	(4)	(4)	(4)	(4)
Asian	400	200	(4)	100
Native American	(4)	(4)	(4)	(4)
Hispanic	100	100	(4)	(4)
Life scientists	61,800	33,200	11,000	13,700
White	55,900	30,400	9,900	12,100
Black	900	500	200	200
Asian	4,500	2,000	800	1,400
Native American	(4)	(4)	(4)	(4)
Hispanic	800	400	200	200
Psychologists	21,500	12,400	3,200	4,300
White	20,200	11,800	3,000	4,000
Black	600	300	100	200
Asian	300	200	100	100
Native American	(4)	(4)	(4)	(4)
Hispanic	400	100	100	200

Appendix table 20. - continued

Field and racial/ethnic group	Total, four-year colleges & universities (1)	Tenure-track: Tenured	Tenure-track: Not tenured	Non-tenure track
Social scientists	43,800	28,300	8,200	5,100
White	39,300	25,400	7,400	4,600
Black	1,300	900	300	100
Asian	2,700	1,700	500	300
Native American	(4)	(4)	(4)	(4)
Hispanic	600	200	200	200
Engineers	21,500	13,200	4,400	2,000
White	18,000	11,500	3,300	1,600
Black	200	(4)	100	(4)
Asian	3,000	1,500	1,000	300
Native American	100	(4)	(4)	(4)
Hispanic	300	100	(4)	(4)

(1) Includes tenure status unknown and no report.
(2) Detail will not add to total employed because
    a) racial and ethnic categories are not mutually exclusive and
    b) total employed includes other and no report.
(3) Includes members of all racial groups.
(4) Too few cases to estimate.

SOURCE: National Science Foundation, SRS.

Appendix table 21. Doctoral men scientists and engineers in
four-year colleges and universities by field,
racial/ethnic group, and tenure status: 1985

Field and racial/ethnic group	Total, four-year colleges & universities (1)	Tenure-track: Tenured	Tenure-track: Not tenured	Non-tenure track
Total scientists and engineers (2)	170,300	107,500	26,900	23,500
White	152,900	97,600	23,500	20,700
Black	2,600	1,500	400	400
Asian	12,700	7,000	2,700	2,200
Native American	200	200	100	(4)
Hispanic (3)	2,400	1,100	500	500
Scientists	149,300	94,500	22,700	21,600
White	135,200	86,200	20,400	19,100
Black	2,400	1,500	300	400
Asian	9,800	5,500	1,800	1,900
Native American	200	200	(4)	(4)
Hispanic	2,100	1,000	400	500
Physical scientists	26,100	15,700	2,600	4,300
White	23,400	14,200	2,400	3,600
Black	300	100	(4)	100
Asian	2,000	1,100	200	600
Native American	100	100	(4)	(4)
Hispanic	400	200	(4)	(4)
Mathematical scientists	11,900	8,800	1,800	600
White	10,600	8,000	1,600	500
Black	100	100	(4)	(4)
Asian	1,000	600	200	100
Native American	(4)	(4)	(4)	(4)
Hispanic	200	100	100	(4)

Appendix table 21. - continued

Field and racial/ethnic group	Total, four-year colleges & universities (1)	Tenure-track: Tenured	Tenure-track: Not tenured	Non-tenure track
Computer specialists	4,700	2,100	1,200	1,000
White	4,000	1,900	1,000	900
Black	(4)	(4)	(4)	(4)
Asian	600	200	200	100
Native American	(4)	(4)	(4)	(4)
Hispanic	100	100	(4)	(4)
Environmental scientists	6,600	3,900	1,000	1,200
White	6,200	3,700	900	1,100
Black	(4)	(4)	(4)	(4)
Asian	300	200	(4)	100
Native American	(4)	(4)	(4)	(4)
Hispanic	100	(4)	(4)	(4)
Life scientists	48,900	29,200	8,100	8,800
White	44,500	26,900	7,300	7,800
Black	600	300	100	100
Asian	3,400	1,800	700	800
Native American	(4)	(4)	(4)	(4)
Hispanic	600	300	100	200
Psychologists	15,300	10,000	1,900	2,400
White	14,500	9,600	1,800	2,300
Black	400	200	100	100
Asian	200	100	(4)	100
Native American	(4)	(4)	(4)	(4)
Hispanic	300	100	(4)	100

Appendix table 21. - continued

Field and racial/ethnic group	Total, four-year colleges & universities (1)	Tenure-track: Tenured	Tenure-track: Not tenured	Non-tenure track
Social scientists	35,800	24,700	6,100	3,300
White	32,000	22,000	5,400	3,000
Black	1,000	800	200	100
Asian	2,300	1,600	500	200
Native American	(4)	(4)	(4)	(4)
Hispanic	500	200	200	100
Engineers	21,100	13,100	4,200	1,900
White	17,700	11,400	3,200	1,600
Black	200	(4)	100	(4)
Asian	2,900	1,500	900	300
Native American	100	(4)	(4)	(4)
Hispanic	300	100	(4)	(4)

(1) Includes tenure status unknown and no report.
(2) Detail will not add to total employed because
    a) racial and ethnic categories are not mutually exclusive and
    b) total employed includes other and no report.
(3) Includes members of all racial groups.
(4) Too few cases to estimate.

SOURCE: National Science Foundation, SRS.

Appendix table 22. Doctoral women scientists and engineers in four-year colleges and universities by field, racial/ethnic group, and tenure status: 1985

Field and racial/ethnic group	Total, four-year colleges & universities (1)	Tenure-track: Tenured	Tenure-track: Not tenured	Non-tenure track
Total scientists and engineers (2)	31,700	11,800	7,500	9,800
White	28,300	10,600	6,700	8,700
Black	900	400	300	200
Asian	2,100	700	400	900
Native American	(4)	(4)	(4)	(4)
Hispanic (3)	500	200	100	200
Scientists	31,200	11,700	7,300	9,700
White	27,900	10,500	6,600	8,600
Black	900	400	300	200
Asian	2,100	700	400	900
Native American	(4)	(4)	(4)	(4)
Hispanic	500	200	100	200
Physical scientists	2,100	800	300	800
White	1,800	700	300	600
Black	(4)	(4)	(4)	(4)
Asian	300	100	(4)	100
Native American	(4)	(4)	(4)	(4)
Hispanic	100	(4)	(4)	(4)
Mathematical scientists	1,100	700	300	200
White	1,000	500	300	100
Black	(4)	(4)	(4)	(4)
Asian	200	100	(4)	(4)
Native American	(4)	(4)	(4)	(4)
Hispanic	(4)	(4)	(4)	(4)

Appendix table 22. - continued

Field and racial/ethnic group	Total, four-year colleges & universities (1)	Tenure-track: Tenured	Tenure-track: Not tenured	Non-tenure track
Computer specialists	500	100	200	100
White	400	100	100	100
Black	(4)	(4)	(4)	(4)
Asian	(4)	(4)	(4)	(4)
Native American	(4)	(4)	(4)	(4)
Hispanic	(4)	(4)	(4)	(4)
Environmental scientists	500	100	100	200
White	400	100	100	100
Black	(4)	(4)	(4)	(4)
Asian	(4)	(4)	(4)	(4)
Native American	(4)	(4)	(4)	(4)
Hispanic	(4)	(4)	(4)	(4)
Life scientists	12,900	4,000	2,900	4,900
White	11,400	3,500	2,600	4,300
Black	300	200	100	100
Asian	1,100	300	200	500
Native American	(4)	(4)	(4)	(4)
Hispanic	200	100	(4)	100
Psychologists	6,200	2,400	1,300	1,900
White	5,700	2,200	1,200	1,700
Black	300	100	100	100
Asian	200	100	(4)	(4)
Native American	(4)	(4)	(4)	(4)
Hispanic	100	(4)	(4)	(4)

Appendix table 22. - continued

Field and racial/ethnic group	Total, four-year colleges & universities (1)	Tenure-track: Tenured	Tenure-track: Not tenured	Non-tenure track
Social scientists	8,000	3,700	2,200	1,800
White	7,200	3,300	2,000	1,600
Black	300	100	100	(4)
Asian	300	100	100	100
Native American	(4)	(4)	(4)	(4)
Hispanic	100	(4)	(4)	(4)
Engineers	400	100	200	100
White	400	100	200	100
Black	(4)	(4)	(4)	(4)
Asian	100	(4)	(4)	(4)
Native American	(4)	(4)	(4)	(4)
Hispanic	(4)	(4)	(4)	(4)

(1) Includes tenure status unknown and no report.
(2) Detail will not add to total employed because
    a) racial and ethnic categories are not mutually exclusive and
    b) total employed includes other and no report.
(3) Includes members of all racial groups.
(4) Too few cases to estimate.

SOURCE: National Science Foundation, SRS.

Appendix table 23. Doctoral scientists and engineers in four-year colleges and universities by field, racial/ethnic group, and academic rank: 1985

Field and racial/ethnic group	Total, four-year colleges & universities (1)	Academic rank		
		Full professor	Associate Professor	Assistant Professor
Total scientists and engineers (2)	202,000	79,600	48,800	36,500
White	181,100	72,300	43,400	32,500
Black	3,500	1,000	1,200	700
Asian	14,800	5,300	3,400	3,000
Native American	300	100	200	(4)
Hispanic (3)	2,900	700	800	700
Scientists	180,500	69,900	44,100	32,700
White	163,100	63,800	39,500	29,700
Black	3,400	1,000	1,100	700
Asian	11,900	4,300	2,800	2,100
Native American	200	100	100	(4)
Hispanic	2,600	700	700	600
Physical scientists	28,200	12,700	4,700	3,100
White	25,100	11,500	4,200	2,700
Black	300	100	(4)	(4)
Asian	2,300	900	200	200
Native American	100	(4)	(4)	(4)
Hispanic	400	200	.(4)	(4)
Mathematical scientists	13,000	6,500	3,300	2,400
White	11,600	5,900	2,800	2,100
Black	1,100	100	(4)	(4)
Asian	1,100	400	400	300
Native American	(4)	(4)	(4)	(4)
Hispanic	200	100	(4)	100

Appendix table 23. – continued

Field and racial/ethnic group	Total, four-year colleges & universities (1)	Academic rank		
		Full professor	Associate Professor	Assistant Professor
Computer specialists	5,100	1,200	1,400	1,200
White	4,400	1,100	1,200	900
Black	(4)	(4)	(4)	(4)
Asian	600	200	200	200
Native American	(4)	(4)	(4)	(4)
Hispanic	100	(4)	(4)	(4)
Environmental scientists	7,100	2,900	1,400	1,100
White	6,600	2,700	1,300	1,100
Black	(4)	(4)	(4)	(4)
Asian	400	100	100	100
Native American	(4)	(4)	(4)	(4)
Hispanic	100	(4)	(4)	(4)
Life scientists	61,800	21,400	15,100	11,800
White	55,900	19,600	13,600	10,700
Black	900	300	300	200
Asian	4,500	1,400	1,000	800
Native American	(4)	(4)	(4)	(4)
Hispanic	800	200	200	100
Psychologists	21,500	7,900	5,600	4,200
White	20,200	7,600	5,200	3,900
Black	600	100	200	200
Asian	300	100	(4)	100
Native American	(4)	(4)	(4)	(4)
Hispanic	400	(4)	100	100

Appendix table 23. - continued

Field and racial/ethnic group	Total, four-year colleges & universities (1)	Academic rank		
		Full professor	Associate Professor	Assistant Professor
Social scientists	43,800	17,300	12,700	9,000
White	39,300	15,500	11,100	8,200
Black	1,300	400	500	300
Asian	2,700	1,200	900	400
Native American	(4)	(4)	(4)	(4)
Hispanic	600	100	200	200
Engineers	21,500	9,700	4,700	3,800
White	18,000	8,500	3,900	2,800
Black	200	(4)	100	(4)
Asian	3,000	1,000	600	900
Native American	100	(4)	(4)	(4)
Hispanic	300	(4)	100	(4)

(1) Includes instructor, other, and no report.
(2) Detail will not add to total employed because
  a) racial and ethnic categories are not mutually exclusive and
  b) total employed includes other and no report.
(3) Includes members of all racial groups.
(4) Too few cases to estimate.

SOURCE: National Science Foundation, SRS.

Appendix table 24. Doctoral men scientists and engineers in four-year colleges and universities by field, racial/ethnic group, and academic rank: 1985

Field and racial/ethnic group	Total, four-year colleges & universities (1)	Academic rank		
		Full professor	Associate Professor	Assistant Professor
Total scientists and engineers (2)	170,300	74,400	40,900	27,000
White	152,900	67,700	36,400	23,900
Black	2,600	800	900	300
Asian	12,700	4,900	2,900	2,500
Native American	200	100	200	(4)
Hispanic (3)	2,400	600	700	500
Scientists	149,300	64,700	36,300	23,300
White	135,200	59,200	32,600	21,200
Black	2,400	800	800	300
Asian	9,800	4,000	2,300	1,600
Native American	200	100	100	(4)
Hispanic	2,100	600	500	500
Physical scientists	26,100	12,300	4,300	2,600
White	23,400	11,100	3,900	2,400
Black	300	100	(4)	(4)
Asian	2,000	900	200	200
Native American	100	(4)	(4)	(4)
Hispanic	400	200	(4)	(4)
Mathematical scientists	11,900	6,200	2,900	2,000
White	10,600	5,600	2,500	1,800
Black	100	100	(4)	(4)
Asian	1,000	400	300	300
Native American	(4)	(4)	(4)	(4)
Hispanic	200	100	(4)	100

Appendix table 24. - continued

Field and racial/ethnic group	Total, four-year colleges & universities (1)	Academic rank		
		Full professor	Associate Professor	Assistant Professor
Computer specialists	4,700	1,200	1,300	1,000
White	4,000	1,000	1,200	800
Black	(4)	(4)	(4)	(4)
Asian	600	200	200	200
Native American	(4)	(4)	(4)	(4)
Hispanic	100	(4)	(4)	(4)
Environmental scientists	6,600	2,800	1,300	1,000
White	6,200	2,600	1,200	900
Black	(4)	(4)	(4)	(4)
Asian	300	100	100	(4)
Native American	(4)	(4)	(4)	(4)
Hispanic	100	(4)	(4)	(4)
Life scientists	48,900	19,700	12,000	8,300
White	44,500	18,100	10,800	7,600
Black	(4)	200	200	100
Asian	3,400	1,200	900	600
Native American	(4)	(4)	(4)	(4)
Hispanic	600	200	200	100
Psychologists	15,300	6,800	4,100	2,300
White	14,500	6,500	3,900	2,100
Black	400	100	100	100
Asian	200	100	(4)	(4)
Native American	(4)	(4)	(4)	(4)
Hispanic	300	(4)	100	100

Appendix table 24. - continued

Field and racial/ethnic group	Total, four-year colleges & universities (1)	Academic rank		
		Full professor	Associate Professor	Assistant Professor
Social scientists	35,800	15,800	10,400	6,200
White	32,000	14,100	9,100	5,700
Black	1,000	400	400	100
Asian	2,300	1,100	800	300
Native American	(4)	(4)	(4)	(4)
Hispanic	500	(4)	100	200
Engineers	21,100	9,600	4,600	3,600
White	17,700	8,500	3,800	2,700
Black	200	(4)	100	(4)
Asian	2,900	1,000	600	900
Native American	100	(4)	(4)	(4)
Hispanic	300	(4)	100	(4)

(1) Includes instructor, other, and no report.
(2) Detail will not add to total employed because
    a) racial and ethnic categories are not mutually exclusive and
    b) total employed includes other and no report.
(3) Includes members of all racial groups.
(4) Too few cases to estimate.

SOURCE: National Science Foundation, SRS.

Appendix table 25. Doctoral women scientists and engineers in four-year
colleges and universities by field, racial/ethnic
group, and academic rank: 1985

Field and racial/ethnic group	Total, four-year colleges & universities (1)	Academic rank		
		Full professor	Associate Professor	Assistant Professor
Total scientists and engineers (2)	31,700	5,200	7,900	9,500
White	28,300	4,600	7,100	8,600
Black	900	200	300	300
Asian	2,100	400	400	500
Native American	(4)	(4)	(4)	(4)
Hispanic (3)	500	100	100	200
Scientists	31,200	5,200	7,800	9,400
White	27,900	4,600	7,000	8,400
Black	900	200	300	300
Asian	2,100	400	400	500
Native American	(4)	(4)	(4)	(4)
Hispanic	500	100	100	200
Physical scientists	2,100	400	400	400
White	1,800	400	300	400
Black	(4)	(4)	(4)	(4)
Asian	300	(4)	100	(4)
Native American	(4)	(4)	(4)	(4)
Hispanic	100	(4)	(4)	(4)
Mathematical scientists	1,100	300	400	400
White	1,000	200	300	300
Black	(4)	(4)	(4)	(4)
Asian	200	(4)	100	(4)
Native American	(4)	(4)	(4)	(4)
Hispanic	(4)	(4)	(4)	(4)

Appendix table 25. - continued

Field and racial/ethnic group	Total, four-year colleges & universities (1)	Academic rank		
		Full professor	Associate Professor	Assistant Professor
Computer specialists	500	(4)	100	200
White	400	(4)	100	200
Black	(4)	(4)	(4)	(4)
Asian	(4)	(4)	(4)	(4)
Native American	(4)	(4)	(4)	(4)
Hispanic	(4)	(4)	(4)	(4)
Environmental scientists	500	(4)	100	200
White	400	(4)	100	100
Black	(4)	(4)	(4)	(4)
Asian	(4)	(4)	(4)	(4)
Native American	(4)	(4)	(4)	(4)
Hispanic	(4)	(4)	(4)	(4)
Life scientists	12,900	1,800	3,100	3,500
White	11,400	1,500	2,800	3,100
Black	300	100	100	100
Asian	1,100	200	200	300
Native American	(4)	(4)	(4)	(4)
Hispanic	200	(4)	(4)	(4)
Psychologists	6,200	1,100	1,500	1,900
White	5,700	1,000	1,400	1,700
Black	300	(4)	100	100
Asian	200	(4)	(4)	(4)
Native American	(4)	(4)	(4)	(4)
Hispanic	100	(4)	(4)	(4)

Appendix table 25. - continued

Field and racial/ethnic group	Total, four-year colleges & universities (1)	Academic rank		
		Full professor	Associate Professor	Assistant Professor
Social scientists	8,000	1,500	2,300	2,800
White	7,200	1,300	2,000	2,500
Black	300	(4)	100	100
Asian	300	100	100	100
Native American	(4)	(4)	(4)	(4)
Hispanic	100	(4)	(4)	100
Engineers	400	(4)	100	200
White	400	(4)	100	100
Black	(4)	(4)	(4)	(4)
Asian	100	(4)	(4)	(4)
Native American	(4)	(4)	(4)	(4)
Hispanic	(4)	(4)	(4)	(4)

(1) Includes instructor, other, and no report.
(2) Detail will not add to total employed because
    a) racial and ethnic categories are not mutually exclusive and
    b) total employed includes other and no report.
(3) Includes members of all racial groups.
(4) Too few cases to estimate.

SOURCE: National Science Foundation, SRS.

Appendix table 26. Selected employment characteristics of scientists and engineers by field, racial/ethnic group and sex: 1986

Field and racial/ethnic group	Labor force participation rate			Unemployment rate			S/E employment rate		
	Total	Men	Women	Total	Men	Women	Total	Men	Women
Total scientists and engineers (1)	94.5	94.6	93.9	1.5	1.3	2.7	84.7	86.4	75.3
White	94.3	94.4	93.8	1.5	1.3	2.6	84.9	86.4	75.9
Black	97.2	97.6	96.4	3.8	2.8	6.0	76.5	79.1	70.2
Asian	96.3	97.0	93.1	1.8	1.9	1.6	87.7	90.7	72.0
Native American	96.0	95.9	96.8	1.2	1.3	(3)	79.3	80.5	69.4
Hispanic (2)	95.2	96.1	92.2	2.1	2.2	1.7	80.2	83.8	66.5
Scientists	95.3	95.9	94.0	1.9	1.6	2.7	76.7	78.3	72.3
White	95.2	95.8	93.8	1.8	1.5	2.6	77.1	78.6	73.0
Black	97.0	97.2	96.7	3.7	1.6	6.5	68.7	69.7	67.2
Asian	96.1	97.5	93.2	2.3	2.8	1.1	76.9	81.7	66.3
Native American	96.6	96.7	96.4	2.1	2.7	(3)	68.2	68.5	67.3
Hispanic	94.9	96.5	91.9	3.0	3.8	1.4	67.5	71.0	61.2
Physical scientists	93.6	94.1	90.8	1.4	1.2	3.1	91.9	91.8	92.4
White	93.5	94.0	90.2	1.4	1.1	3.1	91.8	91.6	93.4
Black	98.1	98.4	97.6	2.6	2.0	4.2	87.2	89.3	81.8
Asian	93.0	93.5	91.9	1.2	1.3	.9	94.4	94.8	93.5
Native American	80.7	80.7	(3)	(3)	(3)	(3)	100.0	100.0	(3)
Hispanic	94.1	97.3	83.1	3.2	1.3	10.7	96.8	96.7	97.4
Mathematical scientists	94.6	95.4	92.6	1.3	.8	2.7	79.3	81.3	73.8
White	94.2	95.0	92.1	1.3	.7	2.7	79.0	81.2	73.0
Black	98.4	98.4	98.5	1.2	(3)	3.4	90.0	90.5	89.0
Asian	97.9	98.4	94.8	2.3	2.6	(3)	70.3	69.3	77.0
Native American	100.0	100.0	100.0	(3)	(3)	(3)	39.7	66.7	13.8
Hispanic	97.6	97.7	97.4	.9	1.4	(3)	82.6	92.3	67.0
Computer specialists	98.5	99.4	96.5	.8	.6	1.6	77.7	77.2	79.0
White	98.6	99.4	96.6	.8	.5	1.6	78.1	77.5	79.7
Black	99.2	100.0	98.0	1.2	.3	2.7	70.1	69.8	70.6
Asian	97.6	99.3	92.7	1.6	.5	1.0	76.6	76.9	75.5
Native American	100.0	100.0	100.0	1.9	2.2	(3)	52.4	47.8	75.4
Hispanic	96.4	100.0	89.3	.9	1.3	(3)	65.7	69.9	56.5

Appendix table 26. - continued

Field and racial/ethnic group	Labor force participation rate			Unemployment rate			S/E employment rate		
	Total	Men	Women	Total	Men	Women	Total	Men	Women
Environmental scientists	94.5	94.8	92.1	4.4	3.9	8.2	87.4	88.6	78.6
White	94.4	94.7	91.9	4.5	4.0	8.4	88.5	89.8	78.5
Black	97.5	97.1	100.0	.6	.2	2.8	41.3	31.9	100.0
Asian	97.3	97.1	100.0	2.6	2.9	(3)	89.6	91.2	71.7
Native American	93.8	93.0	100.0	(3)	(3)	(3)	74.2	77.9	50.0
Hispanic	95.0	94.5	100.0	4.8	5.3	(3)	84.5	85.4	76.6
Life scientists	93.0	94.1	90.0	2.1	1.7	3.4	82.7	83.2	81.1
White	92.8	93.9	89.5	2.1	1.6	3.4	82.9	83.1	82.1
Black	98.5	98.8	97.9	3.8	1.4	7.4	80.9	83.4	76.9
Asian	94.0	96.1	90.7	2.6	2.1	3.3	85.7	90.4	77.6
Native American	100.0	100.0	100.0	(3)	(3)	(3)	63.3	75.3	41.5
Hispanic	92.2	94.2	89.5	.8	1.3	(3)	71.3	74.6	66.5
Psychologists	95.1	94.9	95.3	2.5	2.2	3.0	68.2	71.9	63.6
White	95.0	94.7	95.4	2.3	1.8	3.0	69.1	71.7	65.7
Black	94.5	97.0	93.3	3.6	1.5	4.6	66.6	80.4	59.3
Asian	99.0	100.0	98.8	4.3	23.0	(3)	28.0	95.2	16.2
Native American	100.0	100.0	100.0	8.5	11.2	(3)	94.3	92.3	100.0
Hispanic	96.1	96.3	95.9	4.3	4.8	3.8	46.3	40.9	51.0
Social scientists	95.4	95.8	94.6	2.4	2.3	2.7	60.7	61.9	58.2
White	95.3	95.8	94.3	2.0	2.0	2.1	61.1	62.3	58.1
Black	95.0	93.7	96.8	6.8	3.4	11.2	53.7	50.8	57.8
Asian	96.1	97.8	92.9	6.4	9.6	(3)	68.4	74.7	57.0
Native American	95.0	100.0	81.1	(3)	(3)	(3)	49.0	34.0	100.0
Hispanic	95.0	95.6	93.8	5.8	8.7	(3)	57.6	57.9	56.9
Engineers	93.8	93.8	93.6	1.2	1.2	2.5	91.9	91.9	93.5
White	93.5	93.5	93.5	1.2	1.1	2.5	91.8	91.7	93.5
Black	97.7	98.0	94.8	4.0	4.2	2.0	90.3	90.2	90.9
Asian	96.5	96.7	93.0	1.5	1.4	3.7	95.4	95.4	94.7
Native American	95.6	95.5	100.0	1.4	1.4	(3)	87.8	87.8	87.5
Hispanic	95.6	95.8	93.4	1.2	1.0	3.2	92.6	92.5	93.5

Appendix table 26. - continued

Field and racial/ethnic group	Underemployment rate			Underutilization rate		
	Total	Men	Women	Total	Men	Women
Total scientists and engineers (1)	2.6	1.9	6.3	4.1	3.2	8.9
White	2.5	1.9	6.1	3.9	3.1	8.5
Black	5.5	3.7	9.7	9.1	6.4	15.2
Asian	2.2	1.8	4.1	3.9	3.6	5.6
Native American	2.4	1.1	13.1	3.6	2.4	13.1
Hispanic (2)	4.8	2.5	13.4	6.7	4.6	14.8
Scientists	4.3	3.3	7.0	6.1	4.8	9.5
White	4.2	3.3	6.7	5.9	4.7	9.1
Black	7.5	5.2	10.8	10.9	6.7	16.7
Asian	3.5	3.0	4.6	5.8	5.8	5.7
Native American	5.0	2.1	14.7	7.0	4.8	14.7
Hispanic	8.2	4.0	15.9	10.9	7.6	17.0
Physical scientists	1.9	1.6	3.5	3.3	2.8	6.5
White	1.7	1.5	3.0	3.1	2.7	6.0
Black	4.6	3.1	8.5	7.1	5.0	12.3
Asian	2.5	2.2	3.3	3.6	3.4	4.1
Native American	(3)	(3)	(3)	(3)	(3)	(3)
Hispanic	1.8	1.7	2.6	5.0	3.0	13.0
Mathematical scientists	3.3	2.0	7.1	4.6	2.8	9.6
White	3.1	1.8	6.8	4.3	2.5	9.3
Black	4.2	5.5	1.8	5.4	5.5	5.1
Asian	3.9	3.3	7.5	6.1	5.9	7.5
Native American	44.0	(3)	86.2	44.0	(3)	86.2
Hispanic	3.6	1.5	6.9	4.4	2.9	6.9
Computer specialists	2.5	2.5	2.5	3.3	3.0	4.0
White	2.4	2.4	2.2	3.2	3.0	3.8
Black	4.2	2.7	6.6	5.4	3.0	9.2
Asian	2.7	2.5	3.4	3.3	3.0	4.3
Native American	(3)	(3)	(3)	1.9	2.2	(3)
Hispanic	5.5	6.6	3.1	6.3	7.8	3.1

Appendix table 26. - continued

Field and racial/ethnic group	Underemployment rate			Underutilization rate		
	Total	Men	Women	Total	Men	Women
Environmental scientists	5.6	4.8	11.6	9.7	8.5	18.8
White	5.5	4.6	11.7	9.7	8.4	19.1
Black	4.4	5.1	(3)	5.0	5.4	2.8
Asian	8.8	9.7	(3)	11.2	12.2	(3)
Native American	15.5	10.2	50.0	15.5	10.2	50.0
Hispanic	9.0	8.9	9.6	13.3	13.7	9.6
Life scientists	4.7	3.1	9.6	6.7	4.7	12.6
White	4.4	3.1	8.5	6.4	4.7	11.6
Black	7.3	3.4	13.7	10.9	4.8	20.1
Asian	7.5	3.2	14.7	9.9	5.2	17.5
Native American	7.7	(3)	2.0	9.7	(3)	2.0
Hispanic	16.2	5.7	31.5	16.9	6.9	31.5
Psychologists	5.7	4.7	6.8	8.1	6.8	9.6
White	5.8	4.8	7.0	8.0	6.6	9.8
Black	4.9	(3)	7.5	8.3	1.5	11.7
Asian	(3)	(3)	(3)	4.3	23.0	(3)
Native American	11.5	(3)	44.6	19.1	11.2	44.6
Hispanic	7.1	5.3	8.7	11.1	9.8	12.2
Social scientists	7.2	5.4	11.1	9.4	7.5	13.6
White	6.9	5.2	10.9	8.8	7.1	12.8
Black	13.1	9.8	17.9	19.0	12.8	27.1
Asian	3.0	4.3	.5	9.2	13.5	(3)
Native American	7.5	9.7	(3)	7.5	9.7	(3)
Hispanic	7.7	.6	20.9	13.1	9.2	20.9
Engineers	1.0	1.0	2.3	2.2	2.1	4.8
White	1.0	.9	2.4	2.1	2.0	4.9
Black	2.0	1.9	2.3	5.8	6.0	4.3
Asian	1.2	1.1	1.9	2.7	2.5	5.5
Native American	1.4	1.5	(3)	2.9	.9	(3)
Hispanic	1.4	1.5	.8	2.6	2.5	4.0

(1) Detail will not average to the total because
    a) racial and ethnic categories are not mutually exclusive and
    b) total employed includes other and no report.
(2) Includes members of all racial groups.
(3) Too few cases to estimate.
NOTE: See technical Notes for definition of rates.
SOURCE: National Science Foundation, SRS.

Appendix table 27. Selected employment characteristics of doctoral scientists and engineers by field, racial/ethnic group, and sex: 1985

Field and racial/ethnic group	Labor force participation rate			Unemployment rate			S/E employment rate		
	Total	Men	Women	Total	Men	Women	Total	Men	Women
Total scientists and engineers (1)	95.1	95.4	93.1	0.8	0.7	1.8	91.3	91.5	89.8
White	94.7	95.1	92.8	1.8	1.7	1.8	91.0	91.2	89.9
Black	97.5	97.8	96.8	1.2	1.1	1.3	85.6	88.0	79.8
Asian	98.2	98.6	95.4	.9	.7	2.6	94.9	95.2	92.6
Native American	96.1	96.8	91.5	.4	(3)	3.1	90.4	89.5	96.8
Hispanic (2)	96.7	96.8	96.4	1.6	.9	5.0	91.2	91.7	88.4
Scientists	94.6	95.0	93.0	.9	.7	1.9	90.8	91.1	89.6
White	94.3	94.7	92.7	.9	.7	1.8	90.7	90.9	89.7
Black	97.3	97.5	96.8	1.3	1.3	1.3	84.5	86.9	79.4
Asian	97.7	98.2	95.3	1.0	.6	2.8	94.5	95.0	92.1
Native American	95.3	96.1	90.8	1.5	(3)	3.4	88.5	87.2	96.5
Hispanic	97.9	98.2	96.4	1.4	.5	5.1	92.5	93.4	88.1
Physical scientists	93.2	93.4	90.6	.9	.8	2.2	90.9	90.9	90.4
White	92.6	92.8	89.8	1.0	.9	2.3	90.3	90.3	89.8
Black	100.0	100.0	100.0	.4	.4	(3)	96.4	98.5	75.5
Asian	97.9	98.5	93.6	.4	.2	1.8	95.9	96.0	94.9
Native American	100.0	100.0	(3)	(3)	(3)	(3)	100.0	100.0	(3)
Hispanic	99.7	100.0	97.3	.6	.4	2.8	97.8	98.2	94.2
Mathematical scientists	96.3	96.7	92.9	.5	.4	1.0	92.5	92.4	92.8
White	96.1	96.4	92.6	.5	.5	.9	92.4	92.3	93.0
Black	100.0	100.0	100.0	(3)	(3)	(3)	94.0	93.7	95.8
Asian	98.4	99.2	93.2	.4	.2	2.1	93.5	93.9	91.0
Native American	100.0	100.0	(3)	(3)	(3)	(3)	100.0	100.0	(3)
Hispanic	99.2	100.0	94.7	(3)	(3)	(3)	100.0	100.0	100.0

Appendix table 27. - continued

Field and racial/ethnic group	Labor force participation rate			Unemployment rate			S/E employment rate		
	Total	Men	Women	Total	Men	Women	Total	Men	Women
Computer specialists	99.9	100.0	99.2	0.0	0.0	0.1	99.2	99.2	99.6
White	99.9	100.0	99.1	.0	.0	.1	99.1	99.0	99.5
Black	100.0	100.0	100.0	(3)	(3)	(3)	98.8	98.7	100.0
Asian	100.0	100.0	100.0	.2	.2	(3)	100.0	100.0	100.0
Native American	100.0	100.0	100.0	(3)	(3)	(3)	100.0	100.0	100.0
Hispanic	100.0	100.0	100.0	(3)	(3)	(3)	100.0	100.0	100.0
Environmental scientists	96.8	96.8	96.1	.6	.6	1.2	96.3	96.4	95.6
White	96.6	96.7	96.1	.7	.6	1.1	96.2	96.3	95.3
Black	99.0	100.0	90.9	(3)	(3)	(3)	100.0	100.0	100.0
Asian	98.9	98.8	100.0	.2	(3)	2.4	97.3	97.1	98.8
Native American	100.0	100.0	(3)	(3)	(3)	(3)	100.0	100.0	(3)
Hispanic	100.0	100.0	100.0	(3)	(3)	(3)	89.6	93.5	38.9
Life scientists	93.7	94.4	91.2	1.1	.9	1.8	94.8	95.1	93.7
White	93.5	94.2	90.7	1.1	.9	1.8	94.8	95.1	93.8
Black	94.4	94.0	95.0	1.3	1.1	1.8	89.0	93.1	81.4
Asian	96.9	97.6	94.9	1.7	1.3	2.8	96.2	96.4	95.4
Native American	88.9	86.6	100.0	1.7	(3)	8.7	95.8	94.8	100.0
Hispanic	96.9	96.9	96.8	1.6	.7	5.2	97.3	97.2	97.6
Psychologists	95.9	96.3	95.0	.9	.6	1.4	91.9	91.7	92.4
White	95.8	96.3	94.9	.8	.5	1.4	92.2	91.9	93.0
Black	99.2	100.0	98.4	2.8	1.4	3.3	80.6	80.9	80.3
Asian	99.0	100.0	97.9	2.5	1.7	3.2	87.8	86.8	89.0
Native American	96.3	100.0	86.4	(3)	(3)	(3)	92.3	93.2	89.5
Hispanic	95.0	94.4	96.0	2.7	(3)	7.9	88.6	89.9	85.9

Appendix table 27. - continued

Field and racial/ethnic group	Labor force participation rate			Unemployment rate			S/E employment rate		
	Total	Men	Women	Total	Men	Women	Total	Men	Women
Social scientists	94.4	94.7	93.1	1.0	0.6	2.7	79.8	80.7	76.0
White	94.1	94.4	92.9	1.0	.6	2.7	79.5	80.3	76.2
Black	97.3	97.6	96.6	2.0	2.0	2.3	77.4	78.4	74.7
Asian	97.3	97.5	96.0	1.2	.6	5.1	87.5	89.4	74.1
Native American	97.7	100.0	83.3	(3)	(3)	(3)	70.1	66.1	100.0
Hispanic	99.2	100.0	95.7	1.4	1.0	3.0	82.3	83.4	77.6
Engineers	97.5	97.5	97.7	.5	.5	.9	93.3	93.3	96.9
White	97.1	97.1	98.0	.5	.5	.9	92.8	92.7	96.2
Black	99.4	100.0	93.0	(3)	(3)	(3)	96.5	96.2	100.0
Asian	99.1	99.1	96.9	.8	.8	.9	95.6	95.5	99.0
Native American	100.0	100.0	100.0	(3)	(3)	(3)	100.0	100.0	100.0
Hispanic	89.9	89.7	100.0	2.9	2.9	(3)	82.6	82.4	90.9

Appendix table 27. - continued

Field and racial/ethnic group	Underemployment rate			Underutilization rate		
	Total	Men	Women	Total	Men	Women
Total scientists and engineers (1)	1.7	1.3	3.9	2.5	2.0	5.6
White	1.6	1.2	3.9	2.4	1.9	5.6
Black	3.4	3.4	3.4	4.5	4.5	4.6
Asian	2.4	2.1	4.3	3.3	2.8	6.8
Native American	2.7	1.6	11.1	3.1	1.6	13.8
Hispanic (2)	2.3	1.6	5.5	3.8	2.5	10.2
Scientists	1.9	1.5	3.9	2.8	2.2	5.7
White	1.8	1.4	3.9	2.7	2.0	5.7
Black	3.7	3.8	3.5	5.0	5.1	4.7
Asian	3.4	3.1	4.5	4.3	3.7	7.1
Native American	3.3	1.9	12.3	3.7	1.9	15.3
Hispanic	2.6	1.9	5.4	3.9	2.4	10.2
Physical scientists	1.0	.8	3.0	1.9	1.6	5.2
White	.8	.6	3.3	1.8	1.5	5.5
Black	.4	(3)	4.1	.8	.4	4.1
Asian	2.6	2.7	2.0	3.0	2.9	3.7
Native American	(3)	(3)	(3)	(3)	(3)	(3)
Hispanic	1.1	.6	4.8	1.7	1.0	7.5
Mathematical scientists	.7	.7	1.3	1.2	1.1	2.3
White	.8	.7	1.3	1.3	1.2	2.2
Black	(3)	(3)	(3)	(3)	(3)	(3)
Asian	.3	.2	1.1	.7	.3	3.1
Native American	(3)	(3)	(3)	(3)	(3)	(3)
Hispanic	3.8	4.4	(3)	3.8	4.4	(3)

163

Appendix table 27. - continued

Field and racial/ethnic group	Underemployment rate			Underutilization rate		
	Total	Men	Women	Total	Men	Women
Computer specialists	0.5	0.3	2.0	0.5	0.3	2.2
White	.4	.2	1.9	.5	.3	2.0
Black	8.2	9.3	(3)	8.5	9.3	(3)
Asian	.4	(3)	3.3	.5	.2	3.3
Native American	(3)	(3)	(3)	(3)	(3)	(3)
Hispanic	6.6	6.8	(3)	6.6	6.8	(3)
Environmental scientists	1.0	.7	5.4	1.6	1.3	6.5
White	1.0	.7	5.5	1.7	1.4	6.6
Black	(3)	(3)	(3)	(3)	(3)	(3)
Asian	1.3	1.0	4.9	1.5	1.0	7.2
Native American	(3)	(3)	(3)	(3)	(3)	(3)
Hispanic	(3)	(3)	(3)	(3)	(3)	(3)
Life scientists	2.2	1.8	3.8	3.3	2.7	5.6
White	2.1	1.6	3.9	3.1	2.5	5.6
Black	3.0	2.4	4.2	4.3	3.4	5.9
Asian	3.4	3.6	2.8	5.0	4.9	5.5
Native American	3.4	3.1	4.8	5.0	3.1	13.0
Hispanic	1.9	1.5	3.5	3.4	2.2	8.6
Psychologists	1.9	1.6	2.7	2.8	2.1	4.1
White	1.9	1.6	2.6	2.7	2.1	4.0
Black	2.4	1.5	3.3	3.2	2.9	3.6
Asian	4.1	1.5	6.9	6.5	3.2	9.9
Native American	12.8	6.8	31.6	12.8	6.8	31.6
Hispanic	3.5	1.8	7.0	6.1	1.8	14.4

Appendix table 27. - continued

Field and racial/ethnic group	Underemployment rate			Underutilization rate		
	Total	Men	Women	Total	Men	Women
Social scientists	3.4	2.7	6.7	4.4	3.3	9.2
White	3.1	2.3	6.5	4.0	2.8	9.0
Black	6.6	7.8	3.2	8.5	9.6	5.5
Asian	7.3	6.3	14.6	8.4	6.8	19.0
Native American	(3)	(3)	(3)	(3)	(3)	(3)
Hispanic	3.4	2.5	7.1	4.7	3.5	9.9
Engineers	.7	.7	1.8	1.2	1.2	2.7
White	.7	.7	1.8	1.2	1.2	2.6
Black	(3)	(3)	(3)	(3)	(3)	(3)
Asian	.6	.5	2.2	1.4	1.3	3.2
Native American	(3)	(3)	(3)	(3)	(3)	(3)
Hispanic	.3	(3)	9.1	3.1	2.9	9.1

(1) Detail will not average to the total because
    a) racial and ethnic categories are not mutually exclusive and
    b) total employed includes other and no report.
(2) Includes members of all racial groups.
(3) Too few cases to estimate.

NOTE: See technical Notes for definition of rates.

SOURCE: National Science Foundation, SRS.

Appendix table 28. Average annual salaries of scientists and engineers by field, racial/ethnic group, and years of professional experience: 1986

Field and racial/ethnic group	Total Employed (1)	Professional Experience								
		1 or less	2-4	5-9	10-14	15-19	20-24	25-29	30-34	35 and over
Total scientists and engineers (1)	$38,400	$24,900	$26,700	$34,000	$37,200	$41,500	$44,400	$45,100	$45,000	$44,700
White	38,700	24,700	26,700	34,100	37,400	41,600	44,700	45,200	45,300	44,700
Black	31,500	19,200	24,400	30,000	29,300	36,200	36,800	43,400	36,500	39,400
Asian	39,100	31,200	29,600	34,800	39,700	42,000	43,500	44,400	42,400	43,800
Native American	41,000	31,200	25,900	33,300	34,600	43,100	44,700	46,900	47,100	43,800
Hispanic (2)	34,600	20,400	24,300	32,000	35,800	39,200	43,200	44,100	47,200	47,500
Scientists	35,700	22,400	24,300	31,200	35,800	40,700	43,400	44,500	45,100	44,800
White	35,900	22,600	24,300	31,500	36,100	40,900	44,000	44,200	45,400	44,700
Black	29,000	15,500	22,700	27,400	26,300	36,600	29,200	46,600	37,000	37,900
Asian	37,000	23,500	28,400	30,900	38,500	40,800	41,500	48,900	45,200	47,100
Native American	40,500	17,000	23,600	32,700	33,600	42,000	48,100	42,300	26,600	47,200
Hispanic	30,600	16,200	21,700	27,900	31,800	38,500	46,000	43,300	48,300	57,100
Physical scientists	40,700	23,700	26,100	31,900	38,000	44,000	47,600	45,800	48,200	46,700
White	40,900	23,700	26,300	32,600	38,100	45,600	47,600	44,800	48,400	46,500
Black	35,600	(3)	20,600	30,900	26,400	34,600	41,200	51,300	44,000	37,500
Asian	39,300	22,900	27,500	26,900	37,100	31,100	46,700	55,400	46,800	55,500
Native American	63,400	(3)	(3)	29,800	(3)	(3)	65,000	61,600	(3)	(3)
Hispanic	41,300	22,400	27,500	19,200	36,900	32,900	61,000	48,900	(3)	60,000
Mathematical scientists	39,800	19,300	27,300	36,500	38,200	40,800	46,800	45,500	45,500	45,000
White	40,000	19,200	27,400	36,800	37,900	40,700	48,700	45,000	46,600	45,500
Black	37,000	16,100	27,100	29,300	37,600	35,900	31,000	46,800	29,100	26,300
Asian	38,500	22,600	31,700	37,500	37,700	32,600	38,900	51,500	41,000	27,600
Native American	22,500	(3)	23,000	(3)	(3)	37,300	(3)	19,900	(3)	(3)
Hispanic	38,700	20,000	28,200	29,700	47,100	45,500	37,200	45,600	(3)	(3)
Computer specialists	37,300	25,200	28,500	35,700	38,400	41,600	44,200	47,200	42,600	43,200
White	37,500	25,000	28,600	35,800	38,700	41,300	45,200	47,200	42,100	43,500
Black	32,200	26,500	25,600	32,200	28,600	41,100	33,000	42,400	46,600	20,000
Asian	37,400	28,000	30,800	35,400	38,700	45,800	37,100	55,600	62,000	28,000
Native American	39,300	(3)	23,700	37,900	39,000	44,000	43,100	28,800	(3)	(3)
Hispanic	31,500	23,300	23,600	36,000	38,900	41,100	40,300	46,800	39,700	(3)

Appendix table 28. - continued

Field and racial/ethnic group	Total Employed (1)	Professional Experience								
		1 or less	2-4	5-9	10-14	15-19	20-24	25-29	30-34	35 and over
Environmental scientists	$37,500	$19,600	$22,600	$34,400	$39,400	$40,500	$47,400	$46,600	$44,600	$49,100
White	37,600	19,600	22,600	34,700	39,300	40,600	47,800	47,000	44,400	48,900
Black	31,800	13,000	20,200	34,900	36,200	(3)	(3)	40,000	(3)	(3)
Asian	40,600	(3)	31,100	34,400	41,100	34,200	45,800	46,200	47,700	(3)
Native American	27,000	17,000	(3)	26,000	27,200	(3)	(3)	5,000	(3)	65,000
Hispanic	40,500	12,400	22,800	42,200	51,200	30,000	38,600	50,300	51,300	(3)
Life scientists	33,100	23,500	19,600	26,500	31,800	40,100	41,100	41,300	47,500	42,500
White	33,200	24,100	19,800	26,400	31,600	40,100	41,200	41,100	47,800	41,900
Black	29,300	1,800	10,900	23,400	32,400	32,100	35,700	40,600	42,800	45,500
Asian	35,700	17,800	19,100	30,300	40,600	46,300	39,700	44,300	40,100	42,200
Native American	40,600	(3)	17,500	35,100	24,300	33,600	45,800	43,800	30,000	55,300
Hispanic	29,700	7,600	16,500	24,600	25,000	45,900	56,400	26,600	53,900	55,900
Psychologists	33,400	21,000	21,200	29,400	34,400	37,200	39,200	41,300	42,400	43,200
White	33,900	22,000	21,100	30,900	35,100	37,200	38,900	41,300	42,500	44,100
Black	26,800	4,000	19,900	24,900	26,100	30,100	37,500	39,900	38,600	34,000
Asian	22,500	(3)	21,000	17,100	37,200	42,400	44,900	47,200	40,900	62,000
Native American	41,200	(3)	36,800	27,600	40,000	43,000	49,200	44,000	24,000	25,000
Hispanic	25,400	22,300	19,500	30,400	7,000	33,700	19,700	(3)	34,900	(3)
Social scientists	31,800	20,300	22,100	27,000	32,800	40,000	40,100	43,000	41,800	44,600
White	32,200	20,500	22,000	27,000	33,700	40,200	41,500	43,000	42,600	44,600
Black	22,800	15,600	22,600	26,200	12,700	35,800	17,200	62,400	13,000	47,700
Asian	38,700	20,100	27,000	44,600	34,600	41,700	44,300	41,500	48,900	44,200
Native American	34,300	(3)	21,000	26,600	32,500	(3)	46,000	28,900	24,000	(3)
Hispanic	25,600	14,500	21,500	13,300	35,900	35,100	47,500	22,900	33,500	(3)
Engineers	40,800	30,000	30,400	37,300	38,700	42,200	45,200	45,400	45,000	44,700
White	41,000	29,400	30,400	37,300	38,700	42,300	45,300	45,700	45,200	44,700
Black	35,700	24,200	29,500	35,300	34,600	35,400	46,100	38,300	36,000	40,000
Asian	40,500	38,100	31,100	39,100	40,500	42,600	44,400	42,000	41,200	41,100
Native American	41,300	35,100	31,400	35,500	35,000	43,300	38,600	50,400	51,800	41,400
Hispanic	38,000	27,400	29,100	36,000	38,600	39,800	41,300	44,400	46,700	45,000

(1) Detail will not average to the total because
    a) racial and ethnic categories are not mutually exclusive and
    b) total employed includes other and no report.
(2) Includes members of all racial groups.
(3) Too few cases to estimate.
NOTE: Salaries computed for individuals employed full-time.
SOURCE: National Science Foundation, SRS.

Appendix table 29. Average annual salaries of men scientists and engineers by field, racial/ethnic group, and years of professional experience: 1986

Field and racial/ethnic group	Total Employed (1)	Professional Experience								
		1 or less	2-4	5-9	10-14	15-19	20-24	25-29	30-34	35 and over
Total scientists and engineers (1)	$39,800	$27,000	$28,000	$35,200	$38,000	$42,200	$44,900	$45,400	$45,300	$45,100
White	40,000	26,600	27,900	35,200	38,000	42,400	45,200	45,500	45,500	45,100
Black	33,500	23,100	26,500	30,300	31,400	36,200	38,300	43,400	36,700	39,600
Asian	40,700	33,500	30,300	38,800	40,600	42,800	43,300	45,400	42,500	42,900
Native American	42,600	26,000	32,100	38,000	34,700	43,200	44,700	48,500	47,800	43,800
Hispanic (2)	36,600	20,700	26,200	34,600	36,100	39,700	43,000	44,200	47,200	47,600
Scientists	38,000	24,400	25,700	32,500	37,000	42,200	44,500	45,300	45,900	46,500
White	38,100	24,400	25,500	32,600	37,000	42,400	45,000	45,000	46,200	46,500
Black	31,400	19,700	25,200	26,400	28,000	36,900	29,400	47,300	37,300	38,400
Asian	40,500	24,600	30,000	38,000	41,500	42,800	42,300	49,800	45,600	53,100
Native American	44,100	17,000	33,500	38,100	34,400	41,300	48,100	44,100	27,000	47,200
Hispanic	33,900	15,600	24,000	32,000	32,700	39,500	45,900	43,100	48,300	58,600
Physical scientists	42,000	25,300	27,900	32,700	38,300	45,000	48,500	45,900	48,500	47,000
White	42,000	25,300	28,000	33,100	38,100	46,500	48,400	44,900	48,500	46,800
Black	39,300	(3)	19,100	32,000	36,000	36,600	44,900	51,300	44,900	37,500
Asian	42,200	23,800	33,500	29,400	37,900	31,000	48,200	56,800	49,600	56,800
Native American	63,400	(3)	(3)	29,800	(3)	(3)	65,000	61,600	(3)	(3)
Hispanic	43,100	38,000	31,100	18,800	39,700	31,100	64,000	48,900	(3)	60,000
Mathematical scientists	42,500	20,500	29,600	38,500	40,500	43,500	47,400	46,900	46,400	41,800
White	42,800	20,700	29,900	38,700	40,300	43,600	49,200	46,500	47,500	41,900
Black	38,400	1,900	31,400	32,100	37,300	39,000	30,300	47,300	42,000	1,900
Asian	39,300	22,600	31,700	43,000	40,300	31,200	39,000	54,600	41,000	27,600
Native American	19,900	(3)	(3)	(3)	(3)	(3)	(3)	19,900	(3)	(3)
Hispanic	42,100	20,000	15,200	38,000	50,800	45,500	40,000	45,600	(3)	(3)
Computer specialists	38,900	26,800	29,400	36,500	39,400	43,000	44,700	47,100	44,700	44,200
White	39,000	26,700	29,200	36,500	39,700	42,500	45,300	47,100	44,300	44,600
Black	34,200	30,300	26,200	34,000	25,500	41,200	45,600	42,400	46,600	20,000
Asian	39,600	29,000	31,900	37,200	41,700	50,800	37,000	55,500	62,000	28,000
Native American	42,400	(3)	32,700	42,000	39,000	44,000	43,100	28,800	(3)	(3)
Hispanic	33,800	22,500	26,300	36,100	38,400	41,100	40,300	46,700	39,700	(3)

Appendix table 29. - continued

Field and racial/ethnic group	Total Employed (1)	Professional Experience								
		1 or less	2-4	5-9	10-14	15-19	20-24	25-29	30-34	35 and over
Environmental scientists	$38,400	$21,100	$23,100	$35,000	$39,200	$41,300	$47,700	$46,800	$44,300	$49,200
White	38,500	21,100	23,100	35,200	39,100	41,500	48,100	47,100	44,100	49,000
Black	29,600	13,000	14,300	34,900	29,900	(3)	(3)	40,000	(3)	(3)
Asian	41,100	(3)	32,000	31,100	41,100	34,200	45,800	46,200	47,700	(3)
Native American	26,700	17,000	(3)	17,400	28,000	(3)	(3)	5,000	(3)	65,000
Hispanic	42,400	17,000	26,100	42,700	51,200	30,000	39,200	50,300	51,300	(3)
Life scientists	35,400	27,900	20,600	28,000	32,400	41,200	42,200	43,100	47,500	43,400
White	35,400	29,100	20,600	27,700	31,900	41,100	42,300	43,100	47,700	42,900
Black	33,300	1,800	18,500	24,100	38,500	32,600	34,900	40,600	45,800	45,500
Asian	40,500	17,800	21,300	38,500	46,000	48,800	40,200	41,100	40,100	42,200
Native American	46,500	(3)	29,700	45,700	23,800	33,600	45,800	50,400	30,000	55,300
Hispanic	35,200	1,800	20,100	24,800	28,400	48,000	65,300	26,600	53,900	58,000
Psychologists	36,500	19,200	23,000	32,000	35,800	39,400	40,400	41,900	42,900	47,400
White	36,600	19,000	23,100	32,400	36,000	39,600	40,200	41,800	43,100	48,900
Black	27,400	(3)	18,500	24,600	28,900	26,300	33,800	43,000	33,600	(3)
Asian	39,600	(3)	21,000	22,400	40,200	43,600	39,000	47,200	40,900	62,000
Native American	41,900	(3)	36,800	(3)	40,000	(3)	49,200	44,000	(3)	25,000
Hispanic	26,400	31,000	20,100	44,400	4,700	36,900	13,800	(3)	34,900	(3)
Social scientists	34,700	22,500	23,700	28,600	36,100	41,200	41,300	44,000	42,600	51,200
White	35,100	22,500	23,400	28,900	36,800	41,800	42,900	44,100	43,600	51,200
Black	23,800	35,000	26,200	20,400	13,000	35,700	16,600	65,000	13,000	47,700
Asian	41,900	20,300	25,000	47,200	39,400	41,500	49,500	42,600	48,900	57,500
Native American	39,100	(3)	28,000	27,800	32,500	(3)	46,000	37,600	24,000	(3)
Hispanic	28,500	14,500	23,800	14,400	36,000	35,100	47,700	22,900	33,500	(3)
Engineers	41,100	30,500	30,400	37,400	38,700	42,200	45,200	45,500	45,000	44,700
White	41,200	29,900	30,400	37,400	38,800	42,300	45,400	45,700	45,200	44,800
Black	35,900	24,600	29,000	35,300	34,500	35,200	46,100	38,300	35,800	40,000
Asian	40,800	38,400	30,700	39,300	40,100	42,800	44,500	43,300	41,200	41,100
Native American	41,500	30,000	30,900	37,600	34,800	43,300	38,600	50,400	51,800	41,400
Hispanic	38,300	27,500	28,900	36,300	38,200	39,800	41,500	44,600	46,700	45,000

(1) Detail will not average to the total because
    a) racial and ethnic categories are not mutually exclusive and
    b) total employed includes other and no report.
(2) Includes members of all racial groups.
(3) Too few cases to estimate.
NOTE: Salaries computed for individuals employed full-time.
SOURCE: National Science Foundation, SRS.

Appendix table 30. Average annual salaries of women scientists and engineers by field, racial/ethnic group, and years of professional experience: 1986

Field and racial/ethnic group	Total Employed (1)	Professional Experience								
		1 or less	2-4	5-9	10-14	15-19	20-24	25-29	30-34	35 and over
Total scientists and engineers (1)	$29,900	$19,900	$23,800	$30,100	$33,100	$35,200	$36,500	$36,200	$39,800	$34,600
White	30,200	19,900	23,800	30,600	33,700	35,200	37,100	36,200	40,000	33,400
Black	26,200	15,500	21,400	29,500	25,100	36,200	28,800	43,300	35,000	35,900
Asian	30,100	23,300	27,700	25,500	25,100	34,500	37,100	31,600	35,100	43,200
Native American	29,600	43,300	21,500	27,900	33,900	42,600	(3)	40,000	24,000	(3)
Hispanic (2)	25,200	19,200	21,200	24,800	33,100	30,300	44,600	39,400	(3)	41,000
Scientists	29,000	19,200	22,200	28,700	32,600	34,700	36,400	37,500	38,500	32,800
White	29,400	19,400	22,300	29,200	33,500	34,600	37,000	36,600	38,800	31,100
Black	25,400	13,900	20,100	28,400	24,600	35,900	28,800	43,300	32,800	35,900
Asian	28,800	21,800	25,900	23,100	31,100	35,200	36,300	42,600	32,100	43,200
Native American	29,100	(3)	19,500	27,800	26,200	42,600	(3)	40,000	24,000	(3)
Hispanic	22,900	17,700	19,400	22,100	28,100	28,400	46,900	47,000	(3)	41,000
Physical scientists	31,300	18,400	21,900	29,100	36,400	35,600	35,800	41,500	40,900	43,600
White	31,800	18,500	21,900	30,400	37,800	37,300	35,000	41,300	43,200	43,800
Black	24,300	(3)	22,100	26,800	14,200	27,100	32,000	(3)	37,000	(3)
Asian	31,400	9,000	22,300	24,800	35,800	31,400	40,500	42,500	32,100	34,000
Native American	(3)	(3)	(3)	(3)	(3)	(3)	(3)	(3)	(3)	(3)
Hispanic	33,900	14,000	15,200	22,800	26,600	35,200	54,300	(3)	(3)	(3)
Mathematical scientists	31,000	17,600	24,500	33,100	33,600	29,000	39,100	32,500	32,000	55,800
White	31,000	17,200	24,700	33,600	33,400	28,900	40,100	30,600	34,400	58,000
Black	32,900	24,500	20,500	26,400	37,100	22,800	36,200	43,300	3,700	37,300
Asian	30,600	(3)	31,100	27,300	27,100	35,600	37,700	4,000	(3)	(3)
Native American	25,000	(3)	23,000	(3)	42,200	37,300	(3)	(3)	(3)	(3)
Hispanic	31,000	(3)	33,200	24,300	42,200	(3)	32,600	(3)	(3)	(3)
Computer specialists	33,200	22,500	27,200	34,300	36,100	37,700	39,600	48,500	20,800	36,100
White	33,700	22,200	27,400	34,600	36,700	37,800	44,400	47,900	20,800	36,100
Black	29,300	23,600	24,800	29,700	33,000	40,800	23,700	(3)	(3)	(3)
Asian	30,800	25,900	28,600	31,000	28,500	34,600	39,900	55,800	(3)	(3)
Native American	20,500	(3)	21,300	33,200	(3)	(3)	(3)	(3)	(3)	(3)
Hispanic	25,800	25,100	20,900	35,400	48,000	(3)	(3)	47,000	(3)	(3)

Appendix table 30. - continued

Field and racial/ethnic group	Total Employed (1)	Professional Experience								
		1 or less	2-4	5-9	10-14	15-19	20-24	25-29	30-34	35 and over
Environmental scientists	$30,100	$14,800	$20,500	$31,700	$41,200	$33,100	$38,200	$31,000	$54,600	$38,900
White	30,100	14,800	20,300	31,700	41,500	33,100	38,200	31,000	54,600	38,900
Black	36,100	(3)	28,100	(3)	40,700	(3)	(3)	(3)	(3)	(3)
Asian	35,100	(3)	29,000	35,900	(3)	(3)	(3)	(3)	(3)	(3)
Native American	28,000	(3)	(3)	30,000	26,000	(3)	(3)	(3)	(3)	(3)
Hispanic	21,200	8,000	13,000	18,800	(3)	(3)	37,400	(3)	(3)	(3)
Life scientists	25,200	16,800	18,400	23,100	29,300	32,800	34,100	33,200	47,200	32,000
White	25,100	16,900	18,900	23,000	30,000	32,700	33,800	29,400	47,900	32,000
Black	21,600	(3)	7,900	22,600	21,200	29,200	39,000	(3)	34,100	(3)
Asian	28,400	(3)	17,800	22,400	33,500	37,300	37,000	47,500	(3)	(3)
Native American	32,500	(3)	15,900	27,500	26,000	(3)	(3)	42,200	(3)	(3)
Hispanic	18,700	12,400	14,400	23,900	17,900	30,100	41,100	(3)	(3)	41,000
Psychologists	29,000	22,400	20,000	27,600	32,100	31,900	36,200	39,200	41,000	31,500
White	29,700	25,000	19,900	29,800	33,500	31,500	36,000	39,000	41,100	31,400
Black	26,600	4,000	20,600	25,100	25,100	33,700	39,700	38,900	44,200	34,000
Asian	19,300	(3)	(3)	16,900	34,900	41,600	48,700	(3)	(3)	(3)
Native American	37,400	(3)	(3)	27,600	(3)	43,000	(3)	(3)	24,000	(3)
Hispanic	24,000	20,000	18,600	25,300	46,600	22,400	57,300	(3)	(3)	(3)
Social scientists	25,000	16,900	19,500	24,700	25,600	34,800	34,800	36,300	36,100	21,500
White	25,200	16,700	19,200	24,100	26,800	34,600	35,600	36,700	36,100	7,400
Black	21,400	13,500	18,800	31,100	12,500	41,300	27,100	60,000	(3)	(3)
Asian	31,700	20,000	29,000	31,500	27,900	42,600	4,200	2,000	(3)	43,400
Native American	21,500	(3)	19,000	24,200	(3)	(3)	(3)	24,000	(3)	(3)
Hispanic	18,700	(3)	18,800	12,700	35,200	(3)	46,600	(3)	(3)	(3)
Engineers	34,300	25,300	30,300	36,600	37,200	40,500	38,400	27,000	44,000	43,500
White	34,300	24,600	30,100	36,600	35,600	41,300	38,300	32,600	44,500	43,500
Black	32,900	22,700	31,600	35,200	36,500	38,500	(3)	(3)	39,000	(3)
Asian	35,000	33,100	32,800	37,200	47,200	27,200	39,400	16,000	39,000	(3)
Native American	34,700	43,000	32,700	28,500	40,400	(3)	(3)	(3)	(3)	(3)
Hispanic	33,900	25,900	30,100	33,800	45,400	40,100	32,900	29,600	(3)	(3)

(1) Detail will not average to the total because
   a) racial and ethnic categories are not mutually exclusive and
   b) total employed includes other and no report.
(2) Includes members of all racial groups.
(3) Too few cases to estimate.
NOTE: Salaries computed for individuals employed full-time.
SOURCE: National Science Foundation, SRS.

Appendix table 31. Average annual salaries of doctoral scientists and engineers by field and sex/racial/ethnic group: 1985

Field and sex	Total Employed (1)	White	Black	Asian	Native American	Hispanic (2)
Total scientists and engineers	$43,200	$43,200	$39,600	$44,000	$42,300	$41,300
Men	44,500	44,500	41,400	45,100	43,100	42,600
Women	35,500	35,400	35,600	35,500	36,100	34,400
Scientists	41,800	41,800	39,100	41,700	40,400	40,000
Men	43,100	43,100	40,800	43,000	41,400	41,300
Women	35,200	35,200	35,400	34,800	33,200	34,300
Physical scientists	45,200	45,500	38,900	43,200	38,800	43,700
Men	45,800	46,000	38,700	44,200	38,800	45,100
Women	37,200	37,500	40,700	35,500	(3)	32,500
Mathematical scientists	42,100	42,100	41,600	41,700	43,000	40,400
Men	42,600	42,700	42,200	42,200	43,000	42,300
Women	36,500	36,200	37,000	38,600	(3)	28,600
Computer specialists	45,500	45,200	48,100	47,200	38,200	45,100
Men	46,300	46,100	49,100	47,800	43,100	45,300
Women	38,300	37,900	44,100	41,600	18,300	40,500
Environmental scientists	45,400	45,200	49,000	47,300	42,200	42,300
Men	45,800	45,600	49,000	48,000	42,200	42,700
Women	38,200	38,200	48,800	36,300	(3)	37,000
Life scientists	40,100	40,200	39,300	39,300	35,600	37,600
Men	41,700	41,800	41,000	41,200	36,700	39,000
Women	33,600	33,500	36,400	33,300	30,300	32,000
Psychologists	39,200	39,300	36,200	38,000	40,000	38,900
Men	40,700	40,700	38,500	39,800	40,000	40,100
Women	35,600	35,600	34,000	35,600	40,100	36,100

Appendix table 31. - continued

Field and sex	Total Employed (1)	White	Black	Asian	Native American	Hispanic (2)
Social scientists	$40,900	$41,000	$39,900	$40,200	$45,700	$39,100
Men	42,000	42,100	41,800	41,000	47,100	39,800
Women	35,900	36,000	35,000	34,200	34,400	36,100
Engineers	50,800	51,400	45,100	48,500	51,000	49,100
Men	50,900	51,600	45,300	48,600	50,600	49,400
Women	43,700	43,500	42,500	44,500	57,000	38,900

(1) Detail will not average to the total because
    a) racial and ethnic categories are not mutually exclusive and
    b) total employed includes other and no report.
(2) Includes members of all racial groups.
(3) Too few cases to estimate.

NOTE: Salaries computed for full-time employed civilians.

SOURCE: National Science Foundation, SRS.

Appendix table 32. High school seniors by sex/racial/ethnic group and curriculum: 1980

Sex/racial/ ethnic group	Total	Percent		
		Academic	General	Vocational
Total	100	39	37	24
Male	100	39	38	23
Female	100	38	36	26
White	100	40	37	23
Black	100	33	35	31
Hispanic	100	27	42	31

SOURCE: Center for Education Statistics, HIGH SCHOOL AND BEYOND: A NATIONAL LONGITUDINAL STUDY FOR THE 1980'S, (Washington, D.C., 1981), p. 3 and unpublished data.

Appendix table 33. College-bound seniors by sex, racial/ethnic group, and curriculum: 1981 & 1985

(Percent)

Curriculum and sex	Total	White	Black	Asian	Native American	Mexican American	Puerto Rican
1981							
Academic	76.4	78.9	61.8	72.8	68.0	65.8	64.6
Male	77.9	80.1	62.8	74.1	70.0	69.2	69.3
Female	75.1	77.9	61.1	71.4	66.0	62.7	60.9
General	15.5	14.2	20.6	20.9	20.3	24.4	16.8
Male	15.6	14.3	22.0	19.9	19.9	22.8	16.9
Female	15.4	14.1	19.7	21.8	20.6	25.9	16.7
Career	7.5	6.4	16.4	5.5	10.8	9.0	17.3
Male	6.1	5.2	14.0	5.1	8.9	7.4	12.4
Female	8.8	7.6	18.0	6.0	12.5	10.6	21.2
1985							
Academic	78.5	81.2	65.1	75.5	68.3	70.4	64.0
Male	79.4	81.8	65.4	75.9	69.9	72.5	66.5
Female	77.8	80.6	64.9	75.1	67.0	68.5	62.0
General	14.0	12.5	19.2	19.0	20.3	20.6	18.0
Male	14.3	12.9	20.8	18.8	20.2	19.7	18.6
Female	13.7	12.2	18.1	19.2	20.4	21.4	17.5
Career	6.9	5.9	14.5	4.6	10.3	8.3	16.6
Male	5.7	4.9	12.6	4.3	8.7	7.0	13.4
Female	8.0	6.8	15.8	4.9	11.6	9.5	19.2

SOURCE: Admissions Testing Program of the College Board, PROFILES, COLLEGE-BOUND SENIORS, annual series, 1981-85, (New York: College Entrance Examination Board).

Appendix table 34. Number of mathematics and science courses attempted by 1980 high school sophomores who graduated in 1982 by sex/racial/ethnic group and high school grade point average

(Percent)

Sex/racial/ ethnic groups	1 year or less	2 yrs	3 yrs	4 yrs	5 years or more	Grade Point Average
MATHEMATICS						
Total	8.3	22.3	28.0	28.6	12.8	2.27
Male	7.1	20.2	25.6	32.0	15.1	2.18
Female	9.6	24.3	30.3	25.3	10.5	2.35
White	9.1	22.2	27.5	29.4	11.8	2.34
Black	5.5	18.9	28.5	30.6	16.5	1.98
Asian	4.3	8.7	20.6	42.7	23.7	2.6
Native American	6.5	33.1	22.3	28.8	9.4	2.19
Hispanic	8.5	25.2	30.5	23.6	12.1	2.04
SCIENCE						
Total	20.8	33.7	24.4	14.8	6.3	2.38
Male	19.3	30.9	25.3	17.3	7.2	2.29
Female	22.3	36.5	23.5	12.3	5.4	2.47
White	20.2	32.4	24.5	16.3	6.6	2.47
Black	20.6	35.5	24.7	12.2	7.0	2.08
Asian	13.1	23.7	28.1	23.3	11.8	2.69
Native American	28.1	30.2	23.0	15.1	3.6	2.13
Hispanic	23.3	38.2	23.5	10.6	4.5	2.07

SOURCE: Center for Education Statistics, HIGH SCHOOL AND BEYOND
TABULATION: MATHEMATICS COURSETAKING BY 1980 HIGH SCHOOL
SOPHOMORES WHO GRADUATED IN 1982 and HIGH SCHOOL AND BEYOND
TABULATION: SCIENCE COURSETAKING BY 1980 HIGH SCHOOL SOPHOMORES
WHO GRADUATED IN 1982, (Washington, D.C., April 1984).

Appendix table 35. Types of mathematics and science courses attempted by 1980 high school sophomores who graduated in 1982 by sex/racial/ethnic group

(Percent)

Sex/racial/ ethnic groups	MATHEMATICS					
	Algebra I	Geometry	Algebra II	Trigonometry	Analysis	Calculus
Total	67.7	54.2	34.3	22.9	8.9	6.9
Male	66.1	53.9	35.2	25.8	9.9	8.2
Female	69.3	54.4	33.5	20.0	7.8	5.7
White	71.2	60.4	38.1	26.3	11.1	8.3
Black	63.7	46.3	29.2	16.2	4.9	3.6
Asian	65.6	68.4	38.7	42.7	17.0	19.4
Native American	56.8	33.8	21.6	13.7	1.4	3.6
Hispanic	60.4	39.7	26.3	14.9	4.1	3.6

Sex/racial/ ethnic groups	SCIENCE						
	Physical Science	Biology	Advanced Biology	Chemistry	Chemistry II	Physics	Physics II
Total	67.8	78.8	18.0	35.5	4.4	16.9	1.7
Male	70.5	77.0	16.4	36.4	5.2	22.1	2.6
Female	65.1	80.7	19.6	34.5	3.6	11.6	0.9
White	67.1	79.2	19.5	39.3	5.1	19.8	2.0
Black	71.1	79.7	15.5	39.8	2.9	11.9	1.0
Asian	52.2	78.7	24.5	58.1	9.1	35.6	7.1
Native American	66.9	70.5	13.7	23.7	2.9	9.4	0.0
Hispanic	69.6	77.9	14.5	25.6	2.6	9.3	0.8

SOURCE: Center for Education Statistics, HIGH SCHOOL AND BEYOND TABULATION: MATHEMATICS COURSETAKING BY 1980 HIGH SCHOOL SOPHOMORES WHO GRADUATED IN 1982 and HIGH SCHOOL AND BEYOND TABULATION: SCIENCE COURSETAKING BY 1980 HIGH SCHOOL SOPHOMORES WHO GRADUATED IN 1982, (Washington, D.C., April 1984).

Appendix table 36. Average number of years of high school mathematics and science coursework taken by college-bound seniors by sex, racial/ethnic group, and type of course: 1981 & 1985

1981

Type of course and sex	Total	White	Black	Asian	Native American	Mexican American	Puerto Rican
Mathematics	3.52	3.55	3.26	3.74	3.31	3.25	3.22
Male	3.68	3.72	3.37	3.86	3.46	3.43	3.42
Female	3.38	3.41	3.20	3.61	3.16	3.08	3.06
Physical science	1.79	1.81	1.57	1.99	1.67	1.46	1.60
Male	2.01	2.04	1.72	2.24	1.85	1.64	1.83
Female	1.59	1.61	1.47	1.74	1.50	1.29	1.42
Biological science	1.40	1.39	1.44	1.50	1.46	1.31	1.39
Male	1.39	1.37	1.46	1.51	1.46	1.31	1.35
Female	1.41	1.40	1.43	1.48	1.47	1.32	1.43

1985

Type of course and sex	Total	White	Black	Asian	Native American	Mexican American	Puerto Rican
Mathematics	3.68	3.72	3.43	3.89	3.46	3.48	3.39
Male	3.80	3.83	3.50	3.96	3.57	3.60	3.54
Female	3.58	3.61	3.38	3.81	3.37	3.36	3.27
Physical science	1.90	1.92	1.68	2.12	1.72	1.52	1.69
Male	2.08	2.11	1.78	2.30	1.87	1.70	1.87
Female	1.74	1.75	1.62	1.94	1.59	1.37	1.54
Biological science	1.42	1.41	1.45	1.50	1.44	1.35	1.45
Male	1.40	1.38	1.45	1.49	1.43	1.34	1.41
Female	1.44	1.43	1.45	1.50	1.44	1.36	1.48

SOURCE: Admissions Testing Program of the College Board, PROFILES, COLLEGE-BOUND SENIORS, annual series, 1981-85, (New York: College Entrance Examination Board).

Appendix table 37. Changes in mean performance on the mathematics
assessment by sex/racial/ethnic group:
1978–1982

Sex/racial/ ethnic group and age	Overall Score 1982	Overall Change 1978–82	Knowledge Score 1982	Knowledge Change 1978–82	Skills Score 1982	Skills Change 1978–82	Understanding Score 1982	Understanding Change 1978–82	Applications Score 1982	Applications Change 1978–82
Total										
9 year olds	56.4	+1.0	68.3	+1.4	50.6	+0.8	41.2	-0.4	39.6	+0.5
13 year olds	60.5	+3.9*	73.8	+4.5*	57.6	+4.0*	60.5	+3.9*	45.6	+2.2*
17 year olds	60.2	-0.2	74.9	+0.2	60.0	+0.3	61.5	-0.3	42.4	-1.1
Male										
9 year olds	55.8	+0.5	67.4	+1.0	50.2	+0.5	41.0	-1.3	40.0	+0.4
13 year olds	60.4	+4.0*	73.8	+4.4*	57.0	+4.2*	60.8	+4.2*	46.1	+2.2*
17 year olds	61.6	-0.4	75.9	0.0	61.1	+0.2	63.1	-1.0	44.6	-1.3
Female										
9 year olds	56.9	+1.4*	69.3	+1.9*	51.1	+1.2	41.4	+0.4	39.2	+0.6
13 year olds	60.6	+3.7*	73.8	+4.5*	58.2	+3.8*	60.2	+3.7*	45.1	+2.3*
17 year olds	58.9	+0.1	73.9	+0.4	58.9	+0.4	60.0	+3.7*	45.1	+2.3*
White										
9 year olds	58.8	+0.7	70.8	+1.2	53.1	+0.6	43.4	-0.8	42.4	+0.6
13 year olds	63.1	+3.2*	76.1	+3.9*	60.4	+3.4*	63.6	+3.6*	47.9	+1.6*
17 year olds	63.1	-0.2	77.3	0.0	63.0	+0.3	64.7	-0.1	45.5	-1.0
Black										
9 year olds	45.2	+2.1	57.8	+3.5*	38.7	+1.6	31.4	+0.9	27.0	-0.6
13 year olds	48.2	+6.5*	63.8	+8.0*	44.0	+6.7*	46.4	5.9*	34.8	+4.4*
17 year olds	45.0	+1.3	62.6	3.0	44.2	+1.8	44.8	-0.2	26.0	-0.2
Hispanic										
9 year olds	47.7	+1.1	58.7	0.0	43.8	+2.5	32.4	-0.2	30.5	+0.6
13 year olds	51.9	+6.5*	65.3	6.3*	49.2	+7.2*	49.7	+5.9*	38.8	+6.0*
17 year olds	49.4	+0.9	66.1	+2.0	48.4	+0.5	49.7	+0.8	31.4	+0.4

*Significant at the 0.05 level

SOURCE: National Assessment of Educational Progress, THE THIRD NATIONAL
MATHEMATICS ASSESSMENT: RESULTS, TRENDS, AND ISSUES, (Report No.
13-MA-01), April 1983, pp. 34, 37, 38, and 51.

Appendix table 38. Changes in mean performance on the science assessment by sex and racial group: 1977-82

Sex and racial group	Inquiry Score 1982	Inquiry Change 1977-82	Science, Technology, and Society Score 1982	Science, Technology, and Society Change 1977-82	Content Score 1982	Content Change 1977-82	Attitude (2) Score 1982	Attitude (2) Change 1977-82
Male								
9 year olds	52.8	-1.1	60.5	3.1*	(1)		67.7	-0.8
13 year olds	58.5	-0.4	59.5	0.9	54.7	0.3	52.8	-2.2
17 year olds	70.2	-2.6*	68.6	-1.4	62.7	-2.2*	49	-0.9
White								
9 year olds	55.9	-1.3	62.7	3.0*	(1)		68.6	-1.1
13 year olds	60.4	-0.8	61.5	0.7	56.8	-0.2	52.6	-3.2*
17 year olds	72.8	-2.6*	71.2	-1.2	65.6	-1.7	48	-1.3
Black								
9 year olds	40.8	3.4	50.7	4.4	(1)		64.1	1.4
13 year olds	48.8	0.6	50.1	1.5	44.6	2.4	53.8	0.8
17 year olds	58.1	-0.1	55.8	0.3	47.8	-1.8	53.8	-0.4
Female								
9 year olds	52.5	-0.9	59.4	2.6*	(1)		65.1	-0.4
13 year olds	57.6	-0.8	55.3	0.3	50.2	-1.0	47.6	-2.6*
17 year olds	69.1	-2.4*	65.4	0.3	56.9	-1.7*	46.6	2.7*
White								
9 year olds	55.3	-1.7	61.3	2.2	(1)		66.2	-0.5
13 year olds	59.7	-1.1	57.4	0.4	52.4	-1.2	47	-2.6*
17 year olds	71.6	-2.5*	67.8	0.2	59.3	-1.6	45.4	3.0*
Black								
9 year olds	41.4	1.9	51.7	4.3	(1)		61.4	-0.2
13 year olds	49.3	0.1	46.8	-0.8	40.6	-0.8	50	-1.7
17 year olds	56.7	-1.9	54.1	2.0	44.4	-1.3	54.5	2.0

* Change is significant at the 0.05 level
(1) Not adminstered at 9 year old level.
(2) For 13 and 17 year olds, "attitude" refers to "attitudes toward science classes."

SOURCE: Science Assessment and Research Project, University of Minnesota, IMAGES OF SCIENCE, (Minneapolis, MN: Minnesota Research and Evaluation Center), June 1983, pp. 101-119.

Appendix table 39. Scholastic Aptitude Test (SAT) scores by sex/racial/ethnic group: 1975-86

VERBAL

Year	Total	Male	Female	White	Black	Asian	Native American	Mexican American	Puerto Rican
1975	434	437	431	NA	NA	NA	NA	NA	NA
1976	431	433	430	451	332	414	388	371	364
1977	429	431	427	448	330	405	390	370	355
1978	429	433	425	446	332	401	387	370	349
1979	427	431	423	444	330	396	386	370	345
1980	424	428	420	442	330	396	390	372	350
1981	424	430	418	442	332	397	391	373	353
1982	426	431	421	444	341	398	388	377	360
1983	425	430	420	443	339	395	388	375	365
1984	426	433	420	445	342	398	390	376	366
1985	431	437	425	449	346	404	392	382	373
1986	431	437	426	NA	NA	NA	NA	NA	NA

MATHEMATICS

Year	Total	Male	Female	White	Black	Asian	Native American	Mexican American	Puerto Rican
1975	472	495	449	NA	NA	NA	NA	NA	NA
1976	472	497	446	493	354	518	420	410	401
1977	470	497	445	489	357	514	421	408	397
1978	468	494	444	485	354	510	419	402	388
1979	467	493	443	483	358	511	421	410	388
1980	466	491	443	482	360	509	426	413	394
1981	466	492	443	483	362	513	425	415	398
1982	467	493	443	483	366	513	424	416	403
1983	468	493	445	484	369	514	425	417	397
1984	471	495	449	487	373	519	427	420	400
1985	475	499	452	490	376	518	428	426	405
1986	475	501	451	NA	NA	NA	NA	NA	NA

NA: Not available

NOTE: Scores range from 200 to 800.

SOURCES: Admissions Testing Program of the College Board, NATIONAL
COLLEGE-BOUND SENIORS, annual series; Lawrence Bielmiller,
"Board Says Minority-Group Scores Helped Push Up Averages
on SAT," CHRONICLE OF HIGHER EDUCATION, vol. XXV, no.8,
20 October 1982, pp. 1 & 10; and Admissions Testing Program
of the College Board, PROFILES, COLLEGE-BOUND SENIORS, annual
series, 1981-85.

Appendix table 40. Scholastic Aptitude Test (SAT) scores for males and females by racial/ethnic group: 1981-1985

Sex and year	White	Black	Asian	Native American	Mexican American	Puerto Rican
VERBAL						
Male						
1981	447	341	402	399	383	377
1982	448	348	402	396	386	378
1983	448	346	396	397	385	379
1984	452	349	401	401	385	380
1985	454	354	406	401	393	385
Female						
1981	437	327	391	383	364	348
1982	440	335	395	380	367	359
1983	439	335	394	381	367	355
1984	439	336	396	381	369	354
1985	444	341	401	384	373	363
MATHEMATICS						
Male						
1981	508	381	538	449	439	428
1982	510	385	538	450	441	424
1983	510	388	537	451	443	427
1984	511	389	541	452	444	426
1985	515	394	540	454	452	435
Female						
1981	459	350	487	402	392	371
1982	459	354	488	400	394	377
1983	460	356	490	402	393	374
1984	464	362	497	406	399	379
1985	468	364	496	406	402	381

NOTE: Scores range from 200 to 800.

SOURCE: Admissions Testing Program of the College Board, PROFILES, COLLEGE-BOUND SENIORS, annual series, 1981-85, (New York: College Entrance Examination Board).

Appendix table 41. Percentile rankings on Scholastic Aptitude Test by sex and racial/ethnic group: 1985

Component and score	ALL COLLEGE-BOUND SENIORS			WHITE			BLACK			ASIAN		
	Total	Male	Female	Total	Male	Female	Total	Male	Female	Total	Male	Female
Verbal												
700-800	1	1	1	1	1	1	0	0	0	1	1	1
650-699	2	3	3	3	3	2	0	0	0	3	3	3
600-649	4	5	5	5	5	5	1	1	1	4	5	4
500-599	19	21	19	23	23	21	6	7	6	16	17	15
400-499	33	33	34	37	36	37	20	21	19	25	25	25
Mathematics												
700-800	4	5	1	4	7	1	0	0	0	10	13	5
650-699	5	7	3	6	8	4	1	1	1	9	11	7
600-649	8	11	7	10	12	7	2	3	1	11	13	10
500-599	26	29	24	29	31	27	10	13	8	27	28	27
400-499	29	26	30	30	26	33	24	26	22	24	21	26

Component and score	NATIVE AMERICAN			MEXICAN AMERICAN			PUERTO RICAN		
	Total	Male	Female	Total	Male	Female	Total	Male	Female
Verbal									
700-800	0	0	0	0	0	0	0	0	0
650-699	1	1	1	1	1	0	1	1	1
600-649	2	3	2	2	2	2	2	2	2
500-599	13	15	11	11	13	9	11	13	9
400-499	29	31	28	27	29	25	24	26	23
Mathematics									
700-800	1	2	0	1	1	0	1	1	0
650-699	2	3	1	2	3	1	2	3	1
600-649	4	6	3	4	6	3	4	6	2
500-599	20	25	16	19	23	15	16	21	11
400-499	29	31	28	31	31	30	26	27	23

SOURCE: Admissions Testing Program of the College Board, PROFILES, COLLEGE-BOUND SENIORS, 1985, (New York: College Entrance Examination Board).

Appendix table 42. Scores for college-bound seniors on achievement tests in mathematics and science by sex/racial/ethnic group: 1985

Achievement and SAT-M tests	Total	Male	Female	White	Black	Asian	Native American	Mexican American	Puerto Rican
Mathematics Level I	540	559	523	544	478	563	497	483	511
SAT-M (1)	563	587	540	569	484	574	518	490	528
Mathematics Level II	658	671	637	660	581	674	614	598	620
SAT-M	649	664	624	655	560	653	597	584	610
Chemistry	576	589	551	575	512	587	537	523	556
SAT-M	632	648	604	634	545	649	573	584	590
Biology	554	574	538	557	479	548	496	496	522
SAT-M	584	612	560	587	491	603	521	525	534
Physics	592	603	547	594	513	593	561	545	538
SAT-M	652	657	630	656	557	661	613	610	590

(1) Score on the mathematics portion of the aptitude test.

NOTE: Scores range from 200 to 800

SOURCE: Admissions Testing Program of the College Board, PROFILES, COLLEGE-BOUND SENIORS, 1985, (New York: College Entrance Examination Board, 1985).

Appendix table 43. Scores for college-bound seniors on advanced placement tests in mathematics and science by sex/racial/ethnic group: 1986

Sex/racial/ethnic group	Biology	Chemistry	Computer Science	Math/ Calculus AB	Math/ Calculus BC	Physics B	Physics C Mechanical	Physics C Electrical & Magnetism
Total	3.15	2.80	2.98	3.09	3.50	2.80	3.47	3.33
Male	3.29	2.93	3.05	3.18	3.57	2.91	3.54	3.39
Female	3.01	2.49	2.58	2.95	3.35	2.46	3.09	3.00
White	3.14	2.77	2.99	3.07	3.44	2.76	3.45	3.32
Black	2.27	1.88	2.05	2.30	3.13	2.04	2.63	2.18
Asian	3.49	3.00	3.06	3.39	3.64	3.02	3.47	3.25
Native American	2.72	2.32	2.17	2.73	3.00	2.87	4.00	3.60
Mexican American	2.50	2.31	2.50	2.75	3.39	2.09	3.00	2.42
Puerto Rican	2.69	2.26	2.57	2.68	3.35	1.63	2.67	3.50
Other Hispanic	2.70	2.42	2.84	2.73	3.37	2.13	2.77	2.65

NOTE: Scores range from 1 to 5: 1 = no recommendation for college credit; 2 = possibly qualified; 3 = qualified; 4 = well qualified; and 5 = extremely well qualified.

SOURCE: Advanced Placement Program, The College Board, 1986 ADVANCED PLACEMENT PROGRAM, NATIONAL SUMMARY REPORTS, (New York: College Entrance Examination Board, 1986).

Appendix table 44a. Intended area of study of college-bound seniors by sex/racial/ethnic group: 1981 & 1985

(Percent)

1981

Area of study	Total	Male	Female	White	Black	Asian	Native American	Mexican American	Puerto Rican
Total	100.0	100.0	100.0	100.0	100.0	100.0	100.0	100.0	100.0
Science & engineering	36.1	46.5	26.8	35.7	35.8	43.7	36.4	38.3	34.9
Biological science	3.3	3.4	3.2	3.4	2.1	3.8	3.3	2.6	2.9
Agriculture	1.5	2.0	1.0	1.7	0.4	0.5	1.6	1.0	0.6
Computer science	5.6	6.5	4.8	5.1	9.0	9.9	5.7	6.2	6.8
Mathematics	1.1	1.2	1.0	1.2	0.7	1.2	0.7	0.6	0.7
Physical science	2.0	3.1	1.0	2.1	0.8	2.1	1.7	1.2	1.1
Engineering	11.8	21.5	3.2	11.4	10.9	19.8	12.0	13.8	10.0
Psychology	3.4	1.4	5.2	3.4	3.8	1.9	3.9	3.5	3.9
Social science	7.4	7.4	7.4	7.4	8.1	4.5	7.5	9.4	8.9
Non-S/E (1)	63.9	53.5	73.2	64.3	64.2	56.3	63.6	61.7	65.1
Business	18.5	17.6	19.4	18.3	21.7	16.3	17.5	18.0	20.9
Education	5.7	2.6	8.6	6.1	5.0	2.1	6.5	5.4	4.9

1985

Area of study	Total	Male	Female	White	Black	Asian	Native American	Mexican American	Puerto Rican
Total	100.0	100.0	100.0	100.0	100.0	100.0	100.0	100.0	100.0
Science & engineering	37.2	47.7	28.1	36.4	38.5	44.9	37.1	39.6	37.6
Biological science	3.1	3.0	3.1	3.1	3.1	4.5	2.6	3.1	2.8
Agriculture	0.9	1.4	0.6	1.1	0.3	0.2	1.3	0.7	0.6
Computer science	7.1	9.4	5.0	6.1	12.8	10.1	7.9	8.1	10.2
Mathematics	1.1	1.2	1.1	1.2	0.8	1.2	1.0	0.7	0.7
Physical science	1.7	2.5	1.0	1.8	0.8	1.9	1.5	1.0	1.0
Engineering	11.7	21.1	3.4	11.2	10.7	20.7	10.7	12.9	9.8
Psychology	4.1	1.6	6.3	4.2	3.6	2.0	4.3	4.6	3.7
Social science	7.5	7.5	7.6	7.7	7.5	4.3	7.8	9.0	8.8
Non-S/E (1)	62.8	52.3	71.9	63.6	61.5	55.1	62.9	60.4	62.4
Business	21.0	19.9	22.0	21.0	23.8	17.4	20.0	20.4	21.3
Education	4.7	13.3	7.0	5.1	3.3	1.6	5.3	4.4	4.3

(1) Detail will not add to total because "other non-S/E" not included.

SOURCE: Admissions Testing Program of the College Board, PROFILES, COLLEGE-BOUND SENIORS, annual series, 1981-85, (New York: College Entrance Examination Board).

Appendix table 44b. SAT mathematics scores of college-bound seniors by intended area of study and sex/racial/ethnic group: 1981 & 1985

Area of study	Total	Male	Female	White	Black	Asian	Native American	Mexican American	Puerto Rican
1981									
Total	466	492	443	483	362	513	425	415	398
Science & engineering	---	---	---	---	---	---	---	---	---
Biological science	507	516	496	513	384	556	461	426	428
Agriculture	435	438	431	441	318	434	388	377	410
Computer science	496	520	464	519	355	528	423	423	379
Mathematics	584	602	562	591	407	597	495	499	527
Physical science	565	577	537	571	418	622	508	498	455
Engineering	541	540	549	555	416	568	500	480	464
Psychology	444	476	435	459	345	492	398	380	366
Social science	473	501	450	491	344	511	425	394	376
Non-S/E	---	---	---	---	---	---	---	---	---
Business	442	468	422	458	331	468	398	388	354
Education	415	412	415	424	310	425	376	356	352
1985									
Total	475	499	452	490	376	518	428	426	405
Science & engineering	---	---	---	---	---	---	---	---	---
Biological science	519	530	511	527	398	571	477	440	440
Agriculture	429	428	430	433	327	473	353	364	410
Computer science	488	516	438	518	363	517	415	427	379
Mathematics	588	603	575	595	433	595	565	510	540
Physical science	578	589	554	584	432	618	533	503	536
Engineering	556	555	561	570	430	573	494	491	478
Psychology	450	482	445	460	362	481	419	396	371
Social science	480	503	460	496	359	519	425	403	384
Non-S/E	---	---	---	---	---	---	---	---	---
Business	450	474	432	464	343	476	403	396	377
Education	426	427	426	436	316	448	381	372	353

SOURCE: Admissions Testing Program of the College Board, PROFILES, COLLEGE-BOUND SENIORS, annual series, 1981-85, (New York: College Entrance Examination Board).

Appendix table 45. Selected characteristics of college-bound seniors by sex/racial/ethnic group: 1985

Selected characteristic	All college-bound seniors			Male			Female		
	Percent	SAT-V	SAT-M	Percent	SAT-V	SAT-M	Percent	SAT-V	SAT-M
A. PARENTS EDUCATION									
1. Father's education	100.0	--	--	100.0	--	--	100.0	--	--
Grade School	3.1	354	402	2.7	364	440	3.4	348	380
Some High School	7.2	373	413	6.5	383	447	7.9	368	389
High School Diploma	21.5	399	440	20.8	406	468	22.2	394	417
Business/Trade School	6.7	412	453	6.4	415	482	6.9	409	434
Some College	17.9	425	465	17.6	429	496	18.0	420	444
Bachelor's degree	17.5	451	503	18.6	455	528	16.5	446	478
Some graduate or professional school	4.9	461	509	5.2	465	534	4.6	457	486
Graduate or professional degree	21.2	474	526	22.2	480	553	20.3	470	501
2. Mother's education	100.0	--	--	100.0	--	--	100.0	--	--
Grade School	2.6	344	403	2.4	352	440	2.7	335	378
Some High School	6.5	369	411	5.8	379	447	7.1	362	386
High School Diploma	31.3	410	452	31.6	415	483	31.0	406	431
Business/Trade School	8.5	421	462	7.9	428	496	9.0	415	441
Some College	21.1	436	481	21.2	442	511	21.0	431	454
Bachelor's degree	14.0	470	522	14.7	475	547	13.3	467	497
Some graduate or professional school	5.9	464	510	6.1	468	535	5.7	459	486
Graduate or professional degree	10.3	469	512	10.4	474	542	10.3	463	487
B. ANNUAL PARENTAL INCOME	100.0	--	--	100.0	--	--	100.0	--	--
Under $6,000	3.6	350	395	3.0	361	437	4.1	344	374
$6,000-11,999	7.9	376	418	7.0	386	450	8.8	370	396
$12,000-17,999	10.2	398	439	9.4	407	472	10.9	393	415
$18,000-23,999	12.1	413	453	11.9	419	483	12.2	410	432
$24,000-29,999	11.7	427	469	11.8	430	499	11.6	422	446
$30,000-39,999	18.6	434	482	19.0	438	508	18.2	431	456
$40,000-49,999	13.4	446	496	13.8	449	521	12.9	442	471
$50,000 or more	22.6	465	517	23.9	469	543	21.4	460	494

Appendix table 45. - continued

Selected characteristic	White			Black			Asian		
	Percent	SAT-V	SAT-M	Percent	SAT-V	SAT-M	Percent	SAT-V	SAT-M
A. PARENTS EDUCATION									
1. Father's education	100.0	--	--	100.0	--	--	100.0	--	--
Grade School	1.6	399	436	6.3	304	339	5.7	306	473
Some High School	5.7	402	440	16.0	306	335	7.9	332	489
High School Diploma	21.0	414	454	31.5	316	341	15.0	353	480
Business/Trade School	6.6	425	466	7.9	334	360	5.6	375	491
Some College	18.2	435	478	17.4	347	370	16.1	375	497
Bachelor's degree	18.9	458	508	8.7	374	392	18.5	405	538
Some graduate or professional school	5.2	468	516	2.8	384	400	4.9	415	534
Graduate or professional degree	22.6	481	530	9.4	394	412	26.2	474	575
2. Mother's education	100.0	--	--	100.0	--	--	100.0	--	--
Grade School	1.1	389	426	3.4	294	331	9.0	308	478
Some High School	4.7	399	435	13.9	300	334	10.5	332	493
High School Diploma	32.3	421	464	30.3	317	344	22.1	368	506
Business/Trade School	8.6	433	476	8.8	332	355	6.5	394	508
Some College	21.7	447	494	21.2	346	368	16.6	403	523
Bachelor's degree	14.8	480	529	8.8	373	390	16.9	443	553
Some graduate or professional school	6.2	471	517	4.3	378	390	5.4	446	556
Graduate or professional degree	10.5	478	523	9.3	384	398	12.9	468	557
B. ANNUAL PARENTAL INCOME	100.0	--	--	100.0	--	--	100.0	--	--
Under $6,000	1.8	415	450	12.9	298	330	7.6	271	464
$6,000-11,999	5.4	420	452	21.0	310	340	13.0	301	483
$12,000-17,999	8.6	424	459	18.9	327	351	12.8	353	501
$18,000-23,999	11.6	429	468	14.8	340	366	12.3	378	507
$24,000-29,999	12.2	434	478	9.2	351	376	9.8	401	521
$30,000-39,999	20.1	440	488	10.6	361	381	14.8	424	523
$40,000-49,999	14.7	450	500	6.4	378	397	10.9	444	546
$50,000 or more	25.6	467	519	6.3	407	430	18.7	478	579

Appendix table 45. - continued

Selected characteristic	Native American			Mexican American			Puerto Rican		
	Percent	SAT-V	SAT-M	Percent	SAT-V	SAT-M	Percent	SAT-V	SAT-M
A. PARENTS EDUCATION									
1. Father's education	100.0	--	--	100.0	--	--	100.0	--	--
Grade School	5.3	332	377	23.0	340	390	15.5	315	338
Some High School	11.9	333	366	15.5	346	385	19.8	327	352
High School Diploma	24.1	360	388	19.3	368	405	24.6	356	378
Business/Trade School	7.7	378	408	5.7	386	421	5.5	374	388
Some College	19.6	398	432	17.0	391	429	13.5	387	416
Bachelor's degree	13.0	411	446	8.1	412	455	8.6	417	439
Some graduate or professional school	4.2	432	466	2.0	421	468	2.3	448	485
Graduate or professional degree	14.2	429	459	9.2	430	471	10.2	434	463
2. Mother's education	100.0	--	--	100.0	--	--	100.0	--	--
Grade School	3.8	312	383	22.7	339	387	14.7	308	337
Some High School	10.6	333	367	17.0	348	388	19.8	327	347
High School Diploma	31.9	373	406	26.7	376	418	28.6	369	393
Business/Trade School	8.9	384	405	7.0	388	423	6.0	380	391
Some College	21.9	407	435	15.1	406	440	15.1	392	418
Bachelor's degree	10.2	435	462	4.8	425	461	6.6	430	452
Some graduate or professional school	4.4	414	463	2.3	426	465	2.9	431	458
Graduate or professional degree	8.4	428	436	4.4	425	460	6.2	425	438
B. ANNUAL PARENTAL INCOME	100.0	--	--	100.0	--	--	100.0	--	--
Under $6,000	7.7	342	371	7.2	328	380	14.0	310	333
$6,000-11,999	13.7	347	376	17.6	343	389	21.9	327	345
$12,000-17,999	13.6	362	387	17.7	361	402	16.6	349	375
$18,000-23,999	13.6	381	405	15.6	372	414	12.5	371	388
$24,000-29,999	11.4	395	423	11.8	379	419	8.9	390	420
$30,000-39,999	16.0	409	440	14.4	395	438	10.6	408	436
$40,000-49,999	10.5	407	444	7.7	409	441	6.7	424	454
$50,000 or more	13.6	423	466	8.0	430	469	8.8	446	487

Appendix table 45. – continued

Selected characteristic	All college-bound seniors			Male			Female		
	Percent	SAT-V	SAT-M	Percent	SAT-V	SAT-M	Percent	SAT-V	SAT-M
C. PLANS FOR FINANCIAL AID	100.0	--	--	100.0	--	--	100.0	--	--
Yes	77.3	431	476	75.9	438	508	78.6	426	450
D. OVERALL HIGH SCHOOL GPA	100.0	--	--	100.0	--	--	100.0	--	--
3.75-4.00	14.5	521	589	13.3	533	626	15.6	512	563
3.50-3.74	11.2	475	534	10.1	488	575	12.3	469	505
3.25-3.49	12.5	453	506	11.8	464	545	13.2	444	476
3.00-3.24	17.3	428	473	17.0	438	509	17.6	418	445
2.75-2.99	12.4	409	446	12.4	419	481	12.4	397	415
2.50-2.74	12.7	390	420	13.2	401	451	12.3	380	391
2.25-2.49	8.6	374	403	9.5	386	433	7.7	363	376
2.00-2.24	6.5	359	383	7.6	469	410	5.5	347	358
Under 2.00	4.2	353	376	5.1	364	402	3.4	337	343
E. DEGREE LEVEL GOALS	100.0	--	--	100.0	--	--	100.0	--	--
Two-year training program	2.5	346	375	2.5	345	392	2.4	347	358
Associate of Arts	2.0	355	371	1.4	356	385	2.6	355	364
BA or BS	32.5	410	450	32.1	411	473	32.9	410	435
MA or MS	26.8	448	502	28.0	453	532	25.7	443	473
MD, PhD, or other professional	18.8	485	536	19.4	495	572	18.3	471	503
Two-year program/degree	4.5	350	373	3.9	349	390	5.0	351	361
Undecided	17.4	408	444	16.7	414	474	18.1	399	421

Appendix table 45. - continued

Selected characteristic	White			Black			Asian		
	Percent	SAT-V	SAT-M	Percent	SAT-V	SAT-M	Percent	SAT-V	SAT-M
C. PLANS FOR FINANCIAL AID	100.0	--	--	100.0	--	--	100.0	--	--
Yes	74.9	448	494	92.4	333	359	80.1	397	521
D. OVERALL HIGH SCHOOL GPA	100.0	--	--	100.0	--	--	100.0	--	--
3.75-4.00	15.6	526	591	4.8	432	479	21.5	504	626
3.50-3.74	11.8	487	540	6.1	395	434	14.2	428	560
3.25-3.49	13.0	464	514	8.8	372	406	14.3	395	524
3.00-3.24	17.5	439	485	15.8	348	378	16.4	381	493
2.75-2.99	12.3	421	456	14.0	333	357	10.0	357	461
2.50-2.74	12.2	405	435	17.5	319	339	9.8	335	440
2.25-2.49	8.0	390	419	13.3	309	331	6.1	327	425
2.00-2.24	5.9	374	401	11.3	299	325	4.6	308	408
Under 2.00	3.7	369	390	8.4	298	319	3.2	311	423
E. DEGREE LEVEL GOALS	100.0	--	--	100.0	--	--	100.0	--	--
Two-year training program	2.3	360	387	3.2	274	307	1.7	258	366
Associate of Arts	2.0	368	381	2.3	287	306	1.2	271	370
BA or BS	33.7	423	462	30.5	316	341	24.7	347	465
MA or MS	26.7	464	517	27.6	348	374	27.4	403	533
MD, PhD, or other professional	17.6	501	552	20.4	383	402	30.9	463	587
Two-year program/degree	4.3	364	384	5.5	279	306	2.9	262	367
Undecided	17.7	420	456	16.1	309	335	14.0	368	476

Appendix table 45. - continued

Selected characteristic	Native American			Mexican American			Puerto Rican		
	Percent	SAT-V	SAT-M	Percent	SAT-V	SAT-M	Percent	SAT-V	SAT-M
C. PLANS FOR FINANCIAL AID	100.0	--	--	100.0	--	--	100.0	--	--
Yes	83.5	387	418	89.1	373	418	90.6	359	382
D. OVERALL HIGH SCHOOL GPA	100.0	--	--	100.0	--	--	100.0	--	--
3.75-4.00	8.7	472	533	11.2	457	527	7.3	468	532
3.50-3.74	8.6	445	481	10.6	411	466	7.9	444	468
3.25-3.49	11.5	415	465	12.2	394	446	9.9	396	437
3.00-3.24	16.8	406	424	17.8	371	416	18.1	373	398
2.75-2.99	13.6	375	413	13.3	361	395	14.3	359	380
2.50-2.74	14.4	349	377	14.0	347	377	15.0	330	353
2.25-2.49	11.8	355	374	9.9	330	355	11.4	326	341
2.00-2.24	8.4	334	358	7.0	320	347	9.2	317	335
Under 2.00	6.1	314	338	4.2	323	342	6.8	311	326
E. DEGREE LEVEL GOALS	100.0	--	--	100.0	--	--	100.0	--	--
Two-year training program	4.3	322	340	3.0	295	340	4.2	305	323
Associate of Arts	3.2	332	343	2.0	305	333	3.6	305	318
BA or BS	30.3	374	408	29.4	357	398	31.7	353	378
MA or MS	24.8	407	447	27.3	388	437	24.0	386	420
MD, PhD, or other professional	18.5	438	465	20.9	415	457	17.9	407	437
Two-year program/degree	7.6	327	341	5.0	300	337	7.9	305	320
Undecided	18.9	361	384	17.4	351	385	18.5	337	357

NOTE: SAT-V = Verbal component of the Aptitude test; SAT-M = mathematics component.

SOURCE: Admissions Testing Program of the College Bpard, PROFILES, COLLEGE-BOUND SENIORS, 1985, (New York: College Entrance Examination Board).

Appendix table 46. Graduate Record Examination (GRE) scores by
sex/racial/ethnic group and undergraduate
major: 1979 & 1985

Undergraduate major and year	Total	Men	Women	White	Black	Asian	Native American	Mexican American	Puerto Rican	Other Hispanic(1)
					VERBAL					
All majors										
1979	488	487	489	511	363	480	459	419	389	465
1985	486	485	486	512	379	481	469	425	385	466
Science and engineering										
1979	495	495	500	523	372	486	472	434	395	479
1985	489	485	494	524	387	482	478	448	390	474
Physical science										
1979	519	514	534	541	391	495	482	509	418	509
1985	503	501	509	536	421	495	496	481	376	507
Mathematical science										
1979	505	510	498	537	364	476	494	420	375	468
1985	485	489	478	536	387	467	502	443	369	499
Engineering										
1979	468	465	497	527	403	459	478	434	390	476
1985	463	458	499	530	432	465	505	461	410	470
Biological science										
1979	492	485	500	521	358	494	447	407	398	473
1985	507	502	511	528	404	503	490	477	390	488
Behavioral science										
1979	507	506	509	528	386	503	483	446	399	481
1985	503	506	501	525	392	500	475	446	399	469
Social science										
1979	454	452	457	484	343	453	451	409	363	465
1985	453	454	451	484	348	471	450	415	370	444

Appendix table 46. - continued

QUANTITATIVE

Undergraduate major and year	Total	Men	Women	White	Black	Asian	Native American	Mexican American	Puerto Rican	Other Hispanic(1)
All majors										
1979	514	555	478	525	358	566	457	422	418	468
1985	534	581	494	538	378	603	485	433	427	489
Science and engineering										
1979	544	575	502	557	375	592	476	455	437	497
1985	568	603	523	574	399	615	515	479	451	515
Physical science										
1979	630	640	600	639	462	658	581	600	532	592
1985	632	642	606	637	494	654	587	600	535	608
Mathematical science										
1979	665	682	636	682	486	660	671	595	550	626
1985	656	669	632	670	497	671	624	589	531	628
Engineering										
1979	654	661	603	675	521	675	570	595	583	624
1985	670	671	663	686	570	685	651	627	588	630
Biological science										
1979	555	577	528	569	381	596	479	448	450	509
1985	571	585	558	582	429	617	530	516	453	537
Behavioral science										
1979	500	522	479	514	366	528	457	427	387	460
1985	508	535	488	518	368	554	466	434	397	450
Social science										
1979	474	501	446	496	337	494	443	413	378	429
1985	476	509	449	492	337	509	482	410	381	433

Appendix table 46. - continued

Undergraduate major and year	Total	Men	Women	White	Black	Asian	Native American	Mexican American	Puerto Rican	Other Hispanic(1)
					ANALYTICAL					
All majors										
1979	503	508	499	529	352	510	457	412	385	460
1985	525	533	518	550	395	541	495	441	407	487
Science and engineering										
1979	517	515	515	547	365	524	471	436	397	483
1985	542	545	538	574	408	547	512	475	422	502
Physical science										
1979	557	555	564	581	406	546	523	516	433	524
1985	571	568	577	601	456	570	558	548	431	549
Mathematical science										
1979	567	568	565	602	401	549	553	467	412	530
1985	589	591	586	637	451	580	577	521	448	569
Engineering										
1979	526	525	534	587	437	533	505	487	439	520
1985	559	553	603	621	495	562	588	545	480	544
Biological science										
1979	521	518	526	553	359	537	456	421	401	484
1985	558	551	564	582	431	562	535	498	413	524
Behavioral science										
1979	511	509	513	535	371	510	468	435	382	473
1985	524	524	524	548	397	529	486	455	415	473
Social science										
1979	461	473	469	506	333	464	455	404	362	448
1985	487	490	485	522	366	495	475	431	381	452

(1) Primarily Latin American.

NOTE: Scores range from 200 to 800.

SOURCES: Cheryl L. Wild, A SUMMARY OF DATA COLLECTED FROM GRADUATE
RECORD EXAMINATION TEST-TAKERS DURING 1978-79, DATA SUMMARY
REPORT #4 and Henry Roy Smith III, A SUMMARY OF DATA COLLECTED
FROM GRADUATE RECORD EXAMINATION TEST-TAKERS DURING 1984-85,
DATA SUMMARY REPORT #10, (Princeton N.J.: Educational Testing
Service).

Appendix table 47. Science and engineering bachelor's degree recipients by field and sex: 1975-85

Field	1975	1976	1977	1978	1979	1980	1981	1982	1983	1984	1985
					Total						
Total, all fields	294,920	292,174	288,543	288,157	288,625	291,983	294,867	302,118	307,225	314,666	321,739
Total science	254,855	253,060	246,962	240,746	234,905	232,743	230,799	234,327	234,271	238,135	243,868
Physical sciences	20,896	21,559	22,618	23,175	23,363	23,661	24,175	24,372	23,497	23,759	23,847
Chemistry	10,649	11,107	11,322	11,474	11,643	11,446	11,540	11,316	11,039	10,912	10,701
Physics	3,716	3,544	3,420	3,330	3,338	3,397	3,441	3,475	3,800	3,921	4,111
Geological sciences	3,324	3,362	3,879	4,344	4,503	4,600	5,205	5,542	6,104	6,552	6,313
Other	3,207	3,546	3,997	4,027	3,879	4,218	3,989	4,039	2,554	2,374	2,722
Mathematics	18,346	16,085	14,303	12,701	11,901	11,473	11,173	11,708	12,557	13,342	15,267
Computer sciences	5,039	5,664	6,429	7,224	8,769	11,213	15,233	20,431	24,678	32,435	39,121
Life sciences	72,710	77,301	78,472	77,138	75,085	71,617	68,086	65,041	63,237	59,613	57,812
Biological sciences	56,179	59,012	58,273	56,111	53,454	50,496	47,920	45,806	44,067	42,310	41,933
Agricultural sciences	16,531	18,289	20,199	21,027	21,631	21,121	20,166	19,235	19,170	17,303	15,879
Psychology	51,436	50,363	47,794	45,057	43,012	42,513	41,364	41,539	40,825	40,375	40,237
Social sciences	86,428	82,088	77,349	75,461	72,775	72,266	70,768	71,236	69,477	68,611	67,584
Economics	14,118	14,854	15,342	15,746	16,534	17,954	18,833	19,961	20,556	20,777	20,769
Sociology	31,817	27,970	24,989	22,991	20,545	19,164	17,582	16,324	14,343	13,320	12,129
Political sciences	29,314	28,515	26,576	26,245	25,817	25,658	25,217	25,885	26,020	25,943	26,065
Other	11,179	10,749	10,442	10,479	9,879	9,490	9,136	9,066	8,558	8,571	8,621
Total engineering	40,065	39,114	41,581	47,411	53,720	59,240	64,068	67,791	72,954	76,531	77,871
Aeronautical/astronautical	1,174	1,009	1,078	1,186	1,386	1,424	1,809	2,120	2,127	2,534	2,854
Chemical	3,142	3,203	3,581	4,615	5,655	6,383	6,604	6,814	7,256	7,558	7,222
Civil	7,790	8,059	8,376	9,265	9,941	10,442	10,752	10,570	10,054	9,750	9,208
Electrical	10,246	9,874	10,018	11,213	12,440	13,902	15,040	16,553	18,184	20,059	21,814
Industrial	2,583	2,241	2,264	2,712	2,804	3,217	3,878	4,044	3,824	4,020	4,009
Mechanical	6,949	6,841	7,771	8,924	10,171	11,863	13,388	13,988	15,729	16,691	16,851
Other	8,181	7,887	8,493	9,496	11,323	12,009	12,597	13,702	15,780	15,919	15,613

Appendix table 47. - continued

Men

Field	1975	1976	1977	1978	1979	1980	1981	1982	1983	1984	1985
Total, all fields	201,578	196,577	191,090	188,097	186,333	186,009	186,425	188,957	191,614	196,650	200,300
Total science	162,373	158,906	151,595	144,193	137,532	132,783	129,474	129,503	128,379	130,952	133,745
Physical sciences	17,058	17,420	18,067	18,188	18,076	18,010	18,195	18,033	17,036	17,168	17,149
Chemistry	8,264	8,610	8,720	8,593	8,530	8,169	8,065	7,703	7,303	7,087	6,807
Physics	3,354	3,156	3,062	2,961	2,939	2,963	3,009	3,014	3,317	3,361	3,550
Geological sciences	2,749	2,756	3,043	3,386	3,445	3,469	3,902	4,126	4,535	4,935	4,753
Other	2,691	2,898	3,242	3,248	3,162	3,409	3,219	3,190	1,881	1,785	2,039
Mathematics	10,646	9,531	8,354	7,455	6,943	6,625	6,392	6,650	7,059	7,428	8,231
Computer sciences	4,083	4,540	4,887	5,360	6,306	7,814	10,280	13,316	15,687	20,369	24,690
Life sciences	51,899	53,512	52,863	50,184	47,537	44,021	40,610	38,115	36,677	34,253	32,663
Biological sciences	37,796	38,714	37,325	34,574	31,997	29,405	26,898	25,141	23,962	22,653	21,922
Agricultural sciences	14,103	14,798	15,538	15,610	15,540	14,616	13,712	12,974	12,715	11,600	10,741
Psychology	24,333	22,987	20,692	18,517	16,649	15,590	14,447	13,756	13,228	12,949	12,815
Social sciences	54,354	50,916	46,732	44,489	42,021	40,723	39,550	39,633	38,692	38,785	38,197
Economics	11,679	11,940	11,815	11,813	11,979	12,524	13,093	13,481	13,718	13,689	13,606
Sociology	13,330	11,379	9,802	8,423	7,155	6,383	5,357	4,886	4,360	4,275	3,759
Political sciences	22,704	21,310	19,079	18,077	17,197	16,446	15,946	16,026	15,792	15,778	15,765
Other	6,641	6,287	6,036	6,176	5,690	5,370	5,154	5,240	4,822	5,043	5,067
Total engineering	39,205	37,671	39,495	43,914	48,801	53,226	56,951	59,454	63,235	65,698	66,555
Aeronautical/astronautical	1,150	980	1,050	1,125	1,320	1,342	1,680	1,949	1,955	2,359	2,613
Chemical	3,001	2,927	3,152	3,899	4,649	5,168	5,336	5,328	5,618	5,661	5,347
Civil	7,640	7,807	7,943	8,575	8,986	9,451	9,628	9,375	8,728	8,441	7,975
Electrical	10,116	9,681	9,750	10,778	11,781	13,000	13,940	15,142	16,405	18,028	19,392
Industrial	2,524	2,154	2,115	2,389	2,376	2,672	3,111	3,092	2,824	2,949	2,842
Mechanical	6,867	6,694	7,535	8,458	9,568	10,981	12,252	12,768	14,284	14,927	15,097
Other	7,907	7,428	7,950	8,690	10,121	10,612	11,004	11,800	13,421	13,333	13,060

Appendix table 47. - continued

Field	1975	1976	1977	1978	1979	1980	1981	1982	1983	1984	1985
					Women						
Total, all fields	93,342	95,597	97,453	100,060	102,292	105,974	108,442	113,161	115,611	118,016	121,439
Total science	92,482	94,154	95,367	96,563	97,373	99,960	101,325	104,824	105,892	107,183	110,123
Physical sciences	3,838	4,139	4,551	4,987	5,287	5,651	5,980	6,339	6,461	6,591	6,698
Chemistry	2,385	2,497	2,602	2,881	3,113	3,277	3,475	3,613	3,736	3,825	3,894
Physics	362	388	358	369	399	434	461	432	483	560	561
Geological sciences	575	606	836	958	1,058	1,131	1,303	1,416	1,569	1,617	1,560
Other	516	648	755	779	717	809	770	849	673	589	683
Mathematics	7,700	6,554	5,949	5,246	4,958	4,848	4,781	5,058	5,498	5,914	7,036
Computer sciences	956	1,124	1,539	1,864	2,463	3,399	4,953	7,115	8,991	12,066	14,431
Life sciences	20,811	23,789	25,609	26,954	27,548	27,596	27,476	26,926	26,560	25,360	25,149
Biological sciences	18,383	20,298	20,948	21,537	21,457	21,091	21,022	20,665	20,105	19,657	20,011
Agricultural sciences	2,428	3,491	4,661	5,417	6,091	6,505	6,454	6,261	6,455	5,703	5,138
Psychology	27,103	27,376	27,102	26,540	26,363	26,923	26,917	27,783	27,597	27,426	27,422
Social sciences	32,074	31,172	30,617	30,972	30,754	31,543	31,218	31,603	30,785	29,826	29,387
Economics	2,439	2,914	3,527	3,933	4,555	5,430	5,740	6,480	6,838	7,088	7,163
Sociology	18,487	16,591	15,187	14,568	13,390	12,781	12,225	11,438	9,983	9,045	8,370
Political sciences	6,610	7,205	7,497	8,620	8,620	9,212	9,859	9,859	10,228	10,165	10,300
Other	4,538	4,462	4,406	4,303	4,189	4,120	3,982	3,826	3,736	3,528	3,554
Total engineering	860	1,443	2,086	3,497	4,919	6,014	7,117	8,337	9,719	10,833	11,316
Aeronautical/astronautical	24	29	28	61	66	82	129	171	172	175	241
Chemical	141	276	429	716	1,006	1,215	1,268	1,486	1,638	1,897	1,875
Civil	150	252	433	690	955	991	1,124	1,195	1,326	1,309	1,233
Electrical	130	193	268	435	659	902	1,100	1,411	1,779	2,031	2,422
Industrial	59	87	149	323	428	545	767	952	1,000	1,071	1,167
Mechanical	82	147	236	466	603	882	1,136	1,220	1,445	1,764	1,754
Other	274	459	543	806	1,202	1,397	1,593	1,902	2,359	2,586	2,553

SOURCE: National Science Foundation, SRS, and Center for Statistics, Department of Education.

199

Appendix table 48. Science and engineering master's degree recipients by field and sex: 1975-85

Field	1975	1976	1977	1978	1979	1980	1981	1982	1983	1984	1985
					Total						
Total, all fields	53,852	54,747	56,731	56,237	54,456	54,391	54,811	57,025	58,868	59,569	61,278
Total science	38,418	38,577	39,842	39,222	38,263	37,545	37,438	38,431	39,147	39,217	40,072
Physical sciences	5,830	5,485	5,345	5,576	5,464	5,233	5,300	5,526	5,288	5,568	5,802
Chemistry	2,006	1,796	1,775	1,892	1,765	1,733	1,667	1,758	1,632	1,677	1,734
Physics	1,577	1,451	1,319	1,294	1,319	1,192	1,294	1,284	1,370	1,535	1,523
Geological sciences	932	1,003	1,047	1,239	1,300	1,295	1,396	1,540	1,552	1,514	1,692
Other	1,315	1,235	1,204	1,151	1,080	1,013	943	944	734	842	853
Mathematics	4,338	3,863	3,698	3,383	3,046	2,868	2,569	2,731	2,839	2,749	2,888
Computer sciences	2,299	2,603	2,798	3,038	3,055	3,647	4,218	4,935	5,321	6,190	7,101
Life sciences	9,618	9,823	10,707	10,711	10,719	10,278	9,731	9,824	9,720	9,330	8,757
Biological sciences	6,931	6,939	7,468	7,227	7,220	6,854	6,299	6,184	6,041	5,717	5,345
Agricultural sciences	2,687	2,884	3,239	3,484	3,499	3,424	3,432	3,640	3,679	3,613	3,412
Psychology	7,104	7,859	8,320	8,194	8,031	7,861	8,039	7,849	8,439	8,073	8,481
Social sciences	9,229	8,944	8,974	8,320	7,948	7,658	7,581	7,566	7,540	7,307	7,043
Economics	2,133	2,093	2,166	1,997	1,960	1,823	1,913	1,968	1,975	1,893	1,994
Sociology	2,112	2,010	1,830	1,611	1,415	1,341	1,240	1,154	1,112	1,008	1,022
Political sciences	2,333	2,192	2,223	2,070	2,038	1,938	1,876	1,955	1,829	1,770	1,500
Other	2,651	2,649	2,755	2,642	2,535	2,556	2,552	2,489	2,624	2,636	2,527
Total engineering	15,434	16,170	16,889	17,015	16,193	16,846	17,373	18,594	19,721	20,352	21,206
Aeronautical/astronautical	477	479	385	411	372	382	408	521	491	562	605
Chemical	990	1,031	1,086	1,237	1,149	1,271	1,268	1,287	1,371	1,517	1,549
Civil	2,771	3,000	2,969	2,691	2,655	2,683	2,894	2,998	3,082	3,151	3,174
Electrical	3,471	3,774	3,788	3,742	3,596	3,842	3,902	4,465	4,532	5,079	5,154
Industrial	1,687	1,751	1,609	1,722	1,502	1,313	1,631	1,656	1,432	1,557	1,463
Mechanical	1,860	1,907	1,953	1,943	1,878	2,060	2,293	2,399	2,511	2,797	3,053
Other	4,178	4,228	5,099	5,269	5,041	5,295	4,977	5,268	6,302	5,689	5,937

Appendix table 48. - continued

Field	1975	1976	1977	1978	1979	1980	1981	1982	1983	1984	1985
					Men						
Total, all fields	42,847	42,675	43,577	42,547	40,416	40,008	39,797	41,049	41,787	41,894	42,980
Total science	27,809	27,094	27,421	26,403	25,213	24,352	23,830	24,139	23,942	23,701	24,102
Physical sciences	4,982	4,660	4,458	4,630	4,472	4,258	4,213	4,325	4,151	4,253	4,450
Chemistry	1,590	1,413	1,327	1,447	1,318	1,286	1,194	1,261	1,167	1,139	1,166
Physics	1,453	1,319	1,193	1,171	1,184	1,074	1,179	1,128	1,208	1,341	1,333
Geological sciences	816	873	926	1,026	1,058	1,058	1,076	1,196	1,199	1,149	1,283
Other	1,123	1,055	1,012	986	912	840	764	740	577	624	668
Mathematics	2,910	2,550	2,398	2,233	1,989	1,832	1,692	1,821	1,859	1,795	1,877
Computer sciences	1,961	2,226	2,332	2,471	2,480	2,883	3,247	3,625	3,813	4,379	5,064
Life sciences	7,207	7,204	7,696	7,485	7,259	6,952	6,451	6,315	6,111	5,728	5,266
Biological sciences	4,858	4,746	4,956	4,695	4,510	4,325	3,853	3,621	3,421	3,167	2,810
Agricultural sciences	2,349	2,458	2,740	2,790	2,749	2,627	2,598	2,694	2,690	2,561	2,456
Psychology	4,059	4,188	4,316	3,931	3,688	3,397	3,371	3,228	3,254	2,980	3,064
Social sciences	6,690	6,266	6,221	5,653	5,325	5,030	4,856	4,825	4,754	4,566	4,381
Economics	1,808	1,759	1,783	1,601	1,568	1,441	1,468	1,483	1,506	1,447	1,509
Sociology	1,304	1,166	1,018	878	745	667	590	525	485	456	456
Political sciences	1,857	1,719	1,719	1,523	1,480	1,423	1,342	1,345	1,286	1,233	1,062
Other	1,721	1,622	1,701	1,651	1,532	1,499	1,456	1,472	1,477	1,430	1,354
Total engineering	15,038	15,581	16,156	16,144	15,203	15,656	15,967	16,910	17,845	18,193	18,878
Aeronautical/astronautical	470	469	377	400	355	373	388	482	454	535	574
Chemical	965	992	1,021	1,150	1,035	1,138	1,105	1,106	1,207	1,323	1,281
Civil	2,697	2,901	2,840	2,559	2,512	2,486	2,687	2,728	2,787	2,825	2,837
Electrical	3,413	3,670	3,654	3,600	3,453	3,658	3,681	4,177	4,239	4,694	4,720
Industrial	1,631	1,670	1,534	1,584	1,374	1,180	1,465	1,446	1,226	1,279	1,236
Mechanical	1,845	1,880	1,904	1,886	1,811	1,962	2,177	2,260	2,362	2,613	2,848
Other	4,017	3,999	4,826	4,965	4,663	4,859	4,464	4,711	5,570	4,924	5,196

Appendix table 48. - continued

Field	1975	1976	1977	1978	1979	1980	1981	1982	1983	1984	1985
					Women						
Total, all fields	11,005	12,072	13,154	13,690	14,040	14,383	15,014	15,976	17,081	17,675	18,298
Total science	10,609	11,483	12,421	12,819	13,050	13,193	13,608	14,292	15,205	15,516	15,970
Physical sciences	848	825	887	946	992	975	1,087	1,201	1,137	1,315	1,352
Chemistry	416	383	448	445	447	447	473	497	465	538	568
Physics	124	132	126	123	135	118	115	156	162	194	190
Geological sciences	116	130	121	213	242	237	320	344	353	365	409
Other	192	180	192	165	168	173	179	204	157	218	185
Mathematics	1,428	1,313	1,300	1,150	1,057	1,036	877	910	980	954	1,011
Computer sciences	338	377	466	567	575	764	971	1,310	1,508	1,811	2,037
Life sciences	2,411	2,619	3,011	3,226	3,460	3,326	3,280	3,509	3,609	3,602	3,491
Biological sciences	2,073	2,193	2,512	2,532	2,710	2,529	2,446	2,563	2,620	2,550	2,535
Agricultural sciences	338	426	499	694	750	797	834	946	989	1,052	956
Psychology	3,045	3,671	4,004	4,263	4,343	4,464	4,668	4,621	5,185	5,093	5,417
Social sciences	2,539	2,678	2,753	2,667	2,623	2,628	2,725	2,741	2,786	2,741	2,662
Economics	325	334	383	396	392	382	445	485	469	446	485
Sociology	808	844	812	733	670	674	650	629	627	552	566
Political sciences	476	473	504	547	558	515	534	610	543	537	438
Other	930	1,027	1,054	991	1,003	1,057	1,096	1,017	1,147	1,206	1,173
Total engineering	396	589	733	871	990	1,190	1,406	1,684	1,876	2,159	2,328
Aeronautical/astronautical	7	10	8	11	17	9	20	39	37	27	31
Chemical	25	39	65	87	114	133	163	181	164	194	268
Civil	74	99	129	132	143	197	207	270	295	326	337
Electrical	58	104	134	142	143	184	221	288	293	385	434
Industrial	56	81	75	138	128	133	166	210	206	278	227
Mechanical	15	27	49	57	67	98	116	139	149	184	205
Other	161	229	273	304	378	436	513	557	732	765	741

SOURCE: National Science Foundation, SRS, and Center for Statistics, Department of Education.

Appendix table 49. Science and engineering doctorate recipients
by field and sex: 1975-86

Field	1975	1976	1977	1978	1979	1980	1981	1982	1983	1984	1985	1986
					Total							
Total, all fields	18,358	17,864	17,416	17,048	17,245	17,199	17,633	17,625	17,931	18,075	18,261	18,792
Total science	15,356	15,030	14,773	14,625	14,755	14,720	15,105	14,979	15,150	15,162	15,094	15,416
Physical sciences	3,710	3,506	3,415	3,234	3,320	3,149	3,210	3,351	3,439	3,459	3,534	3,679
Chemistry	1,776	1,624	1,571	1,544	1,566	1,538	1,612	1,680	1,759	1,765	1,837	1,903
Physics	1,300	1,237	1,150	1,067	1,108	983	1,015	1,014	1,043	1,080	1,080	1,187
Geological sciences	634	645	694	623	646	628	583	657	637	614	617	589
Mathematics	981	855	832	783	744	744	728	720	701	698	688	730
Computer sciences	166	148	132	176	235	218	232	220	286	295	310	399
Life sciences	4,402	4,361	4,266	4,369	4,501	4,715	4,786	4,841	4,749	4,872	4,882	4,790
Biological sciences	3,497	3,573	3,484	3,516	3,646	3,803	3,804	3,890	3,734	3,875	3,771	3,791
Agricultural sciences	905	788	782	853	855	912	982	951	1,015	997	1,111	999
Psychology	2,751	2,883	2,989	3,055	3,091	3,098	3,358	3,158	3,309	3,230	3,072	3,071
Social sciences	3,346	3,277	3,139	3,008	2,864	2,796	2,791	2,690	2,666	2,608	2,608	2,747
Economics	868	855	811	778	780	745	808	737	792	767	786	836
Sociology	680	734	725	610	632	601	605	568	525	515	461	492
Political sciences	749	668	614	603	522	505	445	459	397	419	406	414
Other	1,049	1,020	989	1,017	930	945	933	926	952	907	954	1,005
Total engineering	3,002	2,834	2,643	2,423	2,490	2,479	2,528	2,646	2,781	2,913	3,167	3,376
Aeronautical/astronautical	141	122	115	103	81	81	97	86	106	119	124	118
Chemical	370	314	306	261	287	285	296	306	349	361	440	476
Civil	290	314	269	236	236	240	287	308	354	351	358	387
Electrical	612	592	544	463	533	478	478	544	517	593	631	707
Industrial	92	67	73	51	82	77	66	79	86	84	92	101
Mechanical	325	304	270	282	281	293	282	334	311	336	424	442
Other	1,172	1,121	1,066	1,027	990	1,025	1,022	989	1,058	1,069	1,098	1,145

Appendix table 49. - continued

Field	1975	1976	1977	1978	1979	1980	1981	1982	1983	1984	1985	1986
					Men.							
Total, all fields	15,522	14,883	14,310	13,735	13,662	13,398	13,610	13,482	13,462	13,502	13,606	13,886
Total science	12,572	12,103	11,741	11,365	11,234	11,009	11,181	10,960	10,805	10,740	10,637	10,735
Physical sciences	3,416	3,199	3,112	2,926	2,970	2,763	2,845	2,891	2,971	2,954	2,959	3,074
Chemistry	1,582	1,435	1,391	1,349	1,347	1,283	1,376	1,407	1,462	1,445	1,475	1,507
Physics	1,230	1,182	1,086	1,015	1,035	916	942	930	969	1,001	978	1,078
Geological sciences	604	582	635	562	588	564	527	554	540	508	506	489
Mathematics	882	758	723	672	629	649	616	624	588	583	582	609
Computer sciences	156	132	114	156	204	197	206	200	250	258	277	350
Life sciences	3,553	3,508	3,423	3,411	3,470	3,565	3,565	3,550	3,385	3,526	3,480	3,342
Biological sciences	2,691	2,770	2,697	2,623	2,695	2,750	2,717	2,750	2,503	2,662	2,540	2,515
Agricultural sciences	862	738	726	788	775	815	848	800	882	864	940	827
Psychology	1,878	1,937	1,902	1,928	1,831	1,787	1,885	1,721	1,736	1,611	1,552	1,507
Social sciences	2,687	2,569	2,467	2,272	2,130	2,048	2,064	1,975	1,875	1,808	1,787	1,853
Economics	784	763	740	687	676	643	708	639	663	647	664	672
Sociology	470	511	488	386	400	370	363	354	309	289	227	276
Political sciences	628	554	512	485	427	403	349	353	314	322	298	297
Other	805	741	727	714	627	632	644	629	589	550	596	608
Total engineering	2,950	2,780	2,569	2,370	2,428	2,389	2,429	2,522	2,657	2,762	2,969	3,151
Aeronautical/astronautical	139	122	112	102	81	80	97	85	104	117	119	117
Chemical	366	307	297	256	279	271	285	289	327	336	405	423
Civil	287	310	262	230	234	234	281	296	342	332	340	368
Electrical	603	585	532	451	525	466	464	525	510	579	603	674
Industrial	90	65	68	49	77	70	60	73	80	68	86	87
Mechanical	323	301	267	280	277	289	277	322	305	330	402	428
Other	1,142	1,090	1,031	1,002	955	979	965	932	989	1,000	1,014	1,054

Appendix table 49. - continued

SOURCE: National Science Foundation, SRS.

| | Women | | | | | | | | | | | |
Field	1975	1976	1977	1978	1979	1980	1981	1982	1983	1984	1985	1986
Total, all fields	2,836	2,981	3,106	3,313	3,583	3,801	4,023	4,143	4,469	4,573	4,655	4,906
Total science	2,784	2,927	3,032	3,260	3,521	3,711	3,924	4,019	4,345	4,422	4,457	4,681
Physical sciences	294	307	303	308	350	386	365	460	468	505	575	605
Chemistry	194	189	180	195	219	255	236	273	297	320	362	396
Physics	70	55	64	52	73	67	73	84	74	79	102	109
Geological sciences	30	63	59	61	58	64	56	103	97	106	111	100
Mathematics	99	97	109	111	115	95	112	96	113	115	106	121
Computer sciences	10	16	18	20	31	21	26	20	36	37	33	49
Life sciences	849	853	843	958	1,031	1,150	1,221	1,291	1,364	1,346	1,402	1,448
Biological sciences	806	803	787	893	951	1,053	1,087	1,140	1,231	1,213	1,231	1,276
Agricultural sciences	43	50	56	65	80	97	134	151	133	133	171	172
Psychology	873	946	1,087	1,127	1,260	1,311	1,473	1,437	1,573	1,619	1,520	1,564
Social sciences	659	708	672	736	734	748	727	715	791	800	821	894
Economics	84	92	71	91	104	102	100	98	129	120	122	164
Sociology	210	223	237	224	232	231	242	214	216	226	234	216
Political sciences	121	114	102	118	95	102	96	106	83	97	108	117
Other	244	279	262	303	303	313	289	297	363	357	358	397
Total engineering	52	54	74	53	62	90	99	124	124	151	198	225
Aeronautical/astronautical	2	0	1	1	0	1	0	1	2	2	5	1
Chemical	4	7	3	5	8	14	11	17	22	25	35	53
Civil	3	4	9	6	2	6	6	12	12	19	18	19
Electrical	9	7	12	12	8	12	14	19	7	14	28	33
Industrial	2	2	5	5	5	7	6	6	6	16	6	14
Mechanical	2	3	3	2	4	4	5	12	6	6	22	14
Other	30	31	35	25	35	46	57	57	69	69	84	91

Appendix table 50. Graduate degree attainment rates in science
and engineering by sex

TOTAL

Bachelor's degrees Year	Bachelor's degrees Number	Master's degrees Year	Master's degrees Number	Rate	Bachelor's degrees Year	Bachelor's degrees Number	Doctorates Year	Doctorates Number	Rate
1970	264,122	1972	53,567	20.3	1965	164,936	1972	19,008	11.5
1971	271,176	1973	54,234	20.0	1966	173,471	1973	19,001	11.0
1972	281,228	1974	54,175	19.3	1967	187,849	1974	18,313	9.7
1973	295,391	1975	53,852	17.9	1968	212,174	1975	18,358	8.7
1974	305,062	1976	54,747	17.9	1969	244,519	1976	17,864	7.3
1975	294,920	1977	56,731	19.2	1970	264,122	1977	17,416	6.6
1976	292,174	1978	56,237	19.2	1971	271,176	1978	17,048	6.3
1977	288,543	1979	54,456	18.9	1972	281,228	1979	17,245	6.1
1978	288,157	1980	54,391	18.9	1973	295,391	1980	17,199	5.8
1979	288,625	1981	54,811	19.0	1974	305,062	1981	17,633	5.8
1980	291,983	1982	57,025	19.5	1975	294,920	1982	17,625	6.0
1981	294,867	1983	58,868	20.0	1976	292,174	1983	17,931	6.1
1982	302,118	1984	59,569	19.7	1977	288,543	1984	18,075	6.3
1983	307,225	1985	61,278	19.9	1978	288,157	1985	18,261	6.3
					1979	288,625	1986	18,792	6.5

MEN

Bachelor's degrees Year	Bachelor's degrees Number	Master's degrees Year	Master's degrees Number	Rate	Bachelor's degrees Year	Bachelor's degrees Number	Doctorates Year	Doctorates Number	Rate
1970	195,244	1972	44,010	22.5	1965	128,723	1972	16,905	13.1
1971	198,180	1973	44,474	22.4	1966	133,989	1973	16,551	12.4
1972	203,557	1974	43,630	21.4	1967	143,847	1974	15,706	10.9
1973	211,552	1975	42,847	20.3	1968	158,711	1975	15,522	9.8
1974	213,269	1976	42,675	20.0	1969	181,323	1976	14,883	8.2
1975	201,578	1977	43,577	21.6	1970	195,244	1977	14,310	7.3
1976	196,577	1978	42,547	21.6	1971	198,180	1978	13,735	6.9
1977	191,090	1979	40,416	21.2	1972	203,557	1979	13,662	6.7
1978	188,097	1980	40,008	21.3	1973	211,552	1980	13,398	6.3
1979	186,333	1981	39,797	21.4	1974	213,269	1981	13,610	6.4
1980	186,009	1982	41,049	22.1	1975	201,578	1982	13,482	6.7
1981	186,425	1983	41,787	22.4	1976	196,577	1983	13,462	6.8
1982	188,957	1984	41,894	22.2	1977	191,090	1984	13,502	7.1
1983	191,614	1985	42,980	22.4	1978	188,097	1985	13,606	7.3
					1979	186,333	1986	13,886	7.5

Appendix table 50. - continued

WOMEN

Master's degrees

Bachelor's degrees Year	Number	Master's degrees Year	Number	Rate
1970	68,878	1972	9,557	13.9
1971	72,996	1973	9,760	13.4
1972	77,671	1974	10,545	13.6
1973	83,839	1975	11,005	13.1
1974	91,763	1976	12,072	13.2
1975	93,342	1977	13,154	14.1
1976	95,597	1978	13,690	14.3
1977	97,453	1979	14,040	14.4
1978	100,060	1980	14,383	14.4
1979	102,292	1981	15,014	14.7
1980	105,974	1982	15,976	15.1
1981	108,442	1983	17,081	15.8
1982	113,161	1984	17,675	15.6
1983	115,611	1985	18,298	15.8

Doctorates

Bachelor's degrees Year	Number	Doctorates Year	Number	Rate
1965	36,213	1972	2,103	5.8
1966	39,482	1973	2,450	6.2
1967	44,002	1974	2,067	4.7
1968	53,463	1975	2,836	5.3
1969	63,196	1976	2,981	4.7
1970	68,878	1977	3,106	4.5
1971	72,996	1978	3,313	4.5
1972	77,671	1979	3,583	4.6
1973	83,839	1980	3,801	4.5
1974	91,763	1981	4,023	4.4
1975	93,342	1982	4,143	4.7
1976	95,597	1983	4,469	4.7
1977	97,453	1984	4,573	4.7
1978	100,060	1985	4,655	4.7
1979	102,292	1986	4,906	4.8

SOURCES: Center for Education Statistics and National Science Foundation, SRS.

Appendix table 51. Science and engineering degree recipients by field, racial/ethnic group, and degree level: 1979, 1983, and 1985

Field	1979 Bachelor's (1)	1979 Master's (1)	1979 Doctorates	1983 Bachelor's (1)	1983 Master's (1)	1983 Doctorates
TOTAL (2)						
Total science and engineering	322,195	50,201	13,304	304,082	47,367	13,567
Sciences	264,192	38,784	11,796	240,824	35,011	12,133
Physical science (3)	22,659	4,713	2,560	21,889	4,238	2,603
Mathematical science	11,534	2,571	572	11,470	2,103	439
Computer science	8,392	2,528	166	22,152	3,965	198
Life sciences	71,442	9,697	3,612	57,152	8,268	3,916
Psychology	42,561	7,852	2,760	38,540	7,618	3,025
Social science	107,604	11,423	2,126	89,621	8,819	1,952
Engineering	58,003	11,417	1,508	63,258	12,356	1,434
WHITE						
Total science and engineering	284,852	45,185	11,882	266,414	41,238	12,201
Sciences	232,201	35,103	10,727	210,451	31,052	11,073
Physical science (3)	20,958	4,373	2,289	19,746	3,843	2,370
Mathematical science	10,229	2,352	505	10,031	1,845	395
Computer science	7,404	2,273	153	19,027	3,366	174
Life sciences	64,445	8,909	3,333	50,668	7,531	3,607
Psychology	36,648	7,078	2,550	33,106	6,758	2,767
Social science	92,517	10,118	1,897	77,873	7,709	1,760
Engineering	52,561	10,082	1,155	55,963	10,186	1,128

Appendix table 51. - continued

Field	1979 Bachelor's (1)	Master's (1)	Doctorates	1983 Bachelor's (1)	Master's (1)	Doctorates
			BLACK			
Total science and engineering	18,743	1,988	309	16,799	1,823	305
Sciences	16,968	1,742	289	14,913	1,483	276
Physical science (3)	704	86	40	832	100	26
Mathematical science	652	71	11	629	68	3
Computer science	507	65	1	1,274	118	3
Life sciences	2,837	296	44	2,437	220	58
Psychology	3,218	476	115	2,995	469	112
Social science	9,050	748	78	6,746	508	74
Engineering	1,775	246	20	1,886	340	29
			ASIAN			
Total science and engineering	7,080	1,895	865	10,150	2,901	771
Sciences	5,222	1,045	559	6,844	1,432	524
Physical science (3)	439	160	189	719	206	162
Mathematical science	324	104	46	530	136	34
Computer science	263	149	9	1,125	429	20
Life sciences	1,788	309	188	1,925	258	197
Psychology	781	87	36	819	88	44
Social science	1,627	236	91	1,726	315	67
Engineering	1,858	850	306	3,306	1,469	247

Appendix table 51. - continued

Field	1979 Bachelor's (1)	1979 Master's (1)	1979 Doctorates	1983 Bachelor's (1)	1983 Master's (1)	1983 Doctorates
NATIVE AMERICAN						
Total science and engineering	1,187	163	28	1,065	157	28
Sciences	1,023	139	25	899	121	27
Physical science (3)	63	29	3	66	7	8
Mathematical science	41	8	0	27	6	0
Computer science	11	16	1	72	5	1
Life sciences	233	21	3	211	34	5
Psychology	177	20	10	150	41	9
Social science	498	45	8	373	28	4
Engineering	164	24	3	166	36	1
HISPANIC (4)						
Total science and engineering	10,333	970	220	9,654	1,248	262
Sciences	8,778	755	196	7,717	923	233
Physical science (3)	495	65	39	526	82	37
Mathematical science	288	36	10	253	48	7
Computer science	207	25	2	654	47	0
Life sciences	2,139	162	44	1,911	225	49
Psychology	1,737	191	49	1,470	262	93
Social science	3,912	276	52	2,903	259	47
Engineering	1,555	215	24	1,937	325	29

Appendix table 51. - continued

Field	Bachelor's (1)	Master's (1)	1985 Doctorates

TOTAL (2)

Field	Bachelor's (1)	Master's (1)	Doctorates
Total science and engineering	325,988	50,545	13,150
Sciences	256,443	36,094	11,624
Physical science (3)	22,758	4,563	2,570
Mathematical science	14,143	2,146	402
Computer science	36,487	5,233	203
Life sciences	54,954	7,624	3,881
Psychology	39,179	8,129	2,785
Social science	88,922	8,399	1,783
Engineering	69,545	14,451	1,526

WHITE

Field	Bachelor's (1)	Master's (1)	Doctorates
Total science and engineering	284,349	43,994	11,702
Sciences	223,357	31,808	10,514
Physical science (3)	20,541	4,133	2,329
Mathematical science	12,163	1,873	350
Computer science	31,321	4,303	177
Life sciences	48,248	6,946	3,549
Psychology	33,959	7,220	2,558
Social science	77,125	7,333	1,551
Engineering	60,992	12,186	1,188

Appendix table 51. - continued

Field	Bachelor's (1)	1985 Master's (1)	Doctorates
	BLACK		
Total science and engineering	16,972	1,726	331
Sciences	14,933	1,396	297
Physical science (3)	830	89	31
Mathematical science	770	53	7
Computer science	2,143	180	3
Life sciences	2,417	226	69
Psychology	2,667	426	105
Social science	6,106	422	82
Engineering	2,039	330	34
	ASIAN		
Total science and engineering	13,266	3,254	798
Sciences	8,784	1,703	517
Physical science (3)	763	213	170
Mathematical science	885	164	33
Computer science	2,044	615	17
Life sciences	2,197	254	175
Psychology	845	129	44
Social science	2,050	328	78
Engineering	4,482	1,551	281

Appendix table 51. - continued

Field	Bachelor's (1)	1985 Master's (1)	Doctorates
		NATIVE AMERICAN	
Total science and engineering	1,384	220	40
Sciences	1,175	173	39
Physical science (3)	98	21	4
Mathematical science	59	7	0
Computer science	139	41	0
Life sciences	231	24	17
Psychology	201	37	10
Social science	447	43	8
Engineering	209	47	1
		HISPANIC (4)	
Total science and engineering	10,017	1,351	279
Sciences	8,194	1,014	257
Physical science (3)	526	107	36
Mathematical science	266	49	12
Computer science	840	94	6
Life sciences	1,861	174	71
Psychology	1,507	317	68
Social science	3,194	273	64
Engineering	1,823	337	22

(1) Numbers of bachelor's and master's degrees have not been adjusted
    to the taxonomies used by the National Science Foundation and will
    therefore differ from earned degree data in other NSF publications.
(2) Excludes nonresident alien and "other."
(3) Includes enviromental sciences.
(4) Exclusive of all racial groups.

SOURCES: National Science Foundation, SRS, and Center for Education Statistics.

213

Appendix table 52. Graduate enrollment in science and engineering fields
by sex: 1977-86

Field	1977	1979	1980	1981	1982	1983	1984	1985	1986
					Total				
Total, all fields	323,927	333,943	340,740	347,595	354,717	367,971	379,925	387,020	397,791
Total sciences	254,785	261,681	265,656	267,116	270,123	274,816	283,105	287,079	292,497
Physical sciences	26,855	26,700	26,952	27,382	28,199	29,475	30,487	31,194	32,710
Chemistry	16,020	16,101	16,222	16,347	17,015	17,810	17,973	18,486	19,016
Physics	9,933	9,699	9,898	10,150	10,306	10,811	11,517	11,660	12,578
Other	902	900	832	885	878	854	997	1,048	1,116
Mathematical sciences	16,069	15,063	15,360	15,915	17,199	17,443	17,831	18,106	18,379
Computer sciences	9,108	11,690	13,578	16,437	19,812	23,616	25,364	29,522	30,726
Environmental sciences	13,658	13,854	14,208	14,422	15,174	15,609	15,803	15,741	15,342
Geosciences	8,071	8,532	8,668	8,808	9,621	10,321	10,366	10,383	9,948
Oceanography	1,957	1,867	1,992	2,082	2,091	2,063	2,191	2,090	2,082
Atmospheric sciences	924	852	889	882	889	896	907	964	961
Other	2,706	2,603	2,659	2,650	2,573	2,329	2,339	2,304	2,351
Life sciences (1)	61,076	60,572	60,144	59,079	58,624	58,318	59,073	59,051	60,017
Biological sciences	49,556	48,503	47,890	46,979	46,310	46,028	47,008	47,576	48,692
Agricultural sciences	11,520	12,069	12,254	12,100	12,314	12,290	12,065	11,475	11,325
Psychology	38,628	39,786	40,636	40,691	40,098	41,104	44,305	44,060	43,903
Social sciences	89,391	94,016	94,778	93,190	91,017	89,251	90,242	89,405	91,420
Economics	12,063	12,130	13,132	13,344	13,735	13,587	13,064	12,999	12,830
Sociology	8,864	8,159	8,001	7,816	7,246	6,949	6,861	6,593	6,534
Other social sciences	68,464	73,727	73,645	72,030	70,036	68,715	70,317	69,813	72,056
Total engineering	69,142	72,262	75,084	80,479	84,594	93,155	96,820	99,941	105,294
Aeronautical/astronautical	1,518	1,481	1,737	1,883	1,941	2,408	2,431	2,642	2,907
Chemical	5,201	5,605	6,015	6,496	7,189	7,563	7,445	7,156	6,963
Civil	12,712	13,217	13,502	14,515	14,523	15,406	15,739	15,350	15,508
Electrical	17,406	17,789	19,227	20,193	22,017	25,213	26,846	28,540	30,223
Industrial	10,438	10,714	9,870	10,026	9,870	10,712	11,175	12,532	13,473
Mechanical	8,722	9,251	9,888	10,618	11,467	12,911	13,923	14,111	15,540
Other engineering	13,145	14,205	14,845	16,748	17,587	18,942	19,261	19,610	20,680

Appendix table 52. - continued

Field	1977	1979	1980	1981	1982	1983	1984	1985	1986
				Men					
Total, all fields	238,686	235,515	237,205	237,698	240,868	248,943	254,764	259,671	265,838
Total sciences	173,379	169,280	168,624	165,150	165,247	166,150	169,095	171,710	173,778
Physical sciences	22,816	22,205	22,352	22,366	22,776	23,594	24,201	24,636	25,712
Chemistry	12,936	12,683	12,718	12,544	12,855	13,297	13,263	13,652	13,873
Physics	9,129	8,813	8,950	9,133	9,238	9,609	10,172	10,166	10,994
Other	751	709	684	689	683	688	766	818	845
Mathematical sciences	11,944	11,027	11,272	11,419	12,109	12,222	12,562	12,574	12,795
Computer sciences	7,549	9,367	10,491	12,228	14,366	16,968	18,659	22,326	23,266
Environmental sciences	11,307	10,925	10,940	10,945	11,393	11,634	11,849	11,724	11,328
Geosciences	6,703	6,741	6,743	6,746	7,318	7,808	7,895	7,899	7,575
Oceanography	1,602	1,454	1,505	1,529	1,514	1,497	1,563	1,477	1,431
Atmospheric sciences	850	757	779	758	764	766	769	807	782
Other	2,152	1,973	1,913	1,912	1,797	1,563	1,622	1,541	1,540
Life sciences (1)	42,165	39,960	38,939	37,580	36,335	35,736	35,812	35,445	35,544
Biological sciences	32,712	30,499	29,492	28,210	27,021	26,553	26,875	26,923	27,167
Agricultural sciences	9,453	9,461	9,447	9,370	9,314	9,183	8,937	8,522	8,377
Psychology	20,520	19,427	19,036	17,902	16,980	16,706	17,170	16,609	16,088
Social sciences	57,078	56,369	55,594	52,710	51,288	49,290	48,842	48,396	49,045
Economics	9,749	9,498	10,126	10,139	10,237	10,159	9,791	9,682	9,512
Sociology	4,834	4,243	3,984	3,780	3,376	3,269	3,190	3,111	2,977
Other social sciences	42,495	42,628	41,484	38,791	37,675	35,862	35,861	35,603	36,556
Total engineering	65,307	66,235	68,581	72,548	75,621	82,793	85,669	87,961	92,060
Aeronautical/astronautical	1,485	1,432	1,663	1,816	1,831	2,283	2,298	2,475	2,706
Chemical	4,827	4,991	5,336	5,718	6,288	6,547	6,462	6,140	5,931
Civil	11,752	11,752	11,973	12,778	12,614	13,388	13,551	13,046	13,176
Electrical	16,696	16,856	18,244	18,917	20,466	23,157	24,624	26,132	27,324
Industrial	9,683	9,463	8,520	8,466	8,216	8,769	9,001	10,115	10,774
Mechanical	8,449	8,782	9,354	9,987	10,748	12,106	12,963	13,095	14,385
Other engineering	12,415	12,959	13,491	14,866	15,458	16,543	16,770	16,958	17,764

Appendix table 52. - continued

Field	1977	1979	1980	1981	1982	1983	1984	1985	1986
				Women					
Total, all fields	85,241	98,428	103,535	109,897	113,849	119,028	125,160	127,351	131,954
Total sciences	81,406	92,401	97,032	101,966	104,876	108,666	114,009	115,371	118,720
Physical sciences	4,039	4,495	4,600	5,016	5,423	5,881	6,285	6,559	6,998
Chemistry	3,084	3,418	3,504	3,803	4,160	4,513	4,710	4,835	5,143
Physics	804	886	948	1,017	1,068	1,202	1,345	1,494	1,585
Other	151	191	148	196	195	166	230	230	270
Mathematical sciences	4,125	4,036	4,088	4,496	5,090	5,221	5,269	5,532	5,584
Computer sciences	1,559	2,323	3,087	4,209	5,446	6,648	6,705	7,196	7,460
Environmental sciences	2,351	2,929	3,268	3,477	3,781	3,975	3,954	4,017	4,014
Geosciences	1,368	1,791	1,925	2,062	2,303	2,513	2,471	2,484	2,373
Oceanography	355	413	487	553	577	566	628	613	651
Atmospheric sciences	74	95	110	124	125	130	138	157	179
Other	554	630	746	738	776	766	717	763	811
Life sciences (1)	18,911	20,612	21,205	21,499	22,289	22,582	23,261	23,606	24,474
Biological sciences	16,844	18,004	18,398	18,769	19,289	19,475	20,133	20,653	21,526
Agricultural sciences	2,067	2,608	2,807	2,730	3,000	3,107	3,128	2,953	2,948
Psychology	18,108	20,359	21,600	22,789	23,118	24,398	27,135	27,452	27,815
Social sciences	32,313	37,647	39,184	40,480	39,729	39,961	41,400	41,009	42,375
Economics	2,314	2,632	3,006	3,205	3,498	3,428	3,274	3,317	3,318
Sociology	4,030	3,916	4,017	4,036	3,870	3,680	3,671	3,481	3,558
Other social sciences	25,969	31,099	32,161	33,239	32,361	32,853	34,455	34,211	35,499
Total engineering	3,835	6,027	6,503	7,931	8,973	10,362	11,151	11,980	13,234
Aeronautical/astronautical	33	49	74	67	110	125	133	167	201
Chemical	374	614	679	778	901	1,016	983	1,016	1,032
Civil	960	1,465	1,529	1,737	1,909	2,018	2,189	2,305	2,332
Electrical	710	933	983	1,276	1,551	2,056	2,222	2,408	2,899
Industrial	755	1,251	1,350	1,560	1,654	1,943	2,174	2,417	2,699
Mechanical	273	469	1,534	631	719	805	961	1,016	1,155
Other engineering	730	1,246	1,354	1,882	2,129	2,399	2,489	2,651	2,916

(1) Does not include health sciences.
NOTE: Data were not collected in 1978.
SOURCE: National Science Foundation, SRS.

Appendix table 53. Graduate enrollment in science and engineering fields by racial/ethnic group: 1982-86

Field	1982	1983	1984	1985	1986
TOTAL (2)					
Total science and engineering	289,342	296,693	306,120	308,979	312,883
Sciences	229,957	231,373	237,825	238,368	240,038
Physical sciences	21,254	21,813	22,421	22,256	22,812
Mathematical sciences	12,668	12,482	12,548	12,676	12,471
Computer sciences	15,439	18,068	19,135	22,147	22,872
Environmental sciences	13,290	13,734	13,994	13,832	13,320
Life sciences (1)	50,406	49,548	49,864	49,370	49,305
Psychology	38,704	39,672	42,842	42,461	42,339
Social sciences	78,196	76,056	77,021	75,626	76,919
Engineering	59,385	65,320	68,295	70,611	72,845
WHITE					
Total science and engineering	226,704	240,528	241,759	241,402	245,233
Sciences	183,328	190,546	190,224	188,977	190,655
Physical sciences	17,689	18,663	18,838	18,479	18,800
Mathematical sciences	10,158	10,331	10,016	9,871	9,476
Computer sciences	11,574	13,482	13,638	15,061	15,790
Environmental sciences	11,393	12,371	12,142	11,903	11,663
Life sciences (1)	43,347	43,651	43,868	42,398	42,499
Psychology	30,321	32,702	33,229	34,064	34,087
Social sciences	58,846	59,346	58,493	57,201	58,340
Engineering	43,376	49,982	51,535	52,425	54,578

Appendix table 53. - continued

Field	1982	1983	1984	1985	1986
			BLACK		
Total science and engineering	11,657	12,507	12,745	12,402	12,316
Sciences	10,513	11,088	11,201	10,894	10,756
Physical sciences	553	575	613	547	565
Mathematical sciences	357	404	400	423	448
Computer sciences	528	564	528	578	658
Environmental sciences	103	112	112	127	102
Life sciences (1)	1,273	1,295	1,290	1,409	1,272
Psychology	1,643	1,916	2,200	2,075	2,047
Social sciences	6,056	6,222	6,058	5,735	5,664
Engineering	1,144	1,419	1,544	1,508	1,560
			ASIAN		
Total science and engineering	8,379	9,695	11,274	13,099	14,030
Sciences	5,632	6,233	7,057	7,960	8,591
Physical sciences	697	749	943	972	1,064
Mathematical sciences	492	564	634	692	727
Computer sciences	890	1,099	1,150	1,800	2,039
Environmental sciences	208	243	193	194	177
Life sciences (1)	1,269	1,408	1,548	1,771	1,919
Psychology	441	532	699	683	750
Social sciences	1,635	1,638	1,890	1,848	1,915
Engineering	2,747	3,462	4,217	5,139	5,439

Appendix table 53. - continued

Field	1982	1983	1984	1985	1986
			NATIVE AMERICAN		
Total science and engineering	1,006	1,028	995	881	897
Sciences	835	843	788	751	759
Physical sciences	50	45	86	37	52
Mathematical sciences	42	33	31	27	44
Computer sciences	31	22	48	56	20
Environmental sciences	22	27	23	22	21
Life sciences (1)	117	153	109	111	144
Psychology	139	135	133	158	149
Social sciences	434	428	358	340	329
Engineering	171	185	207	130	138
			HISPANIC (3)		
Total science and engineering	8,405	9,717	10,580	9,749	10,312
Sciences	7,304	8,222	8,923	8,154	8,628
Physical sciences	496	563	541	604	653
Mathematical sciences	290	332	298	267	604
Computer sciences	249	282	260	411	426
Environmental sciences	191	227	272	272	271
Life sciences (1)	1,020	1,135	1,144	1,374	1,372
Psychology	1,471	1,830	2,596	1,749	1,869
Social sciences	3,587	3,853	3,812	3,477	3,433
Engineering	1,101	1,495	1,657	1,595	1,684

(1) Does not include health sciences.
(2) Total includes "other" and "unknown" racial/ethnic background.
(3) Exclusive of all racial groups.
NOTE: Data are for U.S. citizens only.
SOURCE: National Science Foundation, SRS.

Appendix table 54. Major sources of graduate support of 1986 science and engineering doctorate recipients by field and sex

Field of degree	Total Known sources (1)	Federal Fellowships & Traineeships	Total	Fellowships	University		Self
					Teaching Assistantships	Research Assistantships	
TOTAL							
Total science and engineering	11,325	1,388	5,914	634	2,045	3,235	3,203
Science	10,053	1,257	5,196	556	1,941	2,699	2,917
Physical science	1,823	115	1,456	79	406	971	195
Mathematical science	327	29	219	14	167	38	69
Computer science	190	13	87	4	22	61	65
Environmental science	391	26	270	25	52	193	83
Life science	3,309	778	1,710	192	525	993	688
Psychology	2,477	173	710	105	362	243	1,235
Social science	1,536	123	744	137	407	200	582
Engineering	1,272	131	718	78	104	536	286
MEN							
Total science and engineering	7,746	907	4,303	406	1,399	2,498	2,018
Science	6,606	789	3,665	338	1,307	2,020	1,757
Physical science	1,514	90	1,218	65	329	824	159
Mathematical science	264	25	179	12	137	30	52
Computer science	154	10	70	3	15	52	52
Environmental science	316	23	217	20	42	155	66
Life science	2,225	487	1,164	113	352	699	486
Psychology	1,193	83	358	53	176	129	590
Social science	940	71	459	72	256	131	352
Engineering	1,140	118	638	68	92	478	261

Appendix table 54. - continued

Field of degree	Total Known sources (1)	Federal Fellowships & Traineeships	University				Self
			Total	Fellowships	Teaching Assistantships	Research Assistantships	
			WOMEN				
Total science and engineering	3,579	481	1,611	228	646	737	1,185
Science	3,447	468	1,531	218	634	679	1,160
Physical science	309	25	238	14	77	147	36
Mathematical science	63	4	40	2	30	8	17
Computer science	36	3	17	1	7	9	13
Environmental science	75	3	53	5	10	38	17
Life science	1,084	291	546	79	173	294	202
Psychology	1,284	90	352	52	186	114	645
Social science	596	52	285	65	151	69	230
Engineering	132	13	80	10	12	58	25

(1) Detail will not add to total known sources because total includes National (non-U.S. Federal), industry, loans, and other.

SOURCE: National Science Foundation, SRS, unpublished data.

Appendix table 55. Major sources of graduate support of 1986 science and engineering doctorate recipients by racial/ethnic group

Sources of support	White	Black	Asian	Native American	Hispanic (2)
Total known sources	10,295	215	336	42	229
Federal Fellowships and Traineeships	1,195	60	61	4	45
University	5,458	62	165	22	94
Fellowships	578	13	18	2	10
Teaching Assistantships	1,898	23	46	11	36
Research Assistantships	2,982	26	101	9	48
Self	2,936	56	79	14	61
Other (1)	706	37	31	2	29

(1) Includes National (non-U.S. Federal), industry, loans, and other.
(2) Exclusive of all racial groups.

SOURCE: National Science Foundation, SRS, unpublished data.

Appendix table 56. NSF fellowships in science and engineering fields by sex: FY 1975 and FY 1985

FY 1975

Field	Number of Applicants			Number of Awards Offered											
				Total			New			Continuation (1)			Honorable Mention		
	Total	Male	Female	Total	Male	Female	Total	Male	Female	Total	Male	Female	Total	Male	Female
Total, all fields	5,773	3,995	1,778	1,527	1,137	390	550	404	146	977	733	244	2,078	1,544	534
Engineering, Mathematics, and Physical Sciences	2,480	2,081	399	679	614	65	239	213	26	440	401	39	888	807	81
Applied Mathematics	381	284	97	97	82	15	36	29	7	61	53	8	127	112	15
Astronomy	52	46	6	12	12	0	7	7	0	5	5	0	21	19	2
Chemistry	429	337	92	115	101	14	40	34	6	75	67	8	132	113	19
Earth Sciences	280	204	76	80	65	15	33	28	5	47	37	10	81	59	22
Engineering	684	642	42	188	176	12	63	58	5	125	118	7	273	264	9
Mathematics	263	192	71	86	82	4	24	22	2	62	60	2	87	79	8
Physics	391	376	15	101	96	5	36	35	1	65	61	4	167	161	6
Life and Medical Sciences	1,704	1,000	704	408	241	167	163	90	73	245	151	94	539	349	190
Biochemistry, Biophysics, Molecular Biology	395	268	127	89	60	29	35	24	11	54	36	18	128	96	32
Biological Sciences	815	480	335	218	135	83	77	46	31	141	89	52	266	172	94
Biomedical Sciences	494	252	242	101	46	55	51	20	31	50	26	24	145	81	64
Behavioral and Social Sciences	1,589	914	675	440	282	158	148	101	47	292	181	111	651	388	263
Anthropology and Sociology	522	252	270	156	92	64	49	30	19	107	62	45	326	170	156
Psychology	453	247	206	128	80	48	46	33	13	82	47	35	142	85	57
Social Sciences	614	415	199	156	110	46	53	38	15	103	72	31	183	133	50

Appendix table 56. - continued

FY 1985

Number of Awards Offererd

Field	Number of Applicants			Total			New			Continuation			Honorable Mention		
	Total	Male	Female	Total	Male	Female	Total	Male	Female	Total	Male	Female	Total	Male	Female
Total, all fields	4,390	2,776	1,614	1,419	949	470	540	362	178	879	587	292	1,544	1,079	465
Engineering, Mathematics, and Physical Sciences	2,210	1,681	529	719	584	135	277	233	44	442	351	91	756	613	143
Applied Mathematics	355	262	93	112	101	11	45	41	4	67	60	7	169	139	30
Astronomy	30	27	3	10	9	1	3	3	0	7	6	1	5	5	0
Chemistry	337	219	118	114	87	27	41	32	9	73	55	18	95	72	23
Earth Sciences	239	151	88	91	53	38	29	20	9	62	33	29	86	50	36
Engineering	778	635	143	254	200	44	97	82	15	157	118	29	292	245	47
Mathematics	148	105	43	48	42	6	20	19	1	28	23	5	44	40	4
Physics	323	282	41	90	82	8	42	36	6	48	46	2	65	62	3
Life and Medical Sciences	1,347	698	649	431	224	207	163	79	84	268	145	123	455	277	178
Biochemistry, Biophysics, Molecular Biology	413	246	167	125	80	45	48	32	16	77	48	29	186	119	67
Biological Sciences	572	298	274	189	96	93	72	32	40	117	64	53	159	96	63
Biomedical Sciences	362	154	208	117	48	69	43	15	28	74	33	41	110	62	48
Behavioral and Social Sciences	833	397	436	269	141	128	100	50	50	169	91	78	333	189	144
Anthropology and Sociology	214	89	125	76	38	38	25	15	10	51	23	28	89	43	46
Psychology	288	108	180	87	32	55	35	10	25	52	22	30	103	45	58
Social Sciences	331	200	131	106	71	35	40	25	15	66	46	20	141	101	40

(1) Includes only those on tenure in 1975, excluding reinstatements.
SOURCE: National Science Foundation, unpublished data.

224

Appendix table 57. NSF minority fellowships in science and engineering fields: FY 1980 and FY 1985

Field	FY 1980					FY 1985				
	Number of Applicants	Number of Awards Offered			Honorable Mention	Number of Applicants	Number of Awards Offered			Honorable Mention
		Total	New	Continuation			Total	New	Continuation	
Total, all fields	404	127	55	72	130	612	159	60	99	196
Engineering, Mathematics, and Physical Sciences	114	39	14	25	38	243	54	22	32	91
Applied Mathematics	19	5	3	2	7	42	10	3	7	13
Astronomy	1	0	0	0	0	1	0	0	0	1
Chemistry	16	12	4	8	6	36	9	2	7	14
Earth Sciences	12	1	0	1	4	18	6	2	4	3
Engineering	50	10	5	5	17	112	23	11	12	52
Mathematics	6	5	1	4	2	17	3	2	1	7
Physics	10	6	1	5	2	17	3	2	1	1
Life and Medical Sciences	115	38	15	23	39	159	45	15	30	54
Biochemistry, Biophysics, Molecular Biology	27	8	4	4	6	31	12	4	8	12
Biological Sciences	49	15	6	9	18	70	22	8	14	21
Biomedical Sciences	39	15	5	10	15	58	11	3	8	21
Behavioral and Social Sciences	175	50	26	24	53	210	60	23	37	51
Anthropology and Sociology	33	10	3	7	14	32	15	5	10	8
Psychology	67	20	11	9	16	81	20	9	11	20
Social Sciences	75	20	12	8	23	97	25	9	16	23

SOURCE: National Science Foundation, unpublished data.

225

Appendix table 58. Postdoctorates in science and engineering by field
and sex/racial/ethnic group: 1975, 1983, & 1985

1975

Field	Total	Men	Women	White	Black	Asian	Native American	Hispanic (1)
Total scientists and engineers	8,151	6,536	1,615	6,638	82	1,241	7	83
Scientists	7,927	6,319	1,608	6,512	82	1,156	7	83
Physical scientists	2,474	2,227	247	1,938	19	464	4	18
Mathematical scientists	143	133	10	104	2	37	0	0
Computer specialists	2	0	2	2	0	0	0	0
Environmental scientists	268	249	19	239	0	29	0	0
Life scientists	4,309	3,264	1,045	3,549	39	607	3	48
Psychologists	378	206	172	361	14	3	0	12
Social scientists	353	240	113	319	8	16	0	5
Engineers	224	217	7	126	0	85	0	0

1983

Field	Total	Men	Women	White	Black	Asian	Native American	Hispanic (1)
Total scientists and engineers	10,945	7,886	3,059	9,303	215	1,175	11	270
Scientists	10,620	7,588	3,032	9,178	215	975	11	212
Physical scientists	1,951	1,674	277	1,565	69	242	0	30
Mathematical scientists	103	82	21	101	0	2	0	0
Computer specialists	84	62	22	84	0	0	0	0
Environmental scientists	326	278	48	288	0	17	0	7
Life scientists	6,853	4,634	2,219	6,006	52	674	10	138
Psychologists	492	285	207	450	26	12	0	26
Social scientists	811	573	238	684	68	28	1	11
Engineers	325	298	27	125	0	200	0	58

Appendix table 58. - continued

Field	Total	Men	Women	1985 White	Black	Asian	Native American	Hispanic (1)
Total scientists and engineers	11,796	8,406	3,390	9,813	213	1,615	51	249
Scientists	11,398	8,031	3,367	9,674	213	1,356	51	247
Physical scientists	2,303	1,968	335	1,723	94	470	0	55
Mathematical scientists	117	109	8	113	2	2	0	4
Computer specialists	13	11	2	13	0	0	0	0
Environmental scientists	373	331	42	312	4	35	0	24
Life scientists	7,410	4,939	2,471	6,461	92	788	15	129
Psychologists	774	387	387	736	10	15	7	31
Social scientists	408	286	122	316	11	46	29	4
Engineers	398	375	23	139	0	259	0	2

(1) Includes members of all racial groups.

SOURCE: National Science Foundation, SRS.

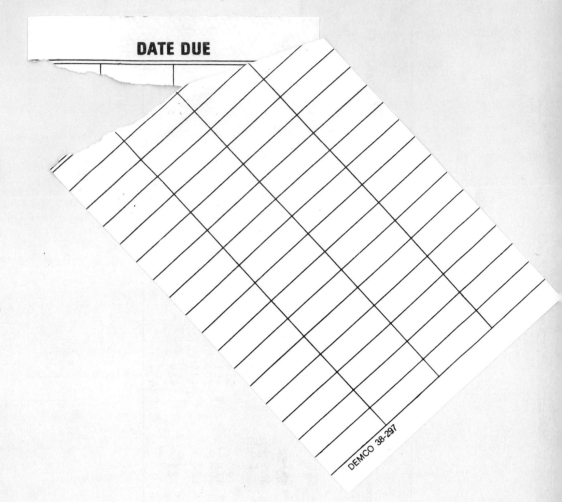

DATE DUE

DEMCO 38-297